# Topics in
# Modern Chemistry

# Topics in

# Modern Chemistry

C. J. Mandleberg

M.A., B.SC. (OXON), F.R.I.C.

*Formerly a Senior Scientific Officer, A.E.R.E., Harwell
and Technical Superintendent, Harbens Ltd.*

CLEAVER-HUME PRESS LTD

LONDON

CLEAVER-HUME PRESS LTD.
*Associated with Macmillan & Co. Ltd*
10-15 Saint Martin's St., W C 2

*First published 1963*

*Demy 8vo, xii + 228 pages,*
*11 tables*

*Printed in Great Britain by*
*Spottiswoode, Ballantyne & Co. Ltd., London and Colchester*

# Foreword

THE FAMOUS ADMIRAL, the late Lord Fisher, was asked to write something over his signature likely to be useful to Cadets at the Naval College. He wrote, 'Favouritism is the secret of efficiency.' I believe that in some instances, nepotism is another such secret, and there are instances of the value of this in history, including the history of science.

And so I urged my nephew to write this book, because I thought he would deal effectively and with clarity and wit with two things that I thought were very wrong in the teaching of young scientists in some countries, and until recently in this one. This he has done.

The first was the idea that a model, such as the brilliant Bohr atom, really represented the thing itself, so that if we could ever see inside an atom, we would see (*pace* Heisenberg) tiny little balls, associated with wave trains, whatever that might mean, whizzing round a central ball, in orbits and 'shells' and spinning like tops. The second was that if a mathematical equation fitted a theory, this was proof that the theory must be correct.

Besides these fallacies, he has covered much more ground, and some more fallacies. I am glad that I bullied my relation into writing this book, and I wish for it the acclaim and success that I think it deserves.

J. H. MANDLEBERG

v

# Contents

# Preface

I MAKE NO APOLOGY for the fact that this is a very personal book about chemistry. Even if I were qualified to do so, I would not want to add another to the many excellent standard general text-books; what I have written is not intended in any way to be a balanced account of the whole field of chemistry. In fact, to some extent, it is deliberately out of balance. I have selected a number of topics which I believe to be important not only for their intrinsic interest, but also because they bring into better perspective the relationships between the chemical elements and their compounds. In many cases, these selected topics are not easily studied by the reader of chemical literature because of the number of different papers in which the work is described; most of this work has been carried out fairly recently and is not yet included in orthodox text-books. I hope that the information which I have gathered together will be of interest to undergraduates in their early years at University, to specialists in particular fields who have all too little time to keep up to date with developments elsewhere, and to those who have ceased to be practising chemists but who want to know something of the directions in which chemical advances are being made.

Nor do I feel that it is necessary to apologize for devoting the first two chapters to an examination of some of the bases of the Chemist's craft. It is generally agreed that science should not only be taught to the few who will become the technocrats of the future, but that it should also form an important part of the general eduction of the many who will not. I do not believe that this object will be achieved by allowing general students a few hours of laboratory work, combined with an attempt to attach their interest by the descriptive chemistry of familiar modern substances such as nylon. Scientific method, its limitations and its potentialities, is more important than the memorizing of the outline of simple redox systems.

If, in what I have written, there is an underlying unity other than personal choice, it is to be found in an attempt to demonstrate the great changes in the mode of chemical thought which have taken place even in so short a time as the last quarter of a century. Inorganic chemistry is no longer predominantly the study of ions in aqueous solution.

ix

Organic and inorganic chemistry have come closer together, but the exploration of the enormous field of covalent inorganic chemistry has really only begun. Although the task of investigating the vast range of non-aqueous ionizing solvents began as long ago as 1890, it has gathered momentum only in recent years. To carry out their investigations, chemists have borrowed techniques from physicists almost before the physical bases of the methods have been solidly established. This is all a far cry from the test-tubes full of aqueous solutions of common ions for analysis which formed a large part of the School and University training of so many Chemists practising today.

However, the one change which must be resisted, is any departure from the standards of scientific integrity. These standards were not established to prove to the world that the scientist is the servant of an ethic superior to that of the common man, but because progress in scientific knowledge can be made only if the standards are strictly observed. A colleague of mine once spent several months attempting to repeat with a substance A some work which had been described in a Journal as being applicable to a group of substances A, B, C and D. In something approaching desperation, he wrote describing his difficulties to the author of the original paper. The latter replied most courteously and apologized for any inconvenience my colleague had suffered; he had found that the process worked so well with substances B, C and D that he had added the apparently similar substance A to the list in his paper although he had not actually tried it. I am afraid that that is a true story.

In writing this book, I have learnt not to place too much reliance on a certain type of Review article. I have used such articles as sources of references to original papers rather than as founts of knowledge. It is surprising in how many of these reviews facts are quoted which do not appear in the original paper to which reference is made, or in which the facts appear, to me at least, as being dangerous distortions of the original author's words. I can only hope that I have not myself fallen into such traps.

I must, however express my sincere gratitude to the authors of the many excellent Review articles which have stimulated my interest and clarified my ideas. In some of these the state of knowledge is summarized so concisely, or an analogy expressed so elegantly, that I have quoted their *ipsissima verba*; in such cases I have made due acknowledgement in the text. If elsewhere, in writing my own text from notes accumulated over a considerable period, I have been guilty of any unintentional plagiarism, I can only apologize.

Finally, I must thank all those who have assisted me in the preparation of this book; in particular, Mr. J. H. Mandleberg who browbeat me into writing it and who has continually encouraged me with helpful criticism, and Dr. H. A. Skinner of Manchester University who read the manuscript and pointed out a number of errors and obscurities. The blame for those that remain must, however, lie entirely at my own door. I also express my special thanks to the staff of the Library of the Chemical Society to whom I have given so much trouble, and who have always displayed such patience and courtesy in finding for me the various publications which I have needed.

C. J. MANDLEBERG

*Ruloe*
*Cheshire*
*March 1963*

# Principal Abbreviations
# and Symbols Used

| | | | |
|---|---|---|---|
| $A$ | Sum of number of neutrons and protons in nucleus | $R$ | Alkyl radical |
| Å.U. | Ångstrom Unit | $T$ | Temperature |
| $E$ | Energy | $t$ | Time |
| GeV | 1000 MeV ('Billion' electron volts) | $V$ | Volume |
| | | $Z$ | Number of protons in nucleus |
| $h$ | Planck's constant | $\beta$ | Bohr magneton |
| $k$ | Gas constant | $\varDelta$ | Dielectric constant |
| kV | Kilovolt | $\lambda$ | Wavelength |
| MeV | Million electron volts | $\nu$ | Frequency |
| $m$ | Mass of a particle | $\chi$ | Magnetic moment |
| $N$ | Number of neutrons in nucleus | | |

In addition, reference is made to the following fundamental particles:

| | | | |
|---|---|---|---|
| $D$ | Deuteron | $\varLambda$ | Lambda particle |
| $e$ | Electron | $\mu$ | Mu-meson (muon) |
| $n$ | Neutron | $\nu$ | Neutrino |
| $p$ | Proton | $\varXi$ | Xi particle |
| $\alpha$ | Alpha particle | $\pi$ | Pi-meson (pion) |
| $\kappa$ | Kappa particle | $\varSigma$ | Sigma particle |
| | | $\tau$ | Tau particle |

The charge which each particle bears may be indicated by a superscript $+$ or $-$, or, in the case of uncharged particles, $^\circ$. 'Anti-particles' are indicated by a bar $^-$ placed over the sign of the corresponding 'real' particle. Particles which decay to more than one secondary particle may have this behaviour indicated by subscript, thus: $\kappa^+_{3\mu}$.

# CHAPTER 1

# Models and Methods

A SCIENCE such as chemistry does not simply advance through the observation and measurement of phenomena. Measurements are of little value in themselves until they can be connected together in some way which reveals interesting relationships between the types of matter of which the observable world is composed. The very nature of measurements is that they should be expressed in numbers, and the relationships or patterns which are found are often mathematical ones. It is natural to assume that the observations which are made are revealing the presence of something that is really there. From this, it is usually concluded that if there is a mathematical pattern into which a number of different observations may be fitted, then this pattern is also an analogy of something which exists or which happens. It has often been noticed in the past that the form of some such mathematical pattern is similar to that which would be produced by the behaviour of familiar concepts of human experience. This has led to the construction of a model in terms of such concepts, and the apparent validity of the model has often been strengthened by the successful verification of predictions made from it.

Many models have been extremely useful but in some cases they have proved a hindrance to progress rather than enabling fresh advances to be made. It has often become more and more difficult to reconcile the accepted model with newly-discovered facts. The model, which was first put forward as an analogy to the mathematics, became as 'real' as its subject. It was tacitly accepted that a macroscopic model of the observed phenomena had been constructed, and that this would continue to reproduce on a large scale all the known observations. The model would in fact be a complete working model. Much work and ingenuity went into devising ever more involved mechanisms to reproduce, for instance, the behaviour of the luminiferous ether. It is probable that if this effort had been diverted from the model to devising further experiments, our knowledge of radiation and its inter-action with matter would have developed more rapidly.

In the last fifty years, the status of models has declined, but their nature and purpose have become better understood. It is now accepted that a model is unlikely to be a working model. It is however still possible to find evidence of a strongly held conviction that the structure of matter and its behaviour ought to be capable of being duplicated in a mental model composed of familiar concepts. The failure in some instances of theoreticians

1

to depict such a model, or even to acknowledge that it is possible to put one forward, is a real obstacle to the acceptance of some modern theories. Where illustrative models have been devised, the failure to understand their uses and their limitations sometimes gives rise to a feeling of frustration, and a conviction that the 'explanation' in terms of the model only tends to create more confusion. In other cases, the failure to put forward a wholly satisfactory model is sometimes considered in some way to invalidate the theoretical relations which have been evolved.

The source of much of this confusion is an inability to distinguish between the reality of the model and the reality of the 'thing-in-itself' or subject. It has been necessary for succeeding generations to realize more or less painfully that atoms were not 'really' like very small billiard balls, and that electrons were not 'really' even smaller ball-bearings circulating in planetary orbits. However, the billiard ball atom and the ball-bearing electron were, and to a limited extent still are, useful models. They were valuable in suggesting fresh lines of experimental and theoretical investigation. Neither model was 'right' in the sense that it was a wholly accurate representation of its subject, the 'thing-in-itself' but neither was entirely 'wrong', since for certain purposes each could, and can, be used to form a useful mental image which embraces a part of the observed phenomena. It is, however, essential always to bear in mind that such mental concepts are only models—illustrations or parables—however closely they may appear to reproduce the subject in so far as it is revealed by the data collected by the experimenter. The more closely models seem to resemble the thing-in-itself, the greater is the potential danger attending their use.

The more carefully the experiments have been carried out, and the more percipient the observer, the better the model may be. That is to say, the more closely may the observed phenomena be integrated to form a model which conveys a worthwhile image of the mathematical relationships which have become apparent. This model may be so useful and it may convey such a good mental impression of the way in which the observed phenomena are really integrated, that it comes to exist in the observer's mind as a true picture of, for instance, 'what the atom is really like'. The limitation that the model is only a model is overlooked, and a generation may pass before the attempt is abandoned to force today's data into the restricted frame of yesterday's model. The failure to abandon the model may in the end lead to such inconsistencies or apparent absurdities in the picture which one is asked to visualize, that the mind tends not to question the model to which it has become accustomed, but to reject the new data which cannot be assimilated into the 'classical' picture.

The results of scientific experiments must be communicated and expounded if they are to be of any value. Three stages can be identified in this process. First, the experiments themselves must be described in such a way that the validity of the results may be assessed by others. In the second stage, the results themselves must be quoted. But as has already been said, these results are of small value unless at some time they can be made the subject of a further process which is the correlation of some function of their numerical values in such a way that a self-consistent underlying pattern becomes apparent. It is relevant at this stage to enquire how far this apparent underlying pattern is a real one. For example it is known that any periodic function may be resolved by Fourier analysis into a number of superimposed sine curves. It is probable, however, that it is wrong to regard the sine curve as the real ultimate secret of the periodic properties of matter.

The numerical data derived from experiments are always approximate. The mathematical pattern which the data appear to form is therefore a pattern connecting approximations. The values of measurable quantities which can be predicted from such patterns normally only show approximate agreement with the experimental quantities which are subsequently measured to test the validity of the patterns. It is not therefore possible to be certain of the reality of the complex mathematical relationships which appear to describe the manner in which matter behaves. The intricate mathematical operations which must often be carried out in order to impose a pattern upon the experimental data may need to be complex because of the inadequacy of the data. On the other hand, there is no sound reason for supposing that the manner in which matter reacts with its environment is basically simple—simple, that is to say, in the sense that it can be expressed by a small number of elementary mathematical relationships. It is therefore impossible to say whether the mathematical relationships discovered have in themselves any basic significance. They may be accurate descriptions of the way in which matter behaves, but alternatively the way in which they correlate the approximate data may be fortuitous. Since the reality of the mathematics itself cannot be established, it would not be reasonable to place more reliance upon the model than upon the processes from which it is derived. Better mathematical relations between the data may be achieved, and the old model may not easily be reconciled with them. The model has done science a real disservice if it has become so firmly held that it has become 'real' and if there is strong disinclination on the part of scientists to abandon it.

This correlation with familiar concepts may be desirable for either (or both) of two reasons. Firstly, at some stage a number of mathematically expressed patterns derived from different experiments may be conveniently integrated into a system of law which will serve as a basis for further experimental advances. The formulation of this law may well involve mathematical processes of more or less refinement which a reader who is not specifically familiar with the field under discussion may have some difficulty in following. It is, however, desirable that such laws, and the state of knowledge which became integrated to form them, should be widely appreciated. The most suitable way of doing this may be in the form of a model or picture of the postulated state of things communicated in everyday and non-mathematical terms. It may be noted in passing that even the most profound researchers into the nature of the physical world appear to find it useful occasionally to take stock in this way. Phenomena are often labelled with words which convey a definite visual image, such as 'spin' and 'wave', or which have a certain emotional content, such as 'attraction' and 'neutralization'.

The second reason is that the mathematical relation may be a barren one. There may be no indication as to the direction in which the experimenter should proceed in order to make further advances in knowledge. To take stock in terms of familiar analogies may suggest experimental advances based on the behaviour of the everyday objects. Mathematics is not inductive, and the intuitive suggestions made by the human brain when confronted with visualizable concepts may be of real value to the experimenter. Although there is no exact correspondence between the behaviour of matter on different scales, it is not surprising that some common features pervade all matter.

The term 'visualization' is used in this book to describe the process of translation of the mathematical pattern into familiar concepts. Visualization presents data to the human brain in the way in which it has had most experience of handling observations. Like other living matter, the brain has been subjected to processes of evolution. Natural selection has led to the survival of those beings whose brains in the first place made the optimum correlation of physical events as they were detected by the senses of the individual, and then made from such a correlation the most practically useful deductions. It is in fact rather surprising that an organ which developed in such a fashion should be so successful in interpreting data from meter readings. Such a facility has only had a survival value in very recent times on the evolutionary time scale. When the brain has reduced data of this type to more or less abstract generalizations, it is often able to derive from them certain practical courses of action which can be applied to the 'real' physical world of perception. These actions give rise to further effects, which can be detected by the senses, and appreciated by the brain as events whose occurrence it had already predicted. Some part of the brain is therefore an instrument for connecting past and future events in the world of perception by an abstract chain which has no perceived analogue. If the chain of abstract reasoning is pursued too far, too many possible alternative links can be become apparent. The chain starts to lose contact with the events of the physical world which are the only means of testing the validity of the deductions.

The formulation of the direction which the reasoning should follow may be facilitated by the presentation of a useful model. That is to say, it is advantageous to state the general outline of the physical system about which speculation is being made in terms of those concepts which the process of evolution has best conditioned the brain to handle; such concepts are objects in motion, waves, mass and extension in space and time. There is no doubt that some types of brains have particular characteristics unusually developed. Mathematicians and musicians can perform wholly abstract explorations within the bounds of more or less artificial systems of logical processes. Their conclusions may be of value of themselves, no matter what vistas have been explored. The exploration of physical phenomena must be conducted in a different way. It must not be forgotten that there is an inherent postulate that the phenomena are derived from a universe which exists independently of the observer. The observer is attempting to discover something about this objective universe, and not about an imaginary universe, however interesting, to which he may be led by following subjective mental processes of reasoning.

This correlation of the deductive processes with the observable world has been illustrated in terms of the work of a solar physicist (1):

> If he wants to work out . . . the internal constitution of the sun . . . he formulates a series of differential equations . . . (and) by using suitable boundary conditions, such that the total mass shall be equal to the observed mass, he picks out the solution which he proposes to compare with the sun. The points to notice are that he would regard all other solutions (at least within a certain range) as representing suns whose existence is equally possible, and that he regards the boundary conditions used as 'accidental' to the particular solution selected.

As chemists, we cannot permit ourselves the luxury of regarding all other systems as being equally possible. When we are confronted with an aqueous solution of sodium chloride, it has certain properties for which it is our business to account. It is possible that other suns may exist elsewhere in the universe to which the rejected solutions of the solar physicist will apply. However fragile is the logical basis for the assumption, we assume that our observations and deductions will be valid for all aqueous solutions of sodium chloride of a certain strength. If we find one to which they do not apply, we say either that the observations are in error, or that the aberrant solution is not aqueous sodium chloride. Speculation on other possible sodium chlorides does not help us. It is axiomatic that there are no other types of sodium chloride. If they exist, then they are something else. Chemical speculation must be kept very close to the facts of experiment and observation.

It is this necessity for direct experiment which makes it so important to

2

confine speculation to areas which are accessible to experimental exploration. The delineation of such areas may often be made easier if there is some visualization of the deductions derived from the phenomena. Visualization is a technique, which is used to achieve further advances in our understanding of the properties of the universe. It is a useful device, but it is only a device, just as is the mathematical process of integration or the use of Hamiltonians. It is important to realize also that the mathematics does not 'explain' anything. The use of wave mechanics requires the application of some fairly difficult mathematics, but this does no more than to collate the data in a mathematical form or pattern; model and collation are thoroughly entangled in wave mechanics. Eigenvalues and eigenfunctions do not explain how fundamental particles behave; they connect and describe the observations in a convenient form and the arithmetic can stand by itself as a method of linking together various series of meter readings obtained in a number of different ways. However, useful advances are often made when the brain is able to speculate in terms of visualizable entities such as harmonic oscillators, rotations and similar concepts. In other words, wave mechanics is a method of codifying the performance of a model based on such concepts. Physical matter does not use computers to work out its interactions, and those interactions do not involve 'real' particles or 'real' waves in the sense that there are 'real' billiard balls or 'real' breakers rolling in to the beach.

Every scientist of whatever standing could well say to himself once a day: 'Atoms are not really small billiard balls.' The insidious danger of a model, and particularly of a good model, is that it may be so convenient and so fruitful in suggesting new approaches to its subject matter, that it becomes almost impossible to purge the mind of it when such a process becomes necessary. A model can never be the real thing. Since it is proposed to state some of the conclusions of present-day scientific thought in what will be, implicitly or explicitly, models, it is necessary to examine further the present status of models, and in doing so, to discover why the most satisfactory visualization is still only a model after all.

A railway enthusiast may wish to build a model of the 'Flying Scotsman'. He constructs such a model as accurately as he is able to a scale of 1 to 100. Visually it will appear to be an excellent copy. If a photograph of the model is placed next to a photograph of the original reduced to the same size, the two may appear to be indistinguishable. But although outline, or appearance, or form may appear to be scaled down perfectly, performance will not be scaled down in the same ratio. Suppose that the model is built to be a working model with every part of the mechanism reproduced. The mode of action of the model as assessed by measurable physical data will not be that of the original subject reduced in the same ratio as are its physical dimensions. For instance, heat losses will be a greater proportion of the total fuel consumption owing to the increased surface to mass ratio, and reactions which depend upon tensile strength of the constructional materials or their elastic modulus will differ from those in the subject, since such properties of matter cannot be scaled down but will remain at their original value.

To overcome this failure satisfactorily to reproduce the performance of the subject at the same scale throughout, the model builder may make further models at scales of 50 : 1 or 10 : 1; the problem of the heterogeneity of scale will not be overcome until he reproduces the subject at a scale of 1 : 1, and then, if his copying has been accurate, he will not have made a model of the 'Flying Scotsman', but the 'Flying Scotsman' itself. To make a model perfect in all its parts, he has had to re-create the thing-in-itself. At any other scale than that of the thing-in-itself, the model will differ from its subject.

In general, the greater the difference in scale, the more pronounced become the differences between the performance of the model and the performance of the thing-in-itself. Differences in appearance may be trivial or absent. A scaled-down model of the 'Flying Scotsman' may be adequate in practice for many varied purposes. It may be a satisfactory representation of the theory of the steam engine. Its use in a wind tunnel may lead to valid predictions about the wind resistance of the locomotive of which it is a model. Modifications to the model to produce a more satisfactory stream-line may be accurately scaled up to improve the design of the 'Flying Scotsman' itself. But data which are derived from mechanical action or performance cannot be directly scaled up to give information about the performance of the subject; it may be possible to obtain valid information in this way indirectly, but only by the use of correction factors and assumptions which have been obtained by other methods than from the performance of the model itself. It would be difficult to use the model directly to give information about, for instance, the fuel consumption of the subject or the distortion of the driving wheels at different speeds.

It is worthwhile to consider in rather more detail why this is so, because although this discussion of the activities of a railway model builder is itself only a model of our attempt to visualize the structure of matter on the atomic and sub-atomic scale, the analogy is in some respects sufficiently close for useful conclusions to be drawn. But it must be realized that this illustration is itself only a model. The valid analogies which can be drawn are valid only in principle, and as is the case with all other models, absurdity and confusion can easily be introduced if the model is adopted as the thing-in-itself.

The two principal causes of the limitation of usefulness of the model are therefore that scaling can only apply to one set of parameters, and that some properties of the constituents of matter are not scaled at all. If the scaling is accurate as applied to linear dimensions, then any property of the model which does not depend on the first power of linear dimensions will be scaled in a different ratio. Whereas any linear distance may be measured on the model, and multiplied by the scaling factor to obtain the equivalent distance on the subject, any property which depends on a higher power of the linear dimensions will be scaled in a ratio which is the scaling factor raised to an equivalent power. Area, volume, and mass, and their derived functions such as momentum and energy are examples of such properties. This may not be a serious defect in the model for many purposes; it does however mean that the model is only a valid analogy after mathematical corrections have been applied to the visual image that has been created. For some aspects of the performance of the model these corrections may be of so complicated a nature as to make the model of no use as a visualization of the subject. A rather more subtle point is that whereas the relationship between the linear dimensions and the derived functions may be well known on the scale of the model, other relations may be of great importance on the scale of the subject or vice versa. There is a particular danger here where there is no apparent relationship between two measurable properties on the scale of the model, and it could be assumed that this lack of correlation holds also on the scale of the subject. The effect on the mass of a steam engine of doubling its velocity from five miles per hour to ten miles per hour is very different from the effect on the mass of a particle of doubling its velocity when it is moving at half the speed of light. In fact, the increase in mass in each case may be expressed by the same mathematical relationship, but in the former case, the effect on the mass of doubling the velocity is so small as to be imperceptible. Although in this case the relationship is known, it might be possible to construct a model in which a similar relationship was so obscure that it were overlooked, or the state of knowledge might be such that the relationship had not been established. Alternatively, the state of affairs which obtains in the subject might not be normally attainable on the scale of the model; 'exchange energy' is hard to visualize because it is never perceived to operate in the macroscopic world because the separation of macroscopic objects is usually too great for the forces to have any appreciable effects.

The second cause of the necessary limitation of the usefulness of the model is that some properties are not scaled at all. Dimensionally, angle is such a property, but not one which usually leads to much difficulty or confusion. There are however other properties which may invalidate any deductions made from the model about the mode of action or performance of the subject. To return to the model of the 'Flying Scotsman', there are a number of properties of matter which are inherent in the material of the model and of the subject, and which are impossible to reduce in scale— tensile strength, elastic modulus, melting point, density. Their effect on the performance of the model and of the subject will differ very greatly at their different scales. Some property of matter which has an unknown or negligibly small effect on one scale, may have a different or predominant effect at another scale. The performance of, for instance, the piston in the cylinder will differ at different scales. If the highest standard of surface finish has been obtained on both the cylinder and the piston on the subject scale, no better finish will be obtained on the model scale. But it is possible to conceive a model so small that the surface imperfections were of the same order of size as that of the cylinder diameter itself; the piston might not run in the cylinder at all. At any scale smaller than that of the subject, the effect of such surface imperfections will be of greater relative importance than in the subject itself. But it is important to remember that the surface imperfections were always present, even in the subject. Great caution should be displayed in the use of such phrases as ' other forces come into play on the atomic scale'. The forces, if real, will pervade all nature; they may be present but inappreciable on the larger scale, just as the effect on the mass of the body is imperceptible when its velocity is changed from five to ten miles per hour. If the model is used as too close an analogy the effect of such unperceived factors may be disastrous.

The general conclusion at this stage is therefore that a model may be of great value in assisting the visualization of form, but of little value in describing performance. The nineteenth-century organic chemists interpreted the shape or form of the benzene ring as a plane regular hexagon. Not only has this never been seriously challenged in recent years, but more and more evidence has accumulated to confirm this hypothesis. Adopted as it was in the first place to explain the number of distinguishable isomers produced in substitution reactions, as in fact a useful model upon which further researches could be based, it has been apparently confirmed by the interpretation of techniques such as X-ray diffraction analysis which purport to establish the 'actual positions' of atoms in molecules. There is such a weight of evidence in support of the model that no one today has been able seriously to suggest an alternative. But it is only a model, and it should not be presumed to have too much in common with the conventional shiny black spheres joined by lengths of rigid wire. The ideas of the organic chemists of a hundred years ago about the performance of the benzene ring, or in other words about the mechanism which confers aromatic properties are altogether less trustworthy. Its stability is consonant with modern wave mechanical conceptions of which the theories of 'hybridization' and ' $\pi$-electrons' are mathematical derivations, but these do not easily allow themselves to be visualized in model form, since the processes and interactions involved are ones of which we have no common world experience; the concept of 'resonance' and of '6 electrons being delocalized over the aromatic ring' convey something to us as words, but we are unable to form a coherent model of the situation, however well the logical necessity may be conveyed to us in mathematical terms. The well-known theorem of Pythagoras may be confirmed for a particular case by cutting out paper shapes and fitting them together, but the theorems of wave mechanics admit of no such tangible interpretation.

Another example of the apparent accuracy of a model in determining form is that of the structure of chromosomes. In order to account for linkage and exchange of inherited characteristics, biologists predicated as a working model certain conformations in space of the long chain protein and nucleic acid structure of which chromosomes appear to be composed. Structural analysis has in many instances confirmed that those parts of the chromosomes which the biologists had assumed to lie sufficiently close for linkage to take place, seem to have just such a physical conformation. The actual process of linkage remains obscure. The model appears adequately to represent form, but a model of performance is not so easy to visualize.

Such deductions of form from theoretical reasoning without the means for 'seeing' the actual shapes are great triumphs; the failure to postulate an entirely adequate model for performance is not a defeat. Shape expressed in Cartesian co-ordinates is the same on any scale; linear dimensions may be scaled with accuracy and a fair degree of confidence. It is models of perform-ance which are suspect. Even so, any model may have some value; a 'bad' model may clarify some hypothesis. The development of the physical sciences has progressed as rapidly as has been the case because so many of the foremost theoreticians have been skilled in devising models to assist visualization of their conclusions. It has been found possible in many cases to construct models which have more or less satisfactorily classified certain features of mechanisms which are not easy to appreciate when they are expressed in a rigid mathematical form.Where such models have been used to illustrate other features of the mechanisms, the failure to appreciate the nature of the model itself has sometimes led to grave difficulties.

Those who have developed the ideas of the model-makers, seem very often to have confused the model with the thing-in-itself; they have considered the model to be 'real' in the same sense that the phenomenon which it was intended to illustrate was 'real'. There has always been much speculation about the reality of observations themselves, but this is outside the scope of the present discussion. It is possible that the scientist is confronted by a vast mirage, and that the scale and meter readings upon which physical science is based are themselves an illusion, and that the supposed mathematical relations between them are also illusory. It may be that 'God created the integers; all else is the work of man'.* This is a fertile field for exploration by the metaphysicist and the theologian, and a perfectly legitimate challenge to human reason. It is a barren prospect for

* 'Die ganzen Zahlen hat Gott gemacht; alles anderes ist Menschenwerk'. (Kroneeker.)

the experimental scientist who must accept things in the terms that are presented to him by his experiments (having assured himself as far as he can that both his experiments and his deductions contain no logical inconsistencies) and who must interpret his results in the most realistic way possible. Models have played and will surely continue to play, an important part in this interpretation.

The next important consideration is that data may lead to more than one interpretation, each consistent in itself. Eddington (2) invented the parable of the aged college Bursar who became so involved with the figures of dues and salaries and bills as things with an existence of their own that he thought that he could deduce from them the real laws governing the world of finance. It is probable that when he emerged blinking into the quadrangle, he could not imagine why it was full of young men and what they were doing in the college. Mascall (3) quotes the case of Mathieu's equation, which will exactly represent certain data; he states that such data may be derived from vibrations of an elliptical membrane of a certain type, but also from the motions of a circus artiste supported by another artiste who is propelling himself round the Ring on a large ball. Mascall points out that from the data alone it is impossible to know whether the subject is a membrane or a circus performer. Thus, in working from the data, and particularly from the mathematical interpretation of the data, to the model, no sure conclusions may be drawn about the equivalence of the model with 'reality'.

Since it is impossible to be sure whether the model is only a convenient device, or whether it has any contact with 'reality', there is no disgrace in abandoning a model, or of using one model to illustrate one part of a phenomenon and another to illustrate another part. This is a legitimate procedure even though the second model is inconsistent with, or even pursues an entirely different form of analogy to, the first. The most important decision is that of determining at what point a given model, hitherto fruitful, is no longer of value, and when a second model must be visualized. It may not be necessary to abandon the first model. The second model may not illustrate behaviour for which the first is perfectly adequate. More than one model may have to be maintained in order to interpret different facets of the behaviour of the physical entity under consideration. Atomic and sub-atomic phenomena, for instance, are manifested as if something was sometimes behaving as we are accustomed to observe discrete macroscopic particles behaving, and sometimes in a manner analogous to a train of waves. Three hundred years of argument are summed up in the expression 'wavicle'; argument based on the unsatisfactory premise that since in our world of everyday experience, there were objects which were particles and also objects which were waves, but none which were both, then if small particles behaved apparently like particles or waves, they must 'Really' be particles or waves—but not both at the same time. The fallacies in such reasoning have already been discussed. The data which appears to be derived, for instance, from the motions of particles could alternatively be derived from some other mechanism (the 'Mathieu's equation' argument). On the other hand the discrete particles (or trains of waves) which are mentally scaled up to the size of objects of our normal perception may be influenced by factors which we need not normally take into account when describing the behaviour of macroscopic objects. In that case the details of their behaviour (or their gross behaviour under certain influences) may have no analogy in the macroscopic world (the 'Flying Scotsman' argument). It cannot be repeated too often that the sub-atomic world is not a small-scale counterpart of the macroscopic world which our unaided senses reveal to us. The constituents and phenomena of the sub-atomic world are not billiard balls and violin strings writ small. It is a realm of which our brains have no means of forming a complete picture, because evolution has formed our brains to visualize a different type of experience.

A brain can interpret such a statement as 'The cow is in the field', but each individual particle of which the cow is composed is not located in space in the same qualitative way as the whole cow is located in the field. Again, the equivalence of matter and energy can only be satisfactorily expressed as a mathematical relationship. This is because the smallest piece of matter of which we can form a literal mental impression is equivalent to a release of energy so vast that we cannot form any realistic appreciation of it. If it is stated that the location of an electron in space is in some way connected with 'the square of a wave-mechanical probability function', it is not necessary to make a ragout of the concept of a roulette wheel and of ripples being generated on a pond and then multiply it by itself. The mechanism of location, or the performance of the constituents of matter as we know it is without perceptible parallel on the macroscopic scale of which our senses make us aware. The location of the cow in the field can in principle be expressed in the same terms as the location of the electron, but the uncertainty of its location is as imperceptible as the change in mass of a body when its velocity is changed from five to ten miles per hour. To be sceptical of the intricate mathematical relationships which have been established on the grounds that they do not appear to apply to the large-scale objects of everyday life, is as illogical as the reasoning of the man (also quoted by Mascall) who refused to have anything to do with Life Insurances. He discovered that the companies used the ratio $\pi$ in their actuarial calculations, and he could not believe that the duration of his life could be affected by the relationship between the diameter and circumference of a circle.

It may be regretted that there is no perfect direct correlation between the phenomena we experience in the familiar world, and those revealed to us by physical experiment; it should not however, be a matter for surprise. We are apparently located in infinite space and endless time, and the difficulty in rationalizing either concept does not prevent the investigation of both space and time to the limits of our resources. It is extremely fortunate that the percipience of man has been able to classify the behaviour of the constituents of matter in certain ways and that he has been able to select from the mathematical correlation of the data, certain aspects of the nature of things of which there can be constructed a worthwhile analogy in terms of objects of everyday experience. It may be confusing that the 'Something' about which we have information is sometimes like a wave and sometimes like a particle, but on the other hand, progress in investigation would have been made more difficult if no analogies at all had suggested themselves. There would be few competent chemists if theories of valency could only be taught in the mathematics of wave mechanics. There would be even fewer if the 'dual nature' of the electron had appeared to be so irresolvable that the hypothesis of 'octet formation' which is visualized in terms of particulate electrons, had been therefore considered to be entirely inadmissible.

Before commencing a discussion of some aspects of the present state of physical, and particularly of chemical knowledge, a discussion which will necessarily be largely based on models of the phenomena, it is convenient to describe two models which are of such general application that they enter to some extent into the visualization of all modern physical theories. Firstly, there is the supersession to a greater or less extent of 'cause and effect' by 'probability'. Secondly there is the necessity to regard the concept of an individual entity as a misleading model, because of the over-whelming influence of the environment on the individual. It may be objected that these concepts can hardly be described as 'models' but in the first place 'probability' has such emotional connotations of 'chance' and 'odds' that it almost inevitably leads to a visualization of tossing coins or other random operations. In the second, the conception of an entity in its environment is largely a visual one, because the mathematical treatment is often so complex that appreciable progress is made by a process of what may be termed 'qualitative intuition'.

'Probability' is a concept with which everyone is familiar in everyday life, and the word is often used as a synonym for 'chance'. In modern scientific language, probable is not synonymous with 'likely to happen'; it is more nearly a synonym for 'possible'. This is not strictly true, however. Possible is often contrasted with 'forbidden', but there may be a finite probability that a 'forbidden' event will occur. Probability may be defined as the likelihood that a given event will occur, expressed on a numerical scale where 0 (or 0%) represents absolute impossibility of occurrence, and 1 (or 100%) represents absolute certainty. In fact, it is very rare for a probability to be stated as 0 or 1. The detailed investigation of phenomena seldom leads to a certainty that a given event 'definitely' will (or will not) happen. If a penny is tossed in the air, it is not even certain that it will fall with one face or the other uppermost (i.e. that it will be either heads or tails). It might balance on one edge. It might fly to pieces in the air because of some unrelieved internal stress. Both these 'anomalous' events may have very low probabilities, perhaps $10^{-10}$ or $10^{-20}$ or less. Since the sum of all probabilities must equal 1 (the probability that something perceptible will occur) then the probability of the penny landing with one face or other uppermost will be less than 1; perhaps $(1 - 10^{-10})$. This is, of course, a very high probability, but the usefulness of many models of physical happenings depends on the fact that their interpretation requires the occurrence of an event of very low intrinsic probability, perhaps as low as $10^{-10}$. Many events of low probability are contrary to their supposed analogues in everyday life. Such an event is the 'leak' of a particle through an energy barrier. The apparent phenomenon is that a particle of a certain energy is in a field of force which is bounded by an energy barrier which the particle under consideration is not energetic enough to surmount. There is a finite probability that the particle will leak through the barrier.

For many purposes it is satisfactory to conceive an energy barrier as a hill or wall. In the world of our normal experience, a solid body or particle must be given a certain kinetic energy if it is to be projected over a wall. This energy must be associated with such a sufficient initial velocity that this will not fall to zero under the influence of the opposing gravitational field of the earth before the centre of mass of the body is no lower than the top line of the wall. It would be surprising if at some lower initial velocity which fell to zero at some height less that the top line of the wall, the particle came to rest on the ground on the opposite side of the solid wall to that on which it started. On the sub-atomic scale such an event, in spite of its apparent contradiction to events of everyday experience, may well happen. Such an event becomes completely irrational if the concept of the model is held so strongly that what is visualized is a particle with accurately defined position, mass and velocity relative to a barrier with equally well defined characteristics; that is to say if the phenomenon under consideration is a scaled-down version of everyday objects. It is however, the model (and to some extent the form in which the data is expressed) which is 'wrong', and not that events in nature are 'irrational'. The assumption was made that a particle whose location was known was 'approaching' an energy barrier; the mental picture was, for instance, of a tennis-ball approaching a net. But the position of the particle was never known with any certainty. Each set of co-ordinates in the universe could be referred to a probability that they described the position of the particle. If the particle could be imagined as the solitary inhabitant of an infinite continuum, the probabilities would fall off in a regular manner (if the particle possessed perfect spherical symmetry), and this falling off would be very rapid as the distance between that described by a particular set of co-ordinates and the region of highest probability increased.* The interposition of an energy barrier modifies the distribution of probabilities, and considerably reduces the probability that the particle is on the other side of the barrier, but it does not reduce this to zero. In other words, the model must include the possibility that 'the particle was on the other side of the barrier all the time'. Such a concept is contrary to our normal physical experience. If a number of racquets balls are being hit inside a totally enclosed racquets court, with a force insufficient for any one of them to breach and penetrate the wall (an occurrence so unlikely in a racquets court that we may fairly say that the probability is zero) we do not expect to find any of them outside the court. The balls can be struck by the players because it is possible to predict with a high degree of certainty where the balls are relative to the court and to the player's racquet. If a number of sub-atomic particles are apparently confined within an energy barrier, not only is their position and velocity within the barrier indeterminate, but there is a probability that they can be detected outside the barrier. It is this behaviour of matter that makes it so difficult to appreciate that the answer to 'Is an electron here or there?' is 'Yes!' The answer is not, however, 'Both!'

No model has yet made it necessary for any unit of matter to be in two places at once. We have to accept a universe in which a particular particle cannot be localized, but in which it is uniquely defined. It is one particle, not several. It is not spread over the whole of space, but the probability of its materialization is spread over the whole of space. What manifests itself to us is not a well-defined particle. It is an event the occurrence of which depends on a function of the probability that something will materialize in a certain position in space. We are no longer concerned with a solid defined localized particle, but with the square of the probability function associated with it.

A third model has therefore to be added to the concept of the electron as a particle and the electron as a wave. An electron as a function of the probability of its location is much less easy to visualize than the former two, which have familiar everyday analogues. Each model has its own uses. There is no need to discard one because of the existence of the others. Above all there is no need to 'reconcile' them. None of them is 'real'. None of them is a 'working model'. Each of them may be of assistance in provoking fresh advances in experiment and theory within the area of investigation within which it is of value. But there is no reason to suppose

---

* It could equally well be argued that in such a system (single particle in infinite continuum), the probability was equal over the whole continuum. As a model, the energy distribution envisaged above is adequate for the present discussion.

that all three will be together supplanted by a further model which will describe in terms of everyday analogues something whose behaviour seems to lie outside our everyday experience of macroscopic objects. It may well be that further models will have to be added to those already in existence. Professor Peierls, for instance, has stated the problem of the particle and the potential barrier in terms of the Uncertainty Principle. The particle may be able to get 'through' the barrier because under certain circumstances it is not necessary for energy to be conserved. The principle involved is not peculiar to the atomic scale. It is only on the atomic scale that this lack of conservation leads to detectable consequences. As Professor Peierls puts it (4):

> In intermediate states of the reaction of matter with a field, energy may not be conserved. The uncertainty principle operates in such a way that the energy of a state is not observable if the state exists only for a certain time. More precisely, if a state only exists for a time $\Delta t$, then its energy cannot be known to better that $\Delta E$ where $\Delta t \Delta E$ must be at least the order of the quantum constant $h$. Crudely speaking, a system may borrow an amount of energy for a short time, provided that the loan is returned before it is possible to discover that the amount is missing. For example, the well-known phenomenon of the transition of particles through potential barriers, which is important in the Gamow theory of alpha decay, can be described simply in these terms. The particle can get through the potential barrier notwithstanding the lack of required kinetic energy, provided that the energy is balanced again soon enough to prevent an actual verification of the lack of balance. Qualitatively this explains that the transition is more difficult if the barrier is higher (therefore requiring a bigger loan) or if it extends further (so that it becomes more difficult to restore the balance in a short time).

The only common ground which such models inhabit is that the behaviour of which the models are analogues can be expressed in a universal language of mathematical functions. One of the reasons why the models have been called into existence is that the mathematics involves techniques which are too difficult for many people to handle. Probability is in itself an abstract conception, and as such it is an unsatisfactory model in the sense that there is nothing tangible or physical which can be visualized. The macroscopic world can usually be expressed in terms of cause and effect. On the sub-atomic scale, this is not possible; the cause and effect of common experience are the result of the summation of the probabilities of an immense number of individual events. In such circumstances confident prediction of the course of mass events becomes possible. Cause and effect is a conception which must be treated with great reserve when we are considering events in which single particles are concerned. Such events must be distinguished from what are, in fact, generalizations in which the behaviour of, for instance, one atom of oxygen encountering another atom of oxygen is qualitatively described. Here, the described behaviour is not literally true of the encounter between two particular designated atoms. The phenomenon has been established on a scale on which the behaviour of a large number of atoms was observed, and the deductions extrapolated back to the behaviour of two postulated atoms which serve as models for the process, but have no 'real' existence. This is not a purely metaphysical distinction. It is becoming apparent that many organic functions depend upon the behaviour of comparatively small numbers of individual giant molecules. Energy and its consequent interactions must be distributed among them in a manner to which various levels of probability are attached, but the individuals may be sufficiently few for the effect of atypical energy distributions (which have a finite probability of occurrence) to have a profound effect on the metabolism of the organism of which they form a part. It is at any rate possible that the mechanism of living may be regulated by the concept of probability to a far greater extent than has been believed probable in the past.

The need to visualize the constituents of the structure of matter in an environment where they are subject to the fields of force which pervade any actual part of the universe has made the behaviour of matter more difficult to explore. It is convenient for many purposes to consider *an* electron, *an* atom, *a* molecule, but a single such particle rarely exists in the systems which are examined by experiment. Earlier generations of scientists were apt to disregard the interactions of atomic neighbours when formulating chemical theories, particularly when a theory formed an adequate model for the visualization of some aspects of the phenomenon.

The use of empirical formulae has the effect of conveying the impression, if only to the subconscious mind, that chemistry is concerned with discrete entities—$H_2O$, $NaCl$, $K_3[Fe(CN)_6]$. Their combination in tidy balanced equations seems to symbolize an inevitable and complete reaction which can be pictured as taking place over all the individual members of the species concerned when the reactants are mixed in the correct proportions. In the course of his classic work on the determination of atomic weights, Richards wrote that every substance must be presumed to be impure, and every reaction to be incomplete, until the contrary is proved. It is most important to realize that, in general, substances are impure, and that only a proportion of the reactants in a given reaction follow to completion the course indicated by the equation. It is misleading to visualize one set of reactants recombining to form the products on the right-hand side of the equation, and to extrapolate this mental picture to cover the whole mass of the reacting material.

It is essential to take into account the environment which surrounds the few atoms which are usually considered to represent a chemical system. It is necessary to consider the effect on one particle of a single species of the presence of surrounding particles of the same species. The effect of such interactions is minimized in a gas at low pressures. The mean free path of the constituent molecules is relatively long, and in a container whose dimensions are large compared with the mean free path, collisions with the containing walls are relatively infrequent. The kinetic theory of gases uses as a model the conception of gas molecules as perfectly elastic spheres which are so small that their volume can be neglected in comparison with that of their container. It has been possible to derive on this basis expressions which are equivalent to those gas laws which had been formulated empirically as a result of measurements made on massive quantities of gas. The agreement between the expressions derived from the kinetic model and from the laboratory experiments is often close under conditions which do not approach the critical point. However, it is possible to measure pressure and temperature at constant volume with great accuracy; if this is done, the properties of the gases are found not to be described in detail by the simple gas laws even under conditions far removed from the critical point. As this point is approached, the deviations (or 'anomalies') become more pronounced. This is due to the failure of the model, because, for example, the molecules with which the kinetic theory of gases is concerned are perfectly elastic, and this is not an accurate statement of the properties of real molecules. The interaction between particles of matter at very small distances of approach is complex, and is made up of both attraction and repulsion, each depending inversely on a high power of the distance between the particles. During isothermal compression the mean free path becomes reduced to the same order of magnitude as that distance within which these interactions are comparable with the average kinetic energy of the particles. The departure of the behaviour of the gas from the simple gas laws then becomes appreciable.

As the gas is further compressed, the effect of the environment on each individual particle becomes more and more important relative to its kinetic energy, until the point of condensation into a liquid is reached. In a gas, the spatial distribution of the particles is random; in a liquid there is strong evidence not only for short-range order in the relative positions of the molecules, but also for some long-range order as well. The molecules are sufficiently closely packed for this to be necessary for steric reasons (i.e. because of their shape—the molecules cannot be regarded as spheres). In addition their electric charge distribution will cause them preferentially to adopt the position of lowest potential energy. Although this order tends to be upset by the kinetic movement of the molecules their overall relative arrangement is far from being random.

In a solid, the kinetic energy is manifested almost entirely by oscillations, rotations and vibrations of the constituent particles (ions, atoms, molecules) about mean positions in a lattice; in the case of an ionic crystal, there is no discrete molecule—the crystal itself is in a sense the molecule. In the transition from a rarefied gas to a solid, the influence on any single particle of 'its neighbours progressively increases. This effect of environment has similarly an increasingly large effect on the behaviour of the individual particles themselves, and thereby on the bulk behaviour of the substance. The concept of an individual molecule diminishes rapidly in importance as the substance is reduced to a more condensed state, and the bulk behaviour of the solid becomes more co-operative in nature. Good examples of this are the so-called 'lambda-point' transitions which a number of crystalline substances undergo when they are raised from a lower temperature to a higher one. The lambda point marks a transition from one type of crystal structure to another. This may be visualized in some cases as the point at which the kinetic energy becomes so large that, for instance, a tetrahedral group in the lattice which is oscillating about a certain mean orientation, may occasionally 'swing over' to a corresponding orientation about which it proceeds once more to oscillate. To permit this 'swing over' to occur, there must be an expansion in the lattice parameters. When this phenomenon is investigated experimentally, it is found that there is no univariant transition point corresponding formally to the melting or to the boiling point. As the temperature is raised towards the lambda point, $dV/dT$—the rate of change of volume with change of temperature—increases progressively rapidly until it becomes extremely large. It then attains a much smaller and more nearly constant value which is the normal coefficient of expansion of the solid. However slowly the temperature is raised this behaviour persists. If the temperature is held constant at some point above which $dV/dT$ has started to increase, the transition will not continue to go forward until more energy is put into the system by increasing the temperature. The phenomenon appears to be co-operative in the sense that the higher energy state is accommodated progressively throughout the substance; the lattice at a temperature slightly below that of the transition point (defined as that temperature at which $dV/dT$ is a maximum) can accommodate both kinds of behaviour. The massive substance is behaving as an entity in which the behaviour of one part is controlling and is controlled by the behaviour of the other parts in the same lattice. The concept of a typical molecule, e.g. $NH_4Cl$, has no meaning—under the same external conditions different ammonium groups are behaving in different ways, and we have no means even in principle of pin-pointing which group is behaving in which way. The lambda-point transition is a property of the lattice as a whole, and not of any constituent part of it.

This is an extreme example of the effect of environment upon one individual in a species, but the concept of the effect of environment is insufficiently stressed in the classical teaching of chemistry. Ions in solution react with the solvent and tend to be solvated. The water of crystallization contained in a hydrated crystal is frequently related to the way in which the ions are solvated in solution. The presence of an ion in solution tends to increase the degree of order already existent in the liquid even beyond the first 'sphere of attraction' which contains those solvent molecules which may be associated with the ion in a solvated crystal. Formulae and equations are only a short-hand representation of typical behaviour, and indeed are an abridged representation of the situation which obtains. Not only do they purport to show only one aspect of the situation as it interests the chemist, but they may be an approximation which conceals an important part of the truth.

This raises a difficult problem in the teaching of chemistry. It is possible to teach the bases of the science by the use of a number of simple models, each adequate for the purpose for which it is used. But they are only models. More complicated and more refined models can approximate more closely to the behaviour of matter as far as it has been investigated, but their complication makes them unsuitable for teaching at elementary levels. To stress the incomplete, and indeed inaccurate, nature of the models being used to illustrate a certain point would inevitably confuse the pupil and might make him lose confidence in the value of the knowledge already gained. It is often desirable to challenge accepted ideas, but such a challenge is only fruitful when it is based on a comprehensive knowledge of those accepted ideas and of the data on which they are based. There seems little alternative but to teach at an elementary stage elementary models as if they were true, and progressively to refine them as the student himself progresses. But the student (and the teacher) must not forget that this refinement leads only to a better model, and that the model itself never becomes a literal description of the matter which is under investigation.

## REFERENCES

(1) MCCREA *Reports Progr. Phys.* **16** 321 (1953)
(2) EDDINGTON *Nature of the Physical World* p. 231 (Everyman's Edition, 1935)
(3) MASCALL *Christian Theology and Natural Science* passim (Longman's, London, 1957)
(4) PEIERLS *Reports Progr. Phys.* **18** 423 (1955)

# CHAPTER 2

# Fact and Fiction

THE EXPERIMENTAL approach to scientific discovery is usually accepted as being in need of no justification, and when a scientist interprets the results of his experiments, he often implicitly adopts a number of assumptions without questioning their accuracy and truth. It is difficult to break away from the total acceptance of certain basic concepts and to remember that they are not facts which have been established by some process of revelation which it is impossible to challenge. Progress is not only impeded by fallacious reasoning and by generalizations which are inconsistent with the available evidence, but also by erecting hypotheses upon principles which are wrongly accepted as being established on unshakeable foundations.

The assumption which lies beneath all experimental science is that the universe, and the matter within it, is composed of the stuff which can be investigated by what we know as scientific method. It is not a logical necessity of this assumption that the results of experiments must be capable of being expressed within a theory or law of universal application. If such laws can be found, it is probable that this is because the universe is rational; however, this is a philosophic conclusion and not a scientific one. Scientists become aware that many of their observations about the behaviour of matter can be collated in such a way that patterns and regularities are apparent, and the fact that these regularities can be integrated into laws of apparently universal application considerably strengthens their own inherent belief about the rationality of the universe. It is not, however, a proof that this is true. The apparent universality of the patterns may be a coincidence, and the patterns may be found because they are what is being sought; it would be difficult to imagine a cosmos of so random a nature that no patterns were fortuitously apparent. However, in applying scientific method, there is no useful alternative to accepting the rationality of the subject of the investigations.

The use of experiment to find out about the nature of the universe is accepted as the basis of scientific investigation, but is the experimental approach in fact the only valid and useful one? Is it possible to investigate by using aprioristic arguments, based on some fundamental postulate which can be established by pure reason? For many years it was thought that this was a fruitful approach to the problem of the behaviour of matter; it dominated scientific thinking from the time of Aristotle to that of

Galileo. It was considered that patterns of beautiful simplicity should underlie the appearance of natural objects and phenomena, and that by contemplation of what the creator had inspired men to consider beautiful, such patterns would be revealed. It was felt that simple patterns were logical necessities of this apparent beauty, and that, in particular, it was probable that there was an underlying symmetry. The aprioristic scientist-philosophers thought that they could identify many phenomena which supported their beliefs. For example, at one time the motions of all the known planets could be accounted for by a system based upon the regular figures of three-dimensional geometry. Considerations of symmetry are deeply engrained in our conceptual thinking, and many of the newly-discovered fundamental particles have probably been the more readily accepted because their existence seems to confirm intuitive ideas about the basic symmetry of matter.

No successful demonstration has yet been made that the behaviour of matter can be determined by aprioristic reasoning from a so-called necessary and obvious fundamental postulate. In recent years, one of the most elaborate attempts to do this was made by Eddington. His exposition involved mathematical and logical processes of extreme difficulty; for this reason few scientists have been sufficiently skilled to be able to comment critically on his work, but it is now generally accepted that his attempt did not succeed. Later mathematicians have challenged the validity of his reasoning, and it also seems probable that he introduced other postulates which were in fact not deduced from his original thesis, but were themselves available as the result of experiments. It is impossible to prove that the behaviour of all matter cannot be deduced in this way, but it does seem at the present time that the nature of things can only be discovered by experiment; in deductive reasoning there comes a point at which there is no *a priori* reason for assuming that events must take one course rather than another, and then the need for experiment is paramount.

An ideal experiment is one that unambiguously confirms or rejects the prediction that has been made on the basis of deductive reasoning. Such experiments are, unfortunately, the exception rather than the rule. The Michelson–Morley experiment is often quoted as an example of such an experimentum crucis, but opportunities to put hypotheses to the test in this way are rare. Much of the development of the physical sciences, and of chemistry in particular, has taken place through the accumulation of a vast corpus of experimental data; any fact which can be established by experiment has some value. The less valuable experiments are those which merely establish that if certain operations are carried out in a specified way, certain results which can be expressed in a quantitive form, will occur. Those experiments of more value cast further light upon the validity of some hypothesis, theory or law, and they are of particular importance if they indicate how such a generalization may be extended, restricted, or modified.

An example of this may be taken from the study of organic chemistry. The result of an organic preparation is frequently a pure and aesthetically pleasing product together with a messy tarry residue. The liquid with the pleasant ethereal smell may well demonstrate that somebody's reaction can be carried out between two reagents not hitherto subjected to it. This has some value, because, while it was most probable that the reaction would follow the expected course, it would have been wrong to assume that to be the case without verification by experiment.What is often neglected is the study of the tarry residue which is discreetly, and usually with some difficulty, washed down the sink. It is important to consider the reason why a 100% of the product was not the pleasant smelling liquid. The reaction cannot be said to have been fully studied until the reactions that produced the tar have been investigated. It is through such 'anomalous' results of experiments that knowledge is often advanced. The experimenter must always be careful to observe and record the 'anomalies' in his experiments; the temptation to assign these to 'experimental error' must be resisted until it can be shown how such error arose, and whether the magnitude of the anomaly was similar to that of the expected error.

The consequences of an experiment may be of two different types which are often confused. In the first place the observed effect may be expressed in such a form that the scale and meter readings can be integrated with similar results of other experiments; the combined results then form a hypothesis which now becomes the subject of further tests. Secondly, there is the possibility that the experimenter may comprehend that his observations lead him to a result which is useful in linking together a wide variety of observations, while it cannot be rigidly deduced from any of them. As Caldin points out ( 1a ):

> Chemical theory is committed to atoms and molecules, and they are not deducible from the empirical laws. Dalton did not deduce the atomic theory from the laws of chemical combination; he invented it with the aid of his imagination, and he found that its consequences agreed with the laws.

Caldin goes on to analyse the attitude of chemists to the theories which are accepted as being so basic as to be ultimate truths, and he points out the dangers inherent in this way of thinking. No one now would seriously suggest that the concept of atoms and molecules is one that is in any danger of successful challenge, but equally everyone would accept that the constitution and behaviour of such particles is infinitely more complex than that which Dalton was able to conceive.

Experimental progress does not only depend on painstaking work illuminated by flashes of insight. It is necessary to provide suitable apparatus; this depends upon advances in technology, and its useful employment is consequent upon improvements in techniques. Professor Jones (1b) recently quoted Louis de Broglie as saying:

> There is one special form of the mechanical art in which the machine becomes the servant of intellectual curiosity; this form is experimental technique—the technique which supplies the scientist with the necessary instruments for studying Nature and discovering its laws. Every important step forward by astronomy, physics, chemistry or biology had one essential condition—the previous existence or invention of certain apparatus; and as the sciences sought to extend their advance, so it became necessary for instrumental technique to develop and to expand . . . since experiments depend on the perfection of experimental technique, the machine today is in a sense one of the essentials of intellectual progress.

The lack of suitable apparatus can be a very real obstacle to the advance of knowledge. For example, it may not be possible to design or to construct a valve which will operate satisfactorily under the conditions of the experiment, or a phenomenon may be beginning to show some feature of unusual interest at the lowest pressure which can be obtained by the available pumping system. Other wants may be more complex, and the experiments will have to wait upon the development of a variety of techniques. The interpretation of X-ray diffraction patterns may not be possible without the use of special electronic computers, and the nature of fundamental particles can only be further investigated by the use of massive accelerators whose construction requires the development of both science and technology. There is some truth in the old adage that 'ninety per cent of scientific experiment consists of plumbing'.

When an experiment has been carried out, and the results have been evaluated, it is necessary to communicate the methods and conclusions to others. The difficulty of communication is a fundamental one in the world today, and it appears in one of its most acute forms in the physical sciences. The sheer mass of recorded information makes it impossible for anyone to be familiar with the published results in any but the narrowest field if he is also to have time to do any original work. Such results are sometimes published by lecture and discussion, but more frequently appear as papers in technical journals. As the volume of information accumulates, it becomes increasingly necessary for the data to be collated in review articles and text-books in such a way as to emphasize the discernible patterns which run through the system of chemical knowledge.

When the data are set out in text-books, there is a natural tendency to regard them as authoritative and final, even though the theories and generalizations are regarded with more suspicion. The fact that theories are suspect and open to question is a striking testimony to the success of the present method of scientific teaching. Many of the critics who dislike, for example, the emphasis placed on the teaching of phlogiston theory in elementary chemistry seem to be unaware of this function of inculcating a critical attitude to established thinking. Such theories are not only taught because it is sometimes easier to introduce more modern ideas by showing the historical processes by which they were derived. The process of training a scientist differs from that of training a technologist who must learn to apply certain established facts rather than to question the very bases from which those facts are derived. In demonstrating how phlogiston and the luminiferous ether became outmoded, it is perhaps unfortunate that they are sometimes made to appear ludicrous; at one time, they seemed to be useful generalizations about the known data. The important fact to note is that so much effort was expended in attempting to perpetuate them when they had ceased to be useful concepts firmly based on experiment. However, the examples used in this way must themselves be chosen to keep pace with the general developments in scientific thought; the Rutherford–Bohr atom is beginning to go the way of caloric and 'alternating affinity' and may supersede earlier hypotheses as an example of how strikingly useful theories eventually become outmoded.

Theories pass through stages of growth and subsequent decline. They may originally be regarded as 'stimulating' and pass from this to the stage of being 'useful'; their final degradation is to be regarded as classical. As one author has ironically put it (2): 'the classical view is one that is wrong, but ancient enough to be forgiven', and again, when writing of a certain theory, '... it has been seriously questioned by some authors. Indeed, it has been repudiated in the strongest terms; it is described as classical'. It is unfortunate that some of the taint, which classical theories have acquired, has rubbed off on classical experiments which in no way deserve it. Sillen (3), writing of solubility products says:

> The values obtained some 50 years ago are often more likely to be correct than some of the values published today. In the old days, there were people who took time to purify their reagents, to analyse their solutions, and to repeat their measurements. This race of careful workers ('classical scientists' as Wilhelm Ostwald would have called them) still exists, but one gets the pessimistic feeling that the percentage of sloppy workers is increasing.

Unfortunately, the quality and indeed the accuracy of experimental work is not of a uniformly high level, and before accepting the published accounts, it is necessary to exercise some measure of critical appraisal. Because it is old, it is not necessarily wrong. Because it is new, it is not necessarily right.

Theories are, or should be, based on experimental data, and while the theory may conceivably be of greater validity than the determinations which it purports to summarize, it cannot be tested except by experimental work of the greatest precision attainable. Experimental work is always inadequate, but inadequacy which stems from failure to examine, to control, to verify and to criticize is inexcusable. It may well be that the author of a scientific paper considered that he had done all this, but it is impossible to make an objective appraisal of his work unless all the data from which the conclusions were derived are clearly stated, and the way in which these data were obtained is sufficiently described to permit an independent worker to repeat the experiment and thereby verify the data if he so desires. It must be remembered that publication of the results of experimental work in a scientific journal, however eminent, is not in the nature of an *ex cathedra* pronouncement which cannot be challenged. It is the exact opposite. Publication offers up the method, the data and the interpretation for informed criticism and appraisal by other competent workers.

A critical appraisal of the data which he includes is an important duty of the writer of any text-book.Wherever possible, such a writer should consult the original reports of the conclusions which he quotes. Since his own judgement will be fallible, he will quote references to such original reports so that the interested reader may form his own opinion on the validity of the conclusions. In many cases, modern experiments are very complex, and the conclusions are derived from the data by an extensive deductive process. The way in which the 'results' quoted in a paper have in fact been deduced from the scale and meter readings which were observed by the experimenters should be subjected to careful scrutiny.

The results which are quoted in text-books as facts have usually undergone at least two 'smoothing' processes. The experimental data have been averaged and condensed within the original paper in order to arrive at a tidy conclusion, and then the conclusions from a number of similar papers have been summarized to form a statement which is sufficiently concise to be included in a text-book of manageable size. These processes can conceal possible sources of experimental error of which the original experimenter may have been only too well aware. This can be illustrated by describing the way in which a simple physical property of a compound was recently determined.

The vapour pressure of plutonium tetrafluoride was measured by the present author and a colleague (4) some years before it was possible to publish the results of the work. This paper has not been chosen for discussion because it was of basic importance or described a fundamental advance in technique; the method employed had been developed over a period of a number of years in the U.S.A. by Phipps and others (5). However, this determination illustrates many of the factors which have to be taken into consideration when interpreting experimental results, and by choosing this particular paper for discussion, the number of those who might be offended by its critical appraisal are severely limited. It illustrates the complexity of a comparatively simple experiment, and the way in which scale and meter readings are converted into derived information.

Measurements of vapour pressure are concerned with two variables— the apparent pressure of the vapour and the corresponding temperature. It is usual to obtain a series of such related pairs of results, and from them to plot a vapour pressure curve. This curve can often be described by an equation of the form (log vapour pressure) = a constant + (another constant divided by the absolute temperature), and thermodynamic properties may be deduced from the numerical values of these two constants.

When a substance exerts an appreciable vapour pressure of, for example, 1 mm of mercury or more at some temperature not far removed from room temperature, it is possible to measure the pressure of the vapour either directly against a column of mercury, or indirectly by allowing a diaphragm to be displaced by the vapour pressure, and to be returned to the null position by an applied measured external pressure. The temperature can be measured by a mercury-in-glass thermometer to a high degree of accuracy. Such a technique was for instance used by the same authors with others to measure the vapour pressure of the hexafluoride of plutonium which is 10 mm of mercury at approximately $-8°$ C (6). This method cannot be applied to a solid such as the tetrafluoride which has a vapour pressure of the order of $\frac{1}{1000}$ mm of mercury at $1100°$ C. The procedure developed by Phipps to measure such pressures was an extension of an effusion method devised by Knudsen (7). If a substance is placed in a closed container, in the lid of which there is a small hole, and the container and its surroundings are evacuated, then the vapour of the substance will effuse through the hole in the lid. The rate of effusion will depend upon a number of factors which include the molecular weight of the compound, the dimensions of the effusion orifice and the vapour pressure of the substance at the temperature at which the experiment is conducted. Knudsen devised an expression for the rate at which the vapour effuses, and measured the quantity which had effused in a given time by weighing the container before and after the experiment had taken place.

Assessing the amount of material which effuses by successive weighings of the container is a laborious procedure because the vacuum must be broken, and the container removed for each determination. This is particularly time-consuming when the material is radio-active and the work is carried out in an enclosed box with extensive precautions to avoid contamination. Phipps devised a more rapid and elegant technique. He used a collimator to define a small pencil of the total effusing mass, and calculated the ratio of the number of molecules within such a pencil to the total number effusing. This pencil, or beam, was allowed to impinge on a small disc. A shutter could be withdrawn and replaced so that the time for which the disc was exposed to the beam could be controlled. Since the compound being investigated contained a radio-active species, the quantity of material which had condensed on the tray could be estimated by electronic disintegration counting techniques. Thus, from the number of radio-active disintegrations detected by a counter, and by the use of equations due to Phipps and Knudsen, the vapour pressure of such a compound can be derived. The corresponding temperature can be measured by an optical pyrometer, as was done by Phipps, or by a thermocouple and potentiometer system as was used by the present author.

The vapour pressure equation in this case was not directly derived from measurements of 'temperature' and 'pressure'. The measured variables were a potential difference in millivolts and the number of radio-active disintegrations indicated on the digital display panel of an electronic counter. Uncertainties and the possibility of error were introduced not only at each stage of the actual measurements but also at each stage of the conversion of the figures derived from the measured variables to the values of temperature and pressure which it was desired to establish. The authors were very conscious of the possible introduction of such inaccuracies, and in the 'experimental' part of the paper, they described their exact procedure in some detail, and also the precautions which it had occurred to them to put into practice. In spite of these attempts to reduce the experimental errors, it is possible to list a variety of ways in which inaccuracy was certainly introduced.

1 *Temperature*

(*a*) The thermocouple used was calibrated at certain fixed points up to 803° C, and above this by interpolation from standard tables. The thermocouple cannot have been identical with those from which the tables were compiled; in any case there is not complete agreement about the temperature of reference points above 1000° C

(*b*) The thermocouple was situated within a sleeve in the effusion pot. The junction was near the mass of tetrafluoride within the pot, but there must certainly have been some difference in temperature between them.

(*c*) At low temperatures, effusion was continued for more than an hour at each temperature, and during this period the temperature as measured with the thermocouple/potentiometer appeared to vary by $\pm 5°$ C.

2 *Vapour Pressure*

(*d*) The Knudsen equation is accurately obeyed only if the effusion orifice is absolutely circular and the rim knife-edged. No real hole can have these characteristics.

(e) The mathematical treatment of the fraction of effusing molecules contained in the collimated pencil is not entirely satisfactory; all that could be done about this was to choose conditions which would minimize the uncertainty.

(f) The effusion pot and its cover expanded when heated; the diameter of the effusion hole therefore altered.

(g) The collimator was of glass mounted in a delicate component. The collimation afforded by this system was probably slightly imperfect.

(h) The tray was cooled to liquid oxygen temperature to improve the adhesion of the incident molecules, but this may well have been less than 100%.

(i) A statistical error is inherent in disintegration counting techniques. This is appreciable when measuring the low activities which resulted from the experiment.

This list of possible sources of error is probably not exhaustive, but it covers the major experimental defects. The magnitude of each could be assessed, and the total probable error compared with the 'scatter' of the observed data. It was concluded that this was insufficient to invalidate the final results. It is, however, instructive to see how the possible sources of error can accumulate even in a comparatively simple experiment in which indirect means are used to measure a simple physical property. As the measured variables become more remote from the property which it is desired to evaluate, so does the interpretation becomes less certain. In some experiments the technique may become so complicated that it becomes uncertain whether what is measured is what it was originally intended to measure, and the interpretation can contain logical fallacies which can invalidate the whole work.

The identification of the elements of the highest atomic number is an example of the difficulty of evaluating experimental work of fundamental importance. The evidence of identification is indirect, and there may be more than one possible interpretation of the observed results. It is work of an entirely different quality from, for instance, the extraction of niobium from tantalum residues, and the identification of a new element in the visible and weighable extract.

The four elements of the highest atomic numbers whose identification has so far been claimed are:

| Einsteinium | 99 | E |
| Fermium | 100 | Fm |
| Mendelevium | 101 | Mv |
| Nobelium | 102 | No |

The identification has not been made by normal chemical methods, and these elements have not been produced in visible or weighable quantities.

The evidence for their existence depends upon observations of ionization pulses in electronic disintegration counters.

It is claimed that $_{99}$E and $_{100}$Fm were first detected in radio-active debris from the American thermonuclear explosion in the Pacific in 1952. Plutonium, americium and curium were subsequently bombarded with neutrons at Berkeley; the products of these bombardments were dissolved in acid, and absorbed on ion exchange resin from which they were then eluted. During the course of this elution, activities were observed at the stage at which it was expected that $_{99}$E and $_{100}$Fm should be present; this was based on analogy with the elution behaviour of the lanthanide series. The justification for this analogy was that the behaviour of the lower members of the actinide series, which had previously been well characterized by conventional chemical methods, was very similar during elution to that of the lanthanides. On 16th January, 1953, it was claimed that fermium had been identified chemically, in that 200 disintegrations, corresponding to 200 atoms of the element, had been observed in the expected elution fration.

The fermium isotope prepared was apparently so short-lived that it was useless to attempt to prepare trans-fermium elements by neutron bombardment of $_{100}$Fm. However, improved techniques led to the production of what was, by these standards, a large quantity of einsteinium—$10^9$ atoms. This preparation was bombarded with a helium beam of $10^{14}$ particles/cm$^2$/sec for 1000 sec. It was hoped that in this way approximately 1 atom of mendelevium might be produced in each experiment and a recoil technique was used to separate any atoms which might be formed. The einsteinium was plated on to a gold foil, through the back of which the beam of helium ions was passed. The momentum of this beam was sufficiently great for any atoms of mendelevium which were produced to recoil and be caught on a second gold foil. A decay process was detected which was interpreted as consisting of electron capture by $_{101}^{256}$Mv to form $_{100}^{256}$Fm which then decayed by spontaneous fission. (Spontaneous fission events can be detected with very high efficiency.)

The second gold foil was then dissolved in acid, and the solution absorbed on a Dowex 50 resin column, elution being carried out with $\alpha$-hydroxy isobutyrate ions at 87° C. Five spontaneous fission counts were observed from the combined results of three bombardments, and their position in the elution process appeared to confirm the presence of mendelevium. One hundred atoms were later detected. Further work (8) confirmed the results obtained; $2 \times 10^{12}$ atoms of $^{253}$E were bombarded with helium ions of energies of 24, 29, 36 and 42 MeV and $^{253}$Mv which decayed to $^{253}$Fm by orbital electron capture with a half life of half an hour was identified.

The identification of $_{101}$Mv was regarded as being well established; however, it is when the evidence for the production of $_{102}$No is discussed that it can be seen how far this type of work differs from the classical criteria which were applied to the discovery of new elements. In 1957, an international team of chemists and physicists carried out a programme of experiments using the cyclotron of the Nobel Institute in Stockholm (9). These workers bombarded $^{244}$Cm with ions of $^{13}$C. The recoil technique was used to separate the expected product, but in this case the secondary foil consisted of Tygon with a thickness corresponding to a density of 1 mg/cm$^2$. This foil was separated from the curium target by a thin aluminium foil (density 50–100 $\mu$g/cm$^2$) which was intended to prevent curium contamination of the Tygon. After the bombardment, the Tygon foil was ignited on a platinum plate. The activity on the plate was first counted directly, and the ash was then dissolved off the plate and the solution absorbed on a cation exchange column. When the ions were eluted with $\alpha$-hydroxy-butyrate, an 8·5 MeV activity was observed in the fraction in which it was hoped $_{102}$No would appear. In the first experiment, four such events were observed. It was concluded that the 8·5 MeV activity was due either to an isotope of element 102 or was possibly the result of electron capture decay of an isotope of 102 with a 10-minute half life to a much shorter lived $\alpha$-emitting mendelevium daughter. It was thought that the most likely reactions were

$$^{244}\text{Cm}\ (^{13}\text{C}, 4n)\ ^{253}_{102}\text{No} \quad \text{or} \quad ^{244}\text{Cm}\ (^{13}\text{C}, 6n)\ ^{251}_{102}\text{No}$$

A total of fifty bombardments was carried out using beams having energies between 70 and 100 MeV for about 30 min. The 8·5 MeV activity was observed in twelve of these bombardments, but only from three out of the six curium targets used, and then only in the first two weeks after their preparation. The subsequent failure to observe the activity was attributed to dilution of the target by impurities, radiation damage, and damage by the cyclotron beam.

These results were severely criticized (10). The experiment was repeated in the United States of America, and $^{250}$Fm, $^{245}$Cf and $^{241}$Cf were identified, but no 8·5 MeV activity was found. It was pointed out that the single elution experiment did not provide a clear chemical differentiation from several possible lighter elements. A 10-min. half life was thought to be more probable for $^{257}$102 or $^{259}$102 than for $^{253}$102 or $^{251}$102. The 8·5 MeV activity was attributed to 'a light element impurity or other artifact'.

The authors who made this criticism described their own work in the course of which they also claimed the identification of the element (11). The bombardment procedure was similar; $^{246}$Cm was bombarded with $^{12}$C in a linear ion accelerator. The target material was plated on to a thin metal foil and placed in a container filled with gaseous helium. Up to this point the experiment was based on established techniques of nuclear physics. The ingenuity displayed by the experimenters in devising the subsequent separation technique is one of the factors which makes the validity of the identification very difficult to assess.

The target foil was surrounded with helium so that the gas could absorb the recoil energy of the transmuted atoms which were knocked from the foil. The atoms, or rather ions, would be positively charged. An endless belt which was negatively charged passed below the target foil, and the field strength was sufficiently high for the positive ions to be attracted to this belt. The belt passed under a catcher foil which was charged, relative to the belt, to a higher negative potential. It was postulated that if atoms of element 102 were formed in the bombardment, their decay would cause their daughter atoms to recoil, and that approximately half would recoil in such a direction that they would be picked up by the field of the catcher foil. After the bombardment, the catcher foil was removed, cut into strips, ignited, dissolved, and subjected to absorption and elution on an ion exchange resin. By studying the activities of the various eluted fractions it was considered that a chemical identification of $^{250}$Fm had been made. When the speed of the endless belt was changed, the distribution of the $^{250}$Fm on the catcher foil was altered, and from this change in distribution, the half life of the postulated parent element 102 could be derived. Two atoms of $^{250}$Fm were detected in one experiment, and nine in another.

What is the validity of the claims made to have identified element 102 in these experiments? Was either successful, or were both? The workers at the Nobel Institute identified something which they took to be the disintegration of an atom of nobelium; the American workers inferred its previous presence from the disintegration of its daughter. In each case the chemical evidence depended on analogies in elution behaviour. There are significant unanswered questions implicit in the Swedish work; why was the activity only observed in 24% of the bombardments, and then only from three of the targets used? Why could the results not be repeated in the U.S.A.? Was the difference in the isotopic composition of the Swedish and American targets significant, and if so why? The American workers state that the excitation energy for producing $^{250}$Fm, which was their indicator of element 102, peaked sharply at $70 \pm 5$ MeV. Were the Swedish workers fortunate enough by chance to have used an even more abrupt absorption peak in some of their experiments? These questions apparently remain unanswered.

The experiments on transmutation which have just been described are particularly difficult for a chemist to evaluate. They illustrate in an extreme the problems which confront any writer of a text-book. Is $_{102}$No to be included among the chemical elements? The cost of such experiments is so high both in money and man-power that they are seldom repeated, and no subsequent claims have yet been made. In this type of work it is more likely that different techniques will be evolved, rather than that the original experiments are exhaustively repeated. If identification is subsequently achieved by the use of different techniques, how does this affect the status of the original experiments?

To return for a moment to the simpler and comparatively straight-forward determination of the vapour pressure of plutonium tetrafluoride, the data indicated that a volatile fluoride $PuF_5$ might have been formed. The case for this was critically examined, and the very tentative conclusion was put forward that it might be produced under the given experimental conditions. All the reservations made in the original paper cannot be reproduced if a writer of a text-book wishes to include such findings. It may be that the existence of, for instance $PuF_5$, is convenient in that analogous compounds of other related elements are known to occur, and its preparation might enable a broad useful generalization to be made about the pentahalides of the actinide elements. $PuF_5$ might then join, in standard text-books, a number of other compounds whose existence is still open to question. The reservations would be repeated in a specialized article on, for example, the halides of plutonium or the fluorides of the actinide elements, but not by the writer of a text-book who cannot go into such detail in the case of every individually unimportant compound which he includes. He must make his own assessment of the validity of the observations.

An example of a compound whose existence was quoted for many years on insufficient evidence is the octafluoride of osmium. The preparation of this compound was first reported in 1913 by Ruff and Tschirch (12). The tetroxide of osmium was well known and there seemed to be no good reason at the time why there should not also be an octavalent fluoride; elements were well known to show their highest valency in combination with fluorine. One of the properties of the compound claimed to be the octafluoride was its ability to combine with the fluorides of the alkali metals; salt-like addition compounds were formed with remarkable ease. It was unfortunate, as Sidgwick pointed out (13), that these addition compounds were not analysed, because they were remarkable in that their existence would have involved the covalency maximum of osmium being 9 or 10, and it was difficult to reconcile this with the predictions of electronic valency theory.

Very little work was done on the compound itself, and there are no references to it in the literature for many years after the work of Ruff and Tschirch. It was quoted in text-books as an accepted fact. However, in 1958, Weinstock and Malm were carrying out a comparative study of the hexafluorides of the actinides and of other transition elements. They pointed out (14) that the melting and boiling points of $OsF_8$ as reported by Ruff and Tschirch were anomalous, and were more nearly those which would be expected for $OsF_6$. They repeated the synthesis of '$OsF_8$' and obtained a compound with properties similar to those reported by the earlier German workers. It was a yellow compound which they found melted at $32.1°$ C (Ruff and Tschirch, $34.4$) and boiled at $45.9°$ C (R. and T., $47.3$). They made careful chemical analyses and vapour density measurements, from which they deduced a molecular weight of $307.6 \pm 3.9$, and a F : Os ratio of $6.11 : 1$. The X-ray diffraction pattern was similar to that of $IrF_6$, and the infra-red and Raman spectrum were similar to those of other hexafluorides.

An independent synthesis was carried out by other workers (15) who also measured the magnetic susceptibility. This varied with temperature in the way to be expected for a compound of sexivalent osmium containing two electrons with unpaired spins. The chemical and physical properties of this compound were the same as those found by Weinstock and Malm. The vibrational spectrum was found to be similar to that of the other hexa-fluorides (16). A full theoretical treatment of the optical absorption spectrum could only be reconciled with a hexafluoride structure (17). Finally, the material which was now well characterized as $OsF_6$ was reduced with tungsten carbonyl (18) and a compound $OsF_5$ was produced which appeared to be the same compound as an '$OsF_6$' reported by Ruff and Tschirch. It has been suggested that the early findings were due to the difficulty of obtaining a steady stream of pure fluorine at the date when the experiments were undertaken. '$OsF_8$' was probably $OsF_6$ contaminated with HF. This would account for the reported reactivity with glass of '$OsF_8$'; Weinstock and Malm found that if their $OsF_6$ was completely free from HF, it did not attack glass.

The existence of osmium octafluoride was quoted as a fact in innumerable text-books. Such a statement is an example of those things which achieve the status of truths by processes other than that of scientific method. It is possible to distinguish four classes of such spurious facts.

1. Things that are true by repetition.
2. Things that are true by simplification.
3. Things that are true by 'smoothing' or by omitting irregularities and exceptions.
4. Things that are true within a narrow context, but which are allowed by custom to appear true in a wide context.

It is not always possible to assign a particular mis-statement to a single one of these categories, but the teaching of chemistry abounds with examples of statements which are not in accordance with all the known facts. This is probably inevitable when it is necessary to present an outline to elementary students, but it is doubtful how far it is realized that this is taking place and whether much thought is given to it. Can it be right to teach ideas which not only are at variance with the latest theories, but which also are not in accord with the experimental facts?

Attention was recently drawn to such a statement by Rothery (19):

For many years it has been customary in school text-books to represent acids and bases by means of the Arrhenius picture. Acids are regarded as substances which release hydrogen ions in aqueous solution. The ion is represented as a bare proton $H^+$. A base then produces hydroxyl ions in solution, and acids neutralize bases giving water

$$H^+ + OH^- \longrightarrow H_2O + \text{heat}$$

There are many objections which must be raised to this picture, e.g.

(i) An acid does not release free protons into solution. Hydrogen ions are solvated protons (protons attached to one or more solvent molecules). This is also true of non-aqueous solvents.

(ii) The solvent is an essential agent in acid base reactions. Pure anhydrous acids and bases will not combine without moisture.

Loose statements are often made about trivial properties of compounds. Carbon disulphide has not in fact got an unpleasant smell—when pure it has a rather pleasant sweet ethereal smell. Benzene is only an unreactive compound under certain conditions of reaction; its vapour will take fire and readily become oxidized. Statements of the latter type are excused on the grounds that it is well known that a particular type of unreactivity is implied, in this case unreactivity to the type of reagent which readily attacks unsaturated aliphatic compounds, but it is very doubtful whether the reception of such unscientific statements is the best training for scientific minds. If the problem of scientific communication is to be solved it can only be by making lucid and more accurate statements, and not by vaguer and less accurate ones.

Less trivial properties are often equally badly described. Generations of students have had to memorize the equation which is said to represent the effect of heat on ammonium dichromate:

$$(NH_4)_2Cr_2O_7 = Cr_2O_3 + 4H_2O + N_2$$

It is most improbable that this is quantitatively true, and the equation casts no light on the mechanism of an interesting reaction. Again, the most extraordinary statements are still made about the composition of the common material bleaching powder. This was studied by X-ray diffraction methods in 1935; the results of the investigation have never been contradicted, but they have found their way into few text-books. It appears (20) that bleaching powder forms crystals of variable composition consisting chiefly of $Ca(OCl)_2$ together with some basic chloride $CaCl_2 . Ca(OH)_2 . H_2O$. The basic chloride is a very stable non-deliquescent substance. It is this compound which is responsible for the difficulty of complete chlorination and the non-deliquescent nature of the material.

Sometimes statements are made in good faith on the basis of the best experimental evidence available at the time, but when the statement is refuted as a result of further work, the amendment fails to be made, and the original statement continues to gain authority through repetition. The study of the intensive drying of materials gave rise to a number of statements about the effect of this procedure on various compounds. For instance, it was said that if dinitrogen tetroxide is intensively dried, its vapour pressure increases above that normally found for the compound. It was afterwards demonstrated that the $N_2O_4$ reacted with phosphorus pentoxide, the drying agent used in the experiments, to form $P_2O_5 \cdot 2NO$. This reaction results in the release of oxygen, and gives rise to an apparent increase in vapour pressure (21).

Structural formulae provide many instances of unfortunate representations of compounds. They are particularly subject to the dictates of fashion. The history of such formulae is in itself a fascinating study; the theory of structure in organic chemistry from the time of Wollaston (1808) to the present day has been discussed in an informal and percipient article which throws light on the whole development of organic chemistry (22). The co-ordinate link held a peculiar fascination for formulae writers. Oxy compounds are still sometimes shown with such formulae as

$$ H-O-N \overset{\nearrow O}{\underset{\searrow O}{}} \qquad Cl-\overset{\overset{Cl}{|}}{\underset{\underset{Cl}{|}}{P}}\rightarrow O \qquad \overset{Cl}{\underset{Cl}{}}\overset{\nearrow}{\underset{\searrow}{S}}\overset{O}{\underset{O}{}} \qquad H-O-\overset{\overset{O}{\uparrow}}{\underset{\underset{O}{\downarrow}}{Cl}}\rightarrow O $$

The length of a co-ordinate link should be similar to that of a single bond. It has been pointed out (23) that bonds indicated by arrows in the above formulae are in fact as short or shorter than double bonds. It is more likely, in the words of the authors of this paper, that they are 'old fashioned' double bonds. Such a bond could use $d$-orbitals to form $d_\pi$—$p_\pi$ bonds.

It is perhaps natural to assume that if there is no specific statement to the contrary, statements of experimental fact apply to conditions in which the temperature and pressure are not far removed from normal atmospheric conditions. The study of chemistry at high temperature is however becoming increasingly important; for instance in connexion with so-called homogeneous nuclear reactors. Little work was done on what is now regarded as high temperature chemistry before 1940; the first authoritative review was published in 1956 (24). There is little chemistry at 10,000° K; above this temperature few species containing more than three atoms can exist. Many compounds may be identified at 2000° K, and their valency relationships differ from those which are commonly found at room temperature. At high temperatures, KT is of the same order of magnitude as the separation between electronic energy levels, and most atoms exist in excited states. The oxides of aluminium, for example, illustrate some of the unfamiliar features of chemistry above $1000°$ C. $Al_2O_3$ has a very low vapour pressure, but is has been known for some years that it is more volatile in the presence of aluminium. Analysis of the volatile product, and a study of its spectrum, has shown that in these reducing conditions a lower oxide is formed and that $Al_2O$, but probably not AlO, is stable in the temperature range $1600–2000°$ C (25). Other workers consider that the compound is chiefly present in the form of the ion $[Al_2O]^+$ at $1480°$ C.

The chemistry of boron compounds at high temperature has also been investigated recently because of the interest in boron-containing rocket fuels. For example, under neutral or oxydizing conditions, solid boric oxide $B_2O_3$ evaporates to form gaseous $B_2O_3$, but under reducing conditions, $B_2O_2$ is formed (27); such reducing conditions are obtained when a mixture of boron and boric oxide is heated (28). A gaseous hydroxide HOBO is believed to be formed when boric oxide is vapourized in the presence of water; the properties of this compound have been studied at temperatures up to $1450°$ K (29).

The existence of such compounds as $Al_2O$ and HOBO as stable species under particular conditions of temperature and pressure illustrate the point that words like 'stable' or 'unreactive' should not be used in a loose sense without specifying the conditions under which the stability or the lack of reactivity apply. As Orgel has pointed out (30):

It should perhaps be emphasized that our ideas of stability are in part a consequence of the chemical operations which we find convenient. If water were less common, and the atmosphere more reducing, the carbonyls would perhaps be regarded as the typical transition metal compounds, and the hydrates, higher oxides, etc. as chemical curiosities.

When statements of fact are considered, it is therefore necessary not only to consider the validity of the methods by which the quoted data were obtained, but also the physical conditions to which the deduced results apply. In addition, it must be remembered that there may be assumptions implicit in the reasoning by which the results were deduced. As Caldin also points out in the article referred to above (1):

Chemists nowadays tend to take for granted the general theoretical background of atoms, molecules, energy and quanta; their controversies concern detailed molecular models, as in the theory of reaction mechanisms, or the theory of liquids or of molecular structure.

It is not suggested that accepted ideas of the atomic nature of chemical substances should be jettisoned because some single experiment casts doubt upon the law of constant composition; it is possible to put forward almost irrefutable arguments for the existence of atoms and molecules. On

4

the other hand, many assumptions are made in any discussion of chemical theory, and their validity is not proved by the simple statement that many people believe them to be true.

## REFERENCES

(1) (a) CALDIN *Proc. Chem. Soc.* 269 (1958)
    (b) LOUIS DE BROGLIE Address to the Lycee Pasteur 13th July, 1953, quoted by JONES *Bull. Inst. Phys.* 102 (April, 1962)
(2) WALD The Selig Hecht Memorial Lecture, *Visual Problems of Colour* p. 30. National Physical Laboratory (H.M.S.O., 1957)
(3) SILLEN *J. Inorg. Nuclear Chem.* 8 176 (1958)
(4) MANDLEBERG and DAVIES *J. Chem. Soc.* 2031 (1961)
(5) (a) PHIPPS, SEARS, SEIFERT and SIMPSON *NNES* XIVb paper 6.1a
    (b) PHIPPS, SEARS and SIMPSON ibid. paper 6.1b
    (c) ERWAY and SIMPSON *AECD* 2733 (1948) etc.
(6) MANDLEBERG, RAE, HURST, LONG, DAVIES and FRANCIS *J. Inorg. Nuclear Chem.* 2 358 (1956)
(7) KNUDSEN *Ann. Phys.* 28 75 (1909), 29 179 (1909)
(8) PHILIPS, GATTI, CHESNE, MUGA and THOMPSON *Phys. Rev. Letters* 1 215 (1958)
(9) FIELDS, FRIEDMAN, MILSTED, ATTERLING, FORSLING, HOLM and ASTROM *Phys. Rev.* 107 1460 (1957)
(10) GHIORSO, SIKKELAND, WALTON and SEABORG *Phys. Rev. Letters* 1 17 (1958)
(11) GHIORSO, SIKKELAND, WALTON and SEABORG *Phys. Rev. Letters* 1 18 (1958)
(12) RUFF and TSCHIRCH *Ber.* 46 929 (1913)
(13) SIDGWICK *Chemical Elements and their Compounds* p. 1506 (Clarendon Press, 1950)
(14) WEINSTOCK and MALM *J. Amer. Chem. Soc.* 80 4466 (1958)
(15) HARGREAVES and PEACOCK *Proc. Chem. Soc.* 85 (1959)
(16) (a) WEINSTOCK, CLEASEN and MALM *J. Chem. Phys.* 32 181 (1960)
    (b) MOFFITT, GOODMAN, FRIED and WEINSTOCK *Mol. Phys.* 2 109 (1959)
(17) EISENSTEIN *J. Chem. Phys.* 34 311 (1961)
(18) HARGREAVES and PEACOCK *J. Chem. Soc.* 2618 (1960)
(19) ROTHERY *J. Roy. Inst. Chem.* 85 4 (1961)
(20) BUNN, CLARK and CLIFFORD *Proc. Roy. Soc.* A151 141 (1935)
(21) STODDART (a) *J. Chem. Soc.* 1459 (1938)
    (b) *J. Chem. Soc.* 448 (1945)
(22) FARRAR and FARRAR *Proc. Chem. Soc.* 285 (1959)
(23) PHILIPS, HUNTER and SUTTON *J. Chem. Soc.* 146 (1945)
(24) BREWER and SEARCY *Ann. Rev. Phys. Chem.* 7 259 (1956)
(25) COCHRAN *J. Amer. Chem. Soc.* 77 2190 (1955)
(26) PORTER, SCHISSEL and INGHRAM *J. Chem. Phys.* 23 339 (1955)

(27) (*a*) EVANS, PROSEN and WAYMAN *Thermodynamic and Transport Properties of Gases Liquids and Solids* p. 226 (McGraw–Hill Book Co., N.Y., 1960)

(*b*) WHITE, WALSH and RENTZEPIS *J. Phys. Chem.* **64** 1784 (1960)

(28) INGHRAM, PORTER and CHUPKA *J. Chem. Phys.* **25** 498 (1956)

(29) (*a*) MARGRAVE *J. Phys. Chem.* **60** 715 (1956)

(*b*) WHITE, MANN, WALSH and SOMMER *J. Chem. Phys.* **32** 488 (1960)

(30) ORGEL *An Introduction to Transition Metal Chemistry* p. 132 (Methuen, London, 1960).

# CHAPTER 3

# Fundamental Particles

THE TRADITIONAL definition of an atom was that it was a small indivisible particle. A hundred years ago there was no evidence to show how the atoms of the various elements differed, and for many purposes it was only necessary to accept that there was such a difference. The organic chemists of the nineteenth century, for instance, were primarily concerned with the structural patterns which could be synthesized from the atoms of carbon and of a few other elements, and with the properties of the compounds which resulted from such syntheses. They were handicapped by the lack of a useful theory of valency, and they had difficulty in interpreting the mechanisms of many reactions, but the absence of an electronic theory did not prevent them from making notable discoveries; the progress in organic chemistry in the latter half of the century was very rapid even when judged by the rate of technical advance to which we are accustomed today.

The discovery of radio-activity in the latter years of the nineteenth century made it appear probable that the atom was not an indivisible unit, and that it had a structure of its own; in 1909 Rutherford first described the familiar atomic model in which planetary negative electrons revolved around a positively charged central nucleus. His ideas were developed and extended by Bohr, who put forward in 1913 his hypothesis of electronic orbits and electron 'jumps'. The purpose of this hypothesis was to offer an explanation of the events which take place when radiation and matter interact. The Bohr orbits of the electrons correspond to discrete electronic energy levels, and Bohr suggested that when radiation is absorbed by an atom, an electron jumps into a level of higher energy, the difference between the initial and final energy levels being equal to the quantity of energy absorbed from the radiation. If the electron subsequently falls back into a lower level, energy is once more emitted in the form of radiation. In these events, the unit of energy is the quantum, of magnitude $h\nu$. On the basis of this hypothesis, Bohr calculated the frequency of a number of the lines in the emission spectrum of the hydrogen atom, and the values which he found agreed with those measured by experiment to a very high degree of precision.

The electron is not now conceived as a minute material particle travelling in an orbit fixed in space around an equally material and localized nucleus. Wave mechanics has smeared both the electron and the nucleus into mere probability clouds within which exact location in time and place is meaningless. But the behaviour of the smeared electrons can still be described for many purposes according to the Bohr equations and parameters. The quantum numbers which uniquely describe any electron are still valid for this purpose, even if the picture presented by Bohr of electrons moving in ellipses whose major and minor axes are described by the first two quantum numbers is no longer acceptable. As is so often the case in physical theory, the mathematics remains valid even if the pictorial model becomes so strained in the attempt to accommodate within it every new discovery that it no longer conveys any useful impression of the phenomenon. Part of Bohr's genius is that not only can he derive mathematical expressions of lasting value, but also that he can translate the figures into useful images which enable striking theoretical advances to be made. As Hoffmann says in his brilliant and entertaining book *The Strange Story of the Quantum* (1):

> When Atomic theory falters, he helps it along with an admittedly temporary theory which somehow proves dazzlingly successful. . . . Bohr is the great sustainer and tider-over of atomic physics, a vital catalyst to keep the flickering mental flame alive until it be self-sustaining.

It does not matter how the fundamental particles are visualized as long as it is in a way which is of value in considering a certain problem, and as long as it is remembered that no visual image represents what they are 'really' like. How the particles behave is a different question. If wave-mechanical equations can be set up to describe their behaviour, it is an immense advance, but it must be remembered that the wave mechanics is a mathematical description of behaviour, and that it is not necessary that a mechanistic model can be set up to reproduce the effect of all the terms and operators. If it is useful and convenient to talk of electrons as if they were discrete material entities, there is no reason in a particular case why this should not be done. For instance, in the 1961 edition of his standard work on chemical crystallography, Bunn writes:

> X-rays . . . are produced when rapidly moving electrons accelerated by potentials of some tens of thousands of volts, collide with atoms; the energy released when the electrons are suddenly stopped is given out in the form of electro-magnetic waves . . . (2).

This is a perfectly adequate description of the process within its context. To attempt to describe in this connexion the fundamental particles in any other way than by describing them as particles would make the phenomenon less readily comprehensible. It must therefore be remembered in reading this chapter that all the particles whose behaviour is described are as tenuous as electrons, that in quantum phenomena they appear as particles, that at other times they exhibit some of the properties of waves, and that they would more properly be conceived as existing in space in such a way that their location can only be described in terms of probability functions. Their detection depends on the observation of secondary or tertiary phenomena, or even on events removed from the particle itself by a long chain of interactions, and the confident statements made about their nature and properties are for the most part deductions derived from a wide array of evidence rather than from any one single conclusive observed event.

There have been very few serious attempts to describe the structure of the atom other than within the broad outlines of the Rutherford–Bohr model. All the modern theories which have found a wide measure of acceptance and which have been useful in stimulating advances in experimental discovery have envisaged a positively charged central nucleus in which almost all the mass of the atom is concentrated, and which is surrounded by negatively charged electrons. It is conventional to say that the nucleus is small in comparison with the size of the atom as a whole without defining rigidly what such a statement means. Certain alternative theories of structure have been put forward, for instance that of Tutin (3). These other theories have not been found to be as useful as that of Rutherford and Bohr in developing our ideas of atomic structure. There has been no serious rival to the Rutherford–Bohr atom as an elementary model of atomic processes, although it is now recognized to be a considerable oversimplification of the state of affairs described by the relevant wave-equations. In constructing this model, no attempt was made to describe the structure of the nucleus, nor was this necessary in order to describe the interaction of electrons with radiation. On the other hand, the electron jump between orbits of different energies is not a very satisfactory picture of this interaction. A considerable amount of research, both theoretical and experimental, has been undertaken since 1935, and much information is now available about both nuclear structure and the interaction of matter with radiation. Some of this information is reviewed in this chapter, together with an outline of the state of our present knowledge about some of the known fundamental particles.

Within a nucleus, protons and neutrons are bound together. The binding forces are exceedingly powerful in comparison with attractive forces such as the bond energies with which the chemist is familiar. It is apparent that they cannot be electrostatic in nature since they act on neutral and positively charged particles—all nuclei have a net positive charge. If the nucleus is considered to contain discrete particles, it can be shown that the distance of separation of the constituent nucleons is of the order of $10^{-13}$ cm. (1 Fermi). At such a distance the attractive force between the sub-nuclear particles is 35 times as strong as the proton–proton electrostatic repulsive force, and $10^{38}$ times as strong as the gravitational attraction between the particles (4). Such a force, of enormous power, and neither gravitational nor electrostatic in nature, is difficult to visualize in terms of concepts familiar in the large scale world. Our present understanding of it is based on work by Yukawa (5). His theory of the mechanism by which such a force could operate was entirely mathematical in form. However, his expression which described the force contained a term which could be interpreted as implying the exchange of 'virtual particles' between the protons and neutrons in the nucleus. Yukawa did not claim a 'real' existence for these particles, but as the theory was developed it became apparent that the exchange forces which he described could be accounted for if particles were 'really' exchanged exceedingly rapidly within the nucleus. The theory was further extended by other workers, notably Kemmer (6). It was shown that such particles would have a mass between two and three hundred times that of the electron; they were referred to as 'mesons'.

No particles of mass intermediate between that of the electron and of the neutron had previously been known, but in 1937, two years after the publication of Yukawa's first paper, such a particle was identified during a study of results of cosmic ray interaction with matter. The particle was named a $\mu$-meson (7). In order to perform the exchange function of binding the sub-nuclear particles, it was obviously necessary that the Yukawa meson should interact very strongly with such particles. Unfortunately it was shown that the $\mu$-meson in fact interacted very weakly and was not capable of filling the role assigned to it in Yukawa's theory. Ten years later, however, another type of mesonic particle was identified (8). This particle, known as the $\pi$-meson reacted strongly with neutrons and protons, and its properties corresponded with those which had been postulated by Yukawa for the exchange particles.

High energy particles are necessary for experimental work of this type, so that when nuclei are bombarded by them, the strong intra-nucleon binding forces are overcome and fragments of the nucleus ejected. Until large particle accelerators were built, the only source of very energetic nuclear missiles was the cosmic radiation. This consists of charged particles, which are mainly protons, although there is also a small proportion of the stripped nuclei of heavier elements; nuclei, that is to say, which have become stripped of all their orbital electrons. The origin of the cosmic particles, and the nature of the forces by which they are accelerated to very high speeds is not yet known. The number of particles which can be detected on the earth is at a maximum during violent solar storms, and it is therefore probable that a proportion of the particles is emitted by the sun. It is unlikely that the sun is the source of all the particles, or even of a large proportion of them. The radiation arrives at the earth's surface with an equal intensity from all directions in space. The directions from which particles arrive cannot be identified with the positions of specific heavenly bodies which might emit them. There are two principal theories of their origin, but there is not sufficient evidence to establish either of them. The theory which has been put forward by Bruno Rossi postulates that the particles are emitted with the high energies which they possess when they reach the earth by certain localized objects in the galaxy such as super-novae (9). The most important alternative theory is that due to Fermi. He suggests that the particles are emitted with relatively low energies by ordinary stars of which the sun is one example. The particles are then presumed to be accelerated to very high velocities by the magnetic fields which are supposed to exist in interstellar space.

It has been estimated that each square metre at the top of the earth's atmosphere is crossed by an average of some 1000 cosmic particles per second (10). If the number of particles with a given energy is plotted against the energy which the particles possess, it is found that this number falls off very rapidly as the energy increases. Most of the particles which are detected have energies less than 10 GeV; less than 1 in $10^{10}$ arrives with an energy greater than $10^7$ GeV and only 1 in $10^{14}$ has an energy greater than $10^9$ GeV (1 GeV = 1000 MeV).

The particles in the cosmic radiation were the tools with which the earlier investigations into the structure of the nucleus were carried out. When such energetic particles penetrate sufficiently closely to an atomic nucleus, it may be disrupted, and sub-nuclear particles emitted after the 'collision'. There are two principal methods by which the results of such a reaction may be detected. In the first of these, a cloud chamber is exposed to the cosmic radiation, and a series of photographs are taken in the hope that in one or more of them interesting particle tracks may be visible. The second method uses photographic emulsion in light-tight cases to detect the interesting events. As the particles pass through the packages their tracks are recorded in the sensitive photographic emulsion. If the cosmic particle passes so close to a nucleus of an atom in the emulsion that it can be said to 'collide' with the nucleus, the release of energy results in a star of affected silver bromide particles in the emulsion. Whichever technique is used, the exposure is usually made at a high altitude, for instance in aeroplanes, balloons, rocket missiles, or on the top of a mountain, so that the cosmic ray showers are as little attenuated as possible by previous collisions with gas nuclei in the atmosphere. It is of interest that the most penetrating particles have such high energies that they may be detected in small numbers below the earth's surface, for example at the bottom of coal mines.

The characteristic 'star' in the emulsion package, and the point of reaction in the cloud-chamber photograph have emanating from them tracks which are characteristic of the nuclear reaction which has taken place. From the length of the tracks, their angle of emission and general nature, it is possible to make deductions about the particles which gave rise to them. It was by the use of these methods that the Yukawa particles were first detected.

The mesons were first produced artificially in the proton-synchroton at Berkeley, California. In this machine, protons can be accelerated to high velocities and therefore to high energies; the proton beam of 0·34 GeV is sufficiently energetic to disrupt the nucleus with the production of $\pi$-mesons. The reaction is observed in stacks of photographic emulsion. Two of the earliest artificially induced nuclear reactions recorded in this way were:

$$p+p \longrightarrow \pi^+ + (p+n) \longrightarrow \pi^+ + D \tag{11}$$

$$\pi^+ + D \longrightarrow p+p \tag{12}$$

Excellent qualitative agreement with the predictions of the Yukawa theory was found in this way. It was also possible to make certain other calculations from the measurements of the tracks. There was an unknown matrix element in the calculation, but the equations could be combined in such a way that this element in the two sets of equations cancelled out, and the cross-sections of the reactions were then calculated. It was also shown that the $\pi$-meson had a zero intrinsic spin.

The mesons are ejected from a disrupted nucleus with a very high velocity. They therefore travel through the emulsion for a measurable distance before they decay with the production of other particles, even though their lifetime before undergoing this decay is short.

Soon after the discovery of the positively charged $\pi$-meson, negatively charged and neutral $\pi$-mesons were identified as well as positively and negatively charged $\mu$-mesons. Their decay schemes and other data are summarized in the following table (13):

| Meson | Mass $(m_e)$ | Decay scheme | Lifetime $(sec)$ |
|-------|------|--------------|---------|
| $\pi^{\pm}$ | 273 | $\pi^{\pm} \rightarrow \mu^{\pm} + \nu$ | $2 \cdot 55 \times 10^{-8}$ |
| $\mu^{\pm}$ | 207 | $\mu^{\pm} \rightarrow e^{\pm} + 2\nu$ | $2 \cdot 1 \times 10^{-6}$ |
| $\pi^{\circ}$ | 264 | $\pi^{\circ} \rightarrow 2\gamma$ | $10^{-14}$ |

The mass unit in which sub-atomic masses are expressed ($m_e$) is the rest mass of the electron.

Two further particles are involved in the above decay scheme. These are the positron ($e^+$) and the neutrino ($\nu$). The positron was discovered in 1932 in the course of early cosmic ray studies by C. D. Anderson. This particle is produced together with a negative electron when a photon is converted into matter. Similarly, if a positron and an electron approach sufficiently closely, the particles disappear and a high energy photon is produced. In these two complementary reactions, the energetic changes involved are in accordance with Einstein's law of the equivalence of mass and energy.

The neutrino, like the Yukawa meson, was first postulated as a mathematical device. It was necessary to introduce an electrically neutral particle with zero mass, but with one unit of spin in order to conserve the spin in a reaction such as

$$n \longrightarrow p + e^- + \nu$$

in which a neutron, in Hoffmann's words, 'sheds an electron' and a proton is formed.

The pions and muons were the first members of the series of sub-nuclear particles to be identified. In 1947, $\kappa$-particles were identified during a cloud-chamber investigation of cosmic ray showers at Manchester (14). These particles have a mass in the range 800–1000 times that of an electron, and they are thus intermediate in mass between the mesons, and the nucleons ($n$ and $p$). A positively charged $\kappa$-particle known as a $\tau^+$-particle was identified in 1949, and the decay scheme established (15):

$$\tau^+ \longrightarrow \pi^+ + \pi^+ + \pi^- + 75 \text{ MeV} \quad (10^{-9} \text{ sec})$$

Its mass was shown to be $966\cdot4\ m_e$. The decay schemes of two further $\kappa$-particles were subsequently worked out:

$$\Lambda^\circ \longrightarrow p + \pi^- + 36\cdot9 \text{ MeV} \quad (3 \times 10^{-10} \text{ sec}) \tag{16}$$

$$\theta^\circ \longrightarrow \pi^+ + \pi^- + 214 \text{ MeV} \quad (10^{-10} \text{ sec}) \tag{17}$$

The charged $\kappa$-particles all decay to more than one secondary meson; the $\tau^+$-particle referred to in reference (15) decays to 3 pions and such a particle is described as a $\kappa_{3\pi}^+$-particle. Other similar particles which have been identified include $\kappa_{3\mu}^+$, $\kappa_{2\mu}^+$, $\kappa_{2\pi}^+$ and $\kappa_{3e}^+$. All these were originally discovered during studies of cosmic ray showers. The negatively charged $\kappa^-$-particles are particularly difficult to detect. They are captured by nuclei in the photographic emulsion and behave in the same manner as do electrons, in that they first occupy classical Bohr orbits. The captured particles then cascade down into successive orbits of lower and lower energy, and they are eventually captured by the nucleus itself.

The particles of intermediate mass such as the $\kappa$-particles are sometimes referred to as hyperons. The electron and positron are known as leptons and the heavier particles such as the nucleons (proton and neutron) are known as baryons. Three other baryons, which are also sometimes described as hyperons, are well established. The $\Xi^-$-particle is known as a cascade particle, from its characteristic appearance in emulsion stacks. It rapidly decays to a $\Lambda°$-particle, which in turn soon decays to a proton and a negative pion. The first stage of this decay scheme is (18):

$$\Xi^- \longrightarrow \Lambda° + \pi^- + 65 \text{ MeV}$$

Two types of $\Sigma$-particle have been identified, one negatively and one positively charged. The $\Sigma^-$-particle is also difficult to detect because it undergoes neutron absorbtion.

$$\Sigma^+ \nearrow p + \pi^0 + 116 \cdot 1 \text{ MeV} \tag{19}$$

$$\searrow n + \pi^+ + 110 \text{ MeV} \tag{20}$$

$$\Sigma^- \longrightarrow n + \pi^- + 118 \text{ MeV} \tag{21}$$

When the only high energy particles which could be used in the study of nuclear reactions were the cosmic rays, the characterization of particles and their reactions was extremely difficult. The arrival of a cosmic particle of the right energy at the right time and place is a matter of chance and in order to identify a nuclear reaction of the type under investigation, it was often necessary to examine hundreds or thousands of photographs of cloud chambers or of stacks of photographic emulsion. The research could not be controlled, and the energy of the incident particle could only be deduced from its effects. High energy particle accelerators were built in the ten years after the war, and one of the factors underlying their design was the need to study nuclear reactions. Two of the largest machines constructed for this purpose are the high energy proton-synchrotons at Brookhaven National Laboratory and at the University of California Radiation Laboratory. These are known as the B.N.L. 3 GeV Cosmotron and the U.C.R.L. 6·2 GeV Bevatron respectively.

Well-defined beams of secondary particles may be obtained from these machines when accelerated protons are directed on to suitable targets placed within the accelerator itself. For research into $\kappa$-particles, the internal target is usually made of copper or tantalum. When 4·6 GeV protons are directed on to a tantalum target, a positive beam is produced with an average energy of 0·375 GeV per $cm^2$. A typical beam produced in this way contained 87·3% protons, 3·8% pions, 0·8% positrons and 0·04% $\kappa^+$-hyperons. The remainder of the beam consists of $^2H$, $^3H$, $^3He$ and $^4He$ nuclei (22). In order to produce for study a beam of hyperons and mesons, the beam is passed through an absorption screen. In this, the protons and any other baryons are brought to rest. The positrons are degraded within the screen, and a beam of $\kappa^+$-particles and $\pi^+$-mesons emerge. Before their behaviour is studied in an emulsion stack, the average velocities of the two types of particles are measured by the use of a Cerenkov detector. The momentum of the two types of particles is the same, but since they have different masses, the velocities and therefore the energies are different. When they pass into the emulsion stack, they penetrate to different depths because of this difference in energy. The $\pi^+$-mesons penetrate the further, and since the reactions of the two types of particles take place in different parts of the stack, their behaviour may be studied separately. Approximately sixty-five $\pi^+$-mesons are produced for every $\kappa^+$-particle.

The negative beam at U.C.R.L. consists almost entirely of $\pi$-mesons— 12,000 are produced for every $\kappa^-$-particle. This is because a very high threshold energy of 2·50 GeV is required for the reaction in which the latter are produced. The reaction is a pair reaction, and a $\kappa^+$-particle is also emitted. As well as being produced in this way, $\kappa^+$-particles are also produced in conjunction with a $\Lambda^0$-hyperon instead of with a $\kappa^-$-particle. This reaction has a much lower threshold energy ( 1·57 GeV). It is for these two reasons that the number of $\kappa^+$-particles produced is much larger than that of $\kappa^-$-particles. The particles so far studied in these experiments are $\kappa_{2\mu}$, $\kappa_{2\pi}$, $\tau^+(\kappa_{3\pi})$, $\kappa_{3\mu}$ and $\kappa_{3e}$. The mass of each of these particles has been found to be 966 $\pm$ 1 $m_e$.

The Yukawa $\pi$-meson is the only one of all these particles which is a necessary component of any theory so far put forward to explain the structure of compound nuclei. While the interactions of the meson form a basis for a theory of how the components of the nucleus are held together, it is also important to know in what way nuclear properties may be related to this detailed structure. 'The detailed structure' of the nucleus refers not to the geometrical arrangement of the particles in space in the sense in which crystal structure is used to describe the arrangements of atoms in a lattice, but to the manner in which nuclear particles are distributed among the various energy levels within the nucleus. The models used in describing the situation refer to energy arrangements and not to spatial arrangements. Any idea of a physical packing of particles within a nucleus is probably entirely without meaning. The particles are wave-mechanical particles which are smeared out to fill the small nuclear volume. It is convenient to talk of the forces between particles being very strong at short distances of separation, but it is as misleading to think of a compound nucleus as consisting of a number of localized material particles held rigidly together by strong forces as it is to think of the whole atom as consisting of a nucleus surrounded by small rigid electrons describing fixed localized planetary orbits. The quantum numbers of Bohr theory are easily visualized as describing physical co-ordinates of material electrons; any analogous visualization cannot be undertaken in describing the manner in which nuclei are built up.

The two principal theories of nuclear structure are the shell theory and the liquid drop model. In the shell theory the nucleons are considered to be disposed in discrete energy shells or levels in a similar way to that in which the extra-nuclear electrons are arranged. Several hundred stable and radio-active nuclei are now known; a stable nucleus in this sense indicates one that does not undergo spontaneous decay at an observable or measurable rate. In discussing the shell theory of nuclear structure, the word stable is used in a quite different sense. In this theory, stability is a relative term, which refers to the binding energy of the nucleus. This energy is measured experimentally, and it is then compared with the energy calculated from a formula due to Weizsächer (24). This formula is not based on any particular nuclear model, but is derived from statistical considerations, and contains no term which corresponds to an increase in stability conferred by the completion of a stable energy shell within the nucleus. If the nuclei are tabulated in ascending order of mass, as the table is ascended there is in general a gradual change in nuclear properties, including binding energy. However, at certain points in the table, more or less abrupt changes in such properties occur. When the table of nuclear properties is considered as a whole, these points of abrupt change exhibit a certain regularity or periodicity of occurrence. This regularity is in many ways reminiscent of the periodic properties exhibited by the elements as the nuclear charge increases ('the periodic table of the elements'); however, the periodic regularity of nuclear properties bears no numerical relation to chemical periodicity. The changes in nuclear properties can be correlated with two variables; these are $Z$, the number of protons, and $N$ the number of neutrons within the nucleus.

Weizsächer's equation is:

$$E = c^2(ZM_p + NM_n) - \alpha A + \beta(N-Z)^2/A + \gamma^{2/3} + \epsilon Z^2/A^{1/3}$$

where $M_p$ is the mass of the proton, $M_n$ the mass of the neutron, $A = N + Z$ which is the mass number ($N$ and $Z$ are defined above) and $\alpha$, $\beta$, $\gamma$ and $\epsilon$ are constants. If the measured binding energy is less than $E$ calculated from the formula, the nucleus is said to be more stable, and if higher, it is said to be less stable.

The stability of nuclei assessed in this way is greater for those which contain an even number of nucleons than it is for their neighbours which contain an odd number. Nuclei with even $Z$ and even $N$ form the most stable type (relative to neighbouring nuclei of different types). Those with odd $Z$ and even $N$, or even $Z$ and odd $N$ are more stable than neighbouring nuclei with odd $Z$ and odd $N$ except for the four light nuclei $^2$H, $^6$Li, $^{10}$B, and $^{14}$N.

The predominant stability of even–even nuclei is known as $\alpha$-particle periodicity; in ascending the nuclear table there is a gain in stability each time an additional two protons and two neutrons are incorporated into the nucleus. This does not mean that the $\alpha$-particle is itself a fundamental constituent of the nucleus, or that nuclei are 'built up' of $\alpha$-particles. The $\alpha$-particle is very stable and it is the smallest even–even nucleus which can be formed. It is so stable that when certain unstable nuclei decay it is in the form of $\alpha$-particles that the excess mass fragments are emitted. This does not imply that these fragments are already existing as discrete entities within the nucleus. The $\alpha$-particle periodicity is however the dominating periodic effect in lighter nuclei, and masks the shell structure which is more apparent in nuclei with a mass number of about 20 and above.

As the nuclear table is ascended, at certain mass numbers there are abrupt discontinuities in the general trend of stability. These discontinuities occur when certain numbers of nucleons are present, that is to say at particular values either of $A$ or of $Z$ or of $N$. Such numbers of nucleons are known as 'magic numbers'. These magic numbers appear to denote the structure at which an energy shell within the nucleus becomes 'closed', in a sense analogous to that in which the extra-nuclear shells of electrons become closed when an inert gas structure is reached. At these points, whether the magic number is attained by the number of neutrons or of protons, the nuclear stability is high compared with the corresponding E from Weizsächer's equation. There is a general trend towards stability as the magic number is approached (a trend which is superposed upon the even/odd alternation of stability) and the stability is abruptly decreased in the first nucleus after the magic number. It is this recurring sequence of stability changes which is the strongest qualitative evidence for the existence of an energy shell structure. The apparent shell structure is also manifested in other nuclear properties; the same periodicity is shown by nuclear magnetic moments, nuclear quadrupole moments, and the values of the ground state spins of nuclei with an odd number of nucleons.

The magic numbers occur in two series:

A series: 2, 8, 20, (40)   $( = n(n+1)(n+2)/3)$

B series: 2, (6), (14), (28), 50, 82, 126   $( = n(n^2+5)/3)$

The numbers in parenthesis correspond to those numbers of nucleons at which the change in stability is less marked. These are sometimes referred to as semi-magic. The stability changes among the lighter nuclei are most marked at numbers of nucleons corresponding to the A series, while the most pronounced stability changes among heavier nuclei are observed at nucleon numbers corresponding to those in series B.

Isotopes are nuclei with the same $Z$, but with a different $N$; isotones have the same $N$ but different $Z$. Nuclei in which $Z$ is a magic number often have a large number of isotopes, and those in which $N$ is a magic number commonly have many isotones. Tin nuclei have 50 protons, and there are 10 stable isotopes of the element. There are 7 isotonic nuclei when $N = 82$, and 6 when $N = 50$. Nuclei with 8, 20, 50, 82 and 126 nucleons are particularly abundant in the earth's crust—for instance $^{16}O$ where

$Z = N = 8$, $^{40}$Ca where $Z = N = 20$ and $^{208}$Pb where $Z = 82$, $N = 126$. The capture cross-sections for medium energy neutrons are abnormally low when $N = 50$, 82 or 126. All these facts indicate that the binding energy of a nucleus containing a magic number of nucleons is particularly high. A further interesting example is found in the fission process. When uranium and plutonium undergo fission as a result of bombardment by thermal neutrons, $^{87}$Br and $^{137}$I are formed as fission fragments. $^{87}$Br has 52 neutrons and $^{137}$I has 84. The first decay of both these radio-isotopes occurs by $\beta$-emission; $N$ then becomes 51 and 83 respectively. A rare decay process then occurs. In each case a 'delayed' neutron 'boils off' leaving stable shells of, in the one case, 50 neutrons, and, in the other, 82. Such an occurrence can most easily be interpreted by assuming that the 51st and 83rd neutrons are particularly lightly bound within the nucleus.

These considerations have given rise to the 'shell' model of nuclear structure which, like the Yukawa theory of meson exchange forces, is based on a mathematical model of discrete nucleons. The magnitude of the attractive force between the nuclear particles and its dependence on their distance of separation can be calculated from the theory. These exchange forces must create a potential field within the nucleus. If it is assumed for the purpose of calculation that the density of the nucleons within the nucleus is approximately constant, then the potential field within the nucleus will also be approximately constant, but will decrease very sharply at a distance from the centre which it is customary to define as the nuclear radius. On the basis of these assumptions a three-dimensional potential energy curve can be drawn to represent conditions within the nucleus. The shape of such a curve has been described by Pryce (25) as 'a square well with rounded edges'—a form similar to that of a laboratory beaker. The nucleons have the familiar 'dual nature' of wave-mechanical particles. With each such particle there is associated a wave of definite frequency. Each particle can be considered to be a three-dimensional harmonic oscillator within the potential energy well. It is possible to calculate the possible energy levels within the well which may be inhabited by such oscillators. Since the well has a finite depth and radius, only a finite number of discrete levels will exist. If these levels are allotted integral numbers from zero upwards, such numbers are analogues of the Principal quantum numbers of the Bohr orbits of the extra-nuclear electrons. A 'spin term' must then be introduced, and combined with the energy level term to characterize the spin orbital interaction; this gives rise to a number of energy sub-levels. The exclusion principle is then applied to this energy structure in the sense that only one particle may occupy any given energy sub-level, since it would by definition be indistinguishable from any other particle with identical quantum characteristics. In this way Mayer (26) calculated an energy scheme for bound nucleons in the nucleus, and he found that the number of particles in the closed shells which resulted from this scheme were successively equal to the magic numbers in series B. He further showed that if the spin-orbital interaction is disregarded, the resulting closed shells correspond to the magic numbers in series A. Mayer's scheme has been reviewed by Pryce (loc. cit.) and an abbreviated

TABLE 1

| Harmonic oscillator Number | Levels of square well potential | Spin term | Number of particles in shell | Number of particles up to and including shell |
|---|---|---|---|---|
| 0 | 1s | $1s_{1/2}$ | 2 | 2 |
| 1 | 1p | $1p_{1/2}$ | 4 ⎫ | 8 |
|   |    | $1p_{3/2}$ | 2 ⎭ |   |
| 2 | 1d | $1d_{5/2}$ | 6 ⎫ |   |
|   |    | $1d_{3/2}$ | 4 ⎬ | 20 |
|   | 2s | $2s_{1/2}$ | 2 ⎭ |   |
| 3 | 1f | $1f_{7/2}$ | 8 | 28 |
|   |    | $1f_{5/2}$ | 6 ⎫ |   |
|   | 2p | $2p_{3/2}$ | 4 ⎬ | 50 |
|   |    | $2p_{1/2}$ | 2 ⎪ |   |
|   |    | $1g_{9/2}$ | 10 ⎭ |   |
| 4 | 1g | $1g_{7/2}$ | 8 ⎫ |   |
|   | 2d | $2d_{5/2}$ | 6 ⎪ |   |
|   |    | $2d_{3/2}$ | 4 ⎬ | 82 |
|   | 3s | $3s_{1/2}$ | 2 ⎪ |   |
|   |    | $1h_{11/2}$ | 12 ⎭ |   |
| 5 | 1h | $1h_{9/2}$ | 10 ⎫ |   |
|   | 2f | $2f_{7/2}$ | 8 ⎪ |   |
|   |    | $2f_{5/2}$ | 6 ⎬ | 126 |
|   |    | $3p_{3/2}$ | 4 ⎪ |   |
|   | 3p | $3p_{1/2}$ | 2 ⎪ |   |
|   |    | $1i_{13/2}$ | 14 ⎭ |   |

version of Mayer's table based on that discussed by Pryce, is set out in Table 1.

Within each shell, the energy levels are not widely separated. The order of ascending energy in the levels shown in Table 1 is thought to be an adequate approximation to the real order of the levels within the nucleus, but it may not be accurate in detail. The value of the spin term can be calculated from the nuclear spins which are experimentally measureable quantities, and they are found to correspond closely with those proposed by Mayer.

This is only a brief outline of the shell model, which is itself only a crude attempt to depict nuclear structure. It has been considerably developed in the last five years; much of this progress has been the result of experimental work with high energy protons. The wave length associated with these particles is less than the presumed distances between the sub-nuclear particles, if indeed such a statement has any real meaning. The experimental bombardments appear to show that the nucleus is semi-transparent to such particle/radiation which often seems to pass right through it without interacting with the nucleons.

The most important alternative way of describing the structure of the nucleus is by means of the 'liquid drop' theory. It is possible to replicate the behaviour of a nucleus containing a number of nucleons by a mathematical model which is formally identical with that used to describe the interactions of atoms and molecules in a charged liquid drop. There are a number of different possible treatments of this model—these are all known as 'collective' theories. Such theories are not concerned with the detailed arrangement of the nucleons, but rather with the behaviour of the nucleus as a whole, and in particular with the way in which it behaves during the processes of neutron capture and of fission. The basis of the collective theories is the fact that the quantized energy levels of a rotating body bearing a uniform charge can be expressed by an equation of the form

$$E_\mathrm{I} = kI(I+1)$$

in which $E_I$ is the energy of the $I$th state, $I$ being the angular momentum quantum number of the state. The nuclei whose energy spectra contain levels which can be connected in this way, that is to say which behave as uniformly charged rotators, occur within certain well defined regions of atomic weights. They are found where $A \simeq 20$, $150 < A < 190$ and $A > 220$. In other regions, the spectra of the nuclei with odd numbers of nucleons are not of this type and they can best be interpreted on the assumption that the nuclei have quadrupole moments which involve very large distortions of the nuclear charge. A quadrupole moment describes the situation in which a surface charge is distributed over four regions, two of which are positive and two negative. This type of nucleus appears also to be deformed dimensionally, that is to say it is not spherical. In the regions where the nuclei with odd numbers of nucleons have moments of this type, the energy spectra of the even–even nuclei are formally analogous to those which would be predicted if a nucleus were to be treated as an electrically charged drop of liquid whose surface was vibrating. Vibration spectra of this type occur when the nuclei contain numbers of nucleons which do not form closed shells in the language of shell model theory.

The studies of the detail of sub-nuclear structure were largely initiated by the calculations of binding forces by Yukawa. As has been stated above, the only particle, apart from protons and neutrons, which is a necessary part of structure theory is the Yukawa meson, the $\pi$-meson. There is as yet no theory which correlates all the nuclear particles which have so far been identified, or indeed which can explain why particles of certain masses and charge are found rather than others. A wholly satisfactory theory must account for all such particles. It does not appear to be likely that there are simpler structural units from which all the known particles are derived. It is more probable that a fundamental series of new physical laws awaits discovery, and that the existent particles will be shown to be a logical necessity of such laws. The experimental demonstration of the particles which have been identified has, however, largely been consequent upon the development of the original Yukawa meson theory. As further equations have been set up to correlate the experimental facts which have been discovered, so various wave-mechanical operators have been introduced. Attempts have then been made to correlate these operators with some detectable physical phenomenon, as was done in the case of the Yukawa meson. This process has been a profitable one, but a satisfactory basic theory is still lacking.

One such set of operators was introduced into the equations which described the behaviour of mesons in order to account for the process of creating or annihilating electric charge in the fields of force in which the mesons were moving. These operators were found to have the same effect as if 'anti-particles' became located within the fields of force. The observed phenomena could be explained by postulating that if such anti-particles approach sufficiently closely to the more familiar real particles, then both particle and anti-particle are annihilated with the creation of an equivalent amount of energy which is manifested as a photon. In this sense, the positron is the anti-particle of the negative electron. However the 'anti-ness' of a particle is not simply a question of opposite charge. The situation is more subtle than that. For instance, a certain operator which was introduced into meson theory implied that there should be not only anti-protons, but also anti-neutrons.

It was calculated that anti-protons should be produced in neutron–neutron collisions which took place above a threshold energy of 5·6 GeV. The difficulty of detecting such particles is very great because in most circumstances they would be indistinguishable from ordinary protons until they took part in a proton–anti-proton collision, and both particles were annihilated. A few of the neutrons contained in the cosmic rays have energies greater than 5·6 GeV, but they are so rare that it was unlikely that a suitable collision event would be observed. One of the factors which influenced the design of the Bevatron at Berkeley, California, was the need to produce particles of a high enough energy to give rise to anti-protons; these were in fact identified when bombardments were carried out above the calculated threshold energy. About twenty of these particles can be produced per day at the present time; approximately $10^5$ $\pi$-mesons are produced along with each anti-proton. Measurements of the mass of these particles showed that it was certainly within $5\%$ of that of the the proton. Their velocity when they were produced in the bevatron experiments was $75\%$ of that of light, and their flight could be followed over an 80 ft path before they collided with a proton with consequent annihilation. From this behaviour it was calculated that their lifetime is greater than $10^{-8}$ sec. This is long in comparison with many other particles of comparable mass, and it was concluded that they were in fact stable (27).

The tracks of these particles were observed in photographic emulsion and the energy released in this process was calculated by studying the stars produced at the point of annihilation. This was found to be equivalent to twice the rest mass of a single particle, that is to the mass of a proton plus an anti-proton (28). The successful production and identification of these particles led workers to examine many earlier cosmic ray records. One track of an anti-proton was found although it had not been previously recognized as such (29).

So far in this chapter, the nature of the sub-nuclear particles has been indicated by means of analogies which have borne some relationship to the world of everyday experience. The behaviour of these particles is so far removed from that of anything we experience in the macroscopic world that the analogies can only give a very qualitative picture of the state of affairs within the nucleus. It is impossible to avoid introducing other concepts which cannot be described in familiar terms. One such concept is that of in-variance. The nature of an invariant has been elegantly stated by Bondi (30):

It is the purpose of every physical theory to describe in a concise manner a wide variety of phenomena. In many cases this will necessitate, as part of the theory, a prescription for applying the theory to systems in different states of motion. A prescription of this kind, a code of translation as it were, will generally consist of a mathematical system of trans-formation laws.

It is in the nature of these transformation laws to change most quantities, but to leave some quantities unchanged. These are called the invariants of the transformation, and serve to define its character. A physical statement of what these invariants are is called a principle of relativity, and the fundamental equations of a theory usually define the principle of relativity applicable to it.

It does not matter whether a given system is described in classical terms, or in those appropriate to quantum mechanics. The prescription or code of translation may be applied to it in either case. If a system is undergoing translational motion in a certain direction, it will have a certain component of momentum in that direction. This momentum-component will be conserved independently of the position or motion of the equipment used to observe it. The conservation of momentum in this way is an invariant of the system. The situation is more complex in other types of invariance which are relevant to a further analysis of the behaviour of sub-nuclear particles. One such principle of invariance describes the nature of the potentials which enter into the equations of electromagnetic theory. The situation differs from that of an observer observing the conservation of momentum in that the electromagnetic potentials cannot be physically observed. They may, however, be subjected to a number of mathematical transformations without altering the physical content of the theory. This behaviour is usually referred to as 'gauge invariance'. Unfortunately, this expression does not enable us to visualize, even remotely, a physical phenomenon. It would be a little more meaningful it if were described as the invariance of electric potential gradient. One of the important consequences of gauge invariance is that the total net amount of electric charge must be conserved within an observed system. Admittedly, it is not usual to think of electric charge as a dynamic variable. However, where a reaction takes place in which matter is transmuted into energy, or vice versa, charge may apparently be created or abolished. This does not occur, because if a charged particle is formed by the materialization of $h\nu$, a particle of the opposite charge will also materialize. The total charge thus remains the same in the system.

This behaviour is described in the wave equations by the introduction of a certain operator $\phi$ whose appearance necessitates the action of a second complementary operator $\phi'$. This is the Hermitian conjugate of $\phi$. When $\phi$ describes the production of a particle of a given charge, then the associated $\phi'$ describes the production of an anti-particle of the opposite sign. A further consequence of gauge invariance is the principle known as the conservation of baryons. This states that if there is a reaction in which matter reacts with energy or with other matter, then the total net number of heavy nuclear particles remains the same after the reaction as it was before. The heavy nuclear particles, or baryons, are $p^+$, $n^\circ$, $\Lambda^\circ$, $\Sigma^+$, $\Sigma^-$, $\Sigma^\circ$, $\Xi^\circ$ and $\Xi^-$ with their corresponding anti-particles. If any of these is created by the materialization of a quantum of energy, then the corresponding anti-particle (anti-baryon) is formed. In other words, in any system

$$(\text{number of baryons}) - (\text{number of anti-baryons}) = k$$

where $k$ is constant before and after any reaction which may take place. It is impossible to prove a statement such as this by experiment. All that can be said is that $k$ has been found to be a constant in all reactions so far studied.

It is also necessary to introduce a curious concept to describe another quality to which no physical meaning has so far been attached. This is known as the property of 'strangeness'. Many of the particles so far described are sometimes called 'strange particles'. The 'strangeness' of a particle is the name given to a quantum number which was introduced as an expedient which enabled the complex reactions of such particles to be tabulated in an ordered way. It is hard to say whether this is a purely arithmetic trick or whether it has an actual physical significance which we cannot now (and may never in the future) reduce to a visualizable concept.

The idea of strangeness resulted from what had earlier appeared to be a contradiction. This was manifested when certain high energy nuclear reactions took place. In such reactions there is a very high probability that strange particles will be produced. This is usually expressed by saying that in these reactions there is a high cross-section associated with the production of such particles. When these strange particles are formed, they decay spontaneously to $\pi$-mesons and nucleons ($n^\circ$ and $p^+$) which are not themselves strange particles. Before they undergo such decay, the strange particles exist for times of the order of $10^{-10}$ sec. This short lifetime is comparatively long on the nuclear time-scale. Now when nucleons and $\pi$-mesons interact, the strength of their reaction may be expressed in terms of their 'coupling constant'. This is, in effect, a measure of the degree of stability of particles which subsequently decay, and it is related to the high cross-section associated with the formation of the strange particles. Fermi has derived an expression, which has been shown to be valid when applied to many other systems, in order to connect the coupling constant with the particle lifetime (31). When the coupling constant is calculated from the lifetime of the strange particles, it is found to be too small to account for the high production cross-section. In order to resolve this difficulty, Pais (32) put forward the hypothesis of 'associated production'. He postulated that the 'synthetic' reaction with the high cross-section differed in type from the 'decay' reaction with the long lifetime, and that therefore the coupling constant derived from the long decay time could not be applied to the synthetic reaction of a different type. The difference is that in the strong production interaction, at least two strange particles are always concerned, while in the 'weak' decay interaction only one particle is involved.

Dalitz (33) describes the process as follows:

The associated production interactions do not conflict with slow decay for strange particles since they can only transform one strange particle into a system involving another strange particle. The interaction $\Lambda^\circ \rightleftharpoons N + \bar{\theta}^\circ$ ($\bar{\theta}^\circ$ is the anti-particle to $\theta^\circ$) effects a transition from a $\Lambda^\circ$ particle to a virtual state, it does not give rise to a rapid decay process for the $\Lambda^\circ$ particle as the $\Lambda^\circ$ mass does not provide sufficient energy for this to be a real process.

On this basis it is possible to distinguish three distinct types of particle reactions. The first type is that involving strong nuclear interactions. The proton–meson–neutron interaction is one of these. The meson interacts with the proton and the neutron and a stable nucleus is formed. Strong interactions of this type are always charge independent. This means that the electric charge of the particles concerned is not an important factor in determining the strength of the binding interaction. This is not the case in the second type of interaction which is electromagnetic in type. Here the charge of the particles is of primary importance, unlike charges attracting, and like charges repelling. The so-called weak interactions make up the third type. Examples of this are decay reactions in which neutrons, mesons and positive or negative electrons are concerned.

In the charge-independent reactions of the first type, the most important parameters are the total angular momentum of the system and the parity of the particles. Parity, or isotopic spin, must not be interpreted as being the same as the normal conception of a spinning sphere. The word 'spin' is a useful label for a property which has only three states; a body capable of spin can be spinning clockwise, anti-clockwise, or at rest with zero spin. The isotopic spin is described by the quantum number $T$; this is related to a number known as the 'isotopic spin resultant' which is denoted by $T_3$. $T_3$ is connected with the charge of the nucleons by the expression

$$T_3 = Q - \tfrac{1}{2}$$

where the charge $Q$ is also three-valued having the values $\pm 1$ unit and zero.

In terms of the isotopic spin resultant ($T_3$), the proton and the neutron are equivalent to two states of the same fundamental particle type. They differ in the value of $T_3$ to be assigned to each. It can be seen from the equation

$$T_3 = Q - \tfrac{1}{2}$$

that $T_3$ will have the value of $+\tfrac{1}{2}$ for the proton of charge $+1$ unit, and $-\tfrac{1}{2}$ for the neutron which has a zero charge. They form, as it were, the two components of a doublet energy level of a hypothetical ground state. The use of parity or isotopic spin thus enables certain particles to be classified into related types, but the quantum number $T_3$ is not sufficient to allow a complete classification to be made. The quantum number $S$, the 'Strangeness number' must also be introduced.

The number $S$ has no physical meaning in the terms of the world to which we are accustomed. However, by assigning certain values of $S$ to the particles, it is possible to classify the reactions which they undergo into types according to the value of $S$ before and after the reaction. For instance in all strong reactions, $S$ is conserved. Again, this statement has not been proved, but no strong reactions are known in which $S$ is not conserved. The allotment of these nuclear quantum numbers to the various known particles is set out in the following table due to Dalitz (33).

| Class | Particle | | | $T$ | $S$ | $U$ |
|---|---|---|---|---|---|---|
| Hyperons | $\varXi^- \ (T_3 = -\tfrac{1}{2})$ | $\varXi^\circ \ (T_3 = +\tfrac{1}{2})$ | | $\tfrac{1}{2}$ | $-2$ | $-1$ |
| | $\varSigma^- \ (T_3 = -1)$ | $\varSigma^\circ \ (T_3 = 0)$ | $\varSigma^+ \ (T_3 = +1)$ | $1$ | $-1$ | $0$ |
| | | $\varLambda^\circ \ (T_3 = 0)$ | | $0$ | $-1$ | $0$ |
| Nucleons | | $N^\circ \ (T_3 = -\tfrac{1}{2})$ | $P^+ \ (T_3 = +\tfrac{1}{2})$ | $\tfrac{1}{2}$ | $0$ | $1$ |
| $\kappa$-particles | | $\kappa^\circ \ (T_3 = -\tfrac{1}{2})$ | $\kappa^+ \ (T_3 = +\tfrac{1}{2})$ | $\tfrac{1}{2}$ | $1$ | $1$ |
| Anti-$\kappa$ particles | $\bar{\kappa}^- \ (T_3 = -\tfrac{1}{2})$ | $\bar{\kappa}^\circ \ (T_3 = +\tfrac{1}{2})$ | | $\tfrac{1}{2}$ | $-1$ | $-1$ |
| $\pi$-mesons | $\pi^- \ (T_3 = -1)$ | $\pi^\circ \ (T_3 = 0)$ | $\pi^+ \ (T_3 = +1)$ | $1$ | $0$ | $0$ |

In strong allowed reactions, not only is the strangeness conserved, but so is also the charge ($Q$), the isotopic spin resultant ($T_3$) and the number of baryons ($B$). The reaction $\varLambda^\circ \longrightarrow P^+ + \pi^-$ is therefore weak, because although $Q$ and $B$ are conserved, $T_3$ and $S$ are not. In all slow decay processes, there is a charge of $\pm 1$ unit in strangeness, that is to say $\varDelta S = \pm 1$.

The properties of the baryons, hyperons and mesons were also summarized by Gell-Mann (34) and Nishijima (35) in the following way

| Mass (electron mass units) | Particles | | |
|---|---|---|---|
| 2580 | $\varXi^-$ | $\varXi^\circ$ | |
| 2330 | $\varSigma^-$ | $\varSigma^\circ$ | $\varSigma^+$ |
| 2180 | | $\varLambda^\circ$ | |
| 1830 | | $N^\circ$ | $N^+ \ (= P^+)$ |
| 960 | $\kappa^-$ | $\bar{\kappa}^\circ$ | $\kappa^+$ |
| | | $\kappa^\circ$ | |
| 270 | $\pi^-$ | $\pi^\circ$ | $\pi^+$ |

which is referred to in the literature as the *G–N* scheme. The particles thus form a series of isobaric multiplets which can also be classified in terms of their Strangeness Quantum Numbers.

| $S = -2$ | $S = -1$ | $S = 0$ | $S = +1$ |
|---|---|---|---|
| $\varXi^- \ \varXi^\circ$ | $\varLambda^\circ$ | $N^\circ \ N^+$ | $\kappa^\circ \ \kappa^+$ |
| | $\varSigma^- \ \varSigma^\circ \ \varSigma^+$ | $\pi^- \ \pi^\circ \ \pi^+$ | |
| | $\kappa^- \ \bar{\kappa}^\circ$ | | |

Now that the nuclear quantum numbers have been introduced, it is possible to classify the nuclear interactions in a more systematic way than that which was set out above.

(i) STRONG INTERACTIONS. These are meson baryon interactions which have strong coupling coefficients of the order of 1. $T$ and $T_3$, and therefore also $S$, are conserved in these reactions.

(ii) ELECTROMAGNETIC INTERACTIONS. $T_3$ is conserved but not $T$; $S$ is, however, conserved. They are characterized by the occurrence of the fine structure constant $\frac{1}{137}$ which occurs in the mathematical equations which express the course of the reaction. An example of such an interaction is the emission of radiation by an excited hydrogen atom; the fine structure constant here enters into the calculation of the spectral terms.

(iii) WEAK INTERACTIONS. In these reactions, the coupling coefficients are very small, being of the order of $10^{-14}$. Neither $T_3$, $T$, nor $S$ are conserved, but $S$ always changes by $\pm 1$ unit.

When reactions are classified in this way, it is possible to deduce certain consequences which have been experimentally verified. For example, when strange particles are produced in the strong interaction between $\pi$-mesons and nucleons, they must always be produced in pairs. This is necessary because both pions and nucleons have zero strangeness, but no strange particles have zero strangeness. To conserve the strangeness number before and after the reaction, the two strange particles which result must have equal and opposite strangeness numbers, thus

$$\pi^- + N^+ \longrightarrow \kappa^+ + \kappa^- + N^0$$

(Strangeness:    $0 + 0 \longrightarrow 1 - 1 + 0$ )

In other reactions, $\kappa^+$ and $\kappa^0$ may be produced in association with $\Lambda^\circ$, but $\kappa^-$ and $\bar{\kappa}^\circ$ cannot be produced because they both have the same strangeness as $\Lambda^0$. The type of reaction in which they are produced is

$$\pi^- + N^+ \longrightarrow \kappa^+ + \kappa^-$$

A $\Sigma^0$-particle may decay to a $\Lambda^0$-particle since they both have the same strangeness (36).

$$\Sigma^0 \longrightarrow \Lambda^0 + \gamma (10^{-20} \text{ sec})$$

An interesting reaction is that in which a $\Xi^0$ particle is produced together with two $\kappa^0$-particles. The threshold energy is near the limit of particle acceleration which can be obtained in the bevatron by means of which this reaction has been observed (37).

$\kappa^-$-particles may be absorbed by protons to form hyperons

$$\kappa^- + N^+ \longrightarrow \Lambda^0 + \pi^0$$

Such hyperons may become bound to atomic nuclei to form hyperfragments or mesonic nuclei. In this way, the hypertriton $^3_\Lambda H$ may be formed from a $\Lambda^0$-hyperon and a deuteron (38). The first observed decomposition of the hypertriton was formulated according to the following scheme:

$$^3_\Lambda H \longrightarrow {}^3He + \pi^- + 41.7 \text{ MeV}$$

but other decay modes have been subsequently observed, such as

$$^3_\Lambda H \begin{array}{l} \nearrow P + D + \pi^- \\ \searrow P + P + N + \pi^- \end{array}$$

Another well-established mesonic nuclei (39) is:

$$^4_\Lambda He \longrightarrow {}^2H + P + N$$

All the nuclei shown in the following table have been reported:

| Nucleus | $^3_\Lambda H$ | $^4_\Lambda H$ | $^4_\Lambda He$ | $^5_\Lambda He$ | $(^8_\Lambda Li)$ | $^8_\Lambda Be$ | $^9_\Lambda Be$ | $^{11}_\Lambda C$ | |
|---|---|---|---|---|---|---|---|---|---|
| Binding energy | $-0.3$ | $1.8$ | $1.9$ | $1.6$ | | $5.1$ | $5.1$ | $6.2$ | MeV |

It is not certain whether the mesonic Lithium nucleus should be formulated as $^7Li$, $^8Li$ or $^9Li$. There is no evidence for the existence of a $^2_\Lambda H$ hyperfragment, which may be because a bound state is not possible for the $\Lambda^0$-nucleon system (40). No hypernuclei containing $\Sigma$-particles have yet been reported. $\mu$-mesons, however can form compound particles. This has interesting consequences when nuclear reactions are carried out in liquid hydrogen. $\mu$-mesons can catalyse such reactions, and it has been suggested that this catalytic process takes place in stages as follows (41):

(i) The $\mu$-meson is slowed down by collisions in the liquid hydrogen and then captured by a proton to form a $(p\mu)$ atom.

(ii) The $(p\mu)$ atom then migrates and encounters a deuteron which captures the meson in an exchange reaction. Owing to the difference in reduced mass, this process releases 135 eV to the system.

(iii) The $(d\mu)$ atom slows down by collisions and forms a $(p\mu d)^+$ molecular ion by a process of electron ejection.

(iv) The nuclear reaction $p + d \longrightarrow {}^3He + \gamma$ (5.5 MeV) then occurs; the $\gamma$-ray may then eject the meson. In a process such as this there will be competing reactions due to the natural decay of the meson, and from the possible formation of other compound ions such as $(p\mu p)^+$ and $(d\mu d)^+$.

It has also been suggested that in order to provide a sufficient magnetic field for the depolarization of positive mesons in gases, molecular ions such as $(He_\mu)^+$ may be formed, but this hypothesis is still somewhat speculative (42).

Another process of great interest has recently been described. $\mu$-mesons, and possibly also $\kappa$-mesons and hyperons can be captured into electronic orbitals, and replace an electron therein. The orbital transitions of the captured mesons have been detected in X-ray spectra. From these observations accurate measurements of the meson masses may be made (43). The meson may be subsequently captured from these electronic orbits by the nucleus (44). The compound particles muonium ($\mu^+e^-$) and positronium ($\mu^+e^+$) have been extensively described.

Before leaving the subject of the nuclear particles, it is appropriate to say a few more words about the anti-particles. Their nature is extremely difficul t to understand. It is not hard to visualize the positron as the anti-particle of the electron, but it is very difficult to comprehend an entity which is the anti-particle of the neutron. The situation of the neutrino and the anti-neutrino is more difficult still, and even more complex. The neutrino has a zero mass but possesses a spin. Two types of neutrinos which can be partially visualized are apparently not related in the sense of a particle and its anti-particle. The two types which can be distinguished are that which has its intrinsic spin parallel to the momentum, and that in which the two are anti-parallel. The possession of a momentum by a particle with zero mass is in itself a difficult conception. These two types of neutrino are known as left-handed and right-handed respectively. Since these two are not anti-particles of each other, in Pauli's view (45) there should be two types of anti-particle, anti-left and anti-right as it were. Four particles are thus involved in this treatment, but it is difficult to see which of them are anti-particles of which.

This is therefore rather a barren treatment, and it is more rewarding to consider the alternative hypothesis that for any given momentum there can only be either a left-handed or a right-handed state concerned with any given momentum. This approach gave rise to two hypotheses. In that due to Lee and Yang (46) it is considered that there are two real particles, and that each is the anti-particle of the other. The alternative approach due to Majorana (47) is that the two opposed spin/momentum arrangements are two states of the same particle which is thus its own anti-particle. Although the two hypotheses appear opposed, Serpe (48) has shown that they are formally equivalent.

This view of the neutrino, which is usually referred to as the Majorana neutrino, does not involve any fundamental difference between the two types or states of the neutrino. They are related in the same way as the neutral $\pi$-meson $\pi^0$ is related to its anti-particle; it is not easy to say in what the 'anti-ness' consists; it differs from the state of the $\kappa^0$-meson and its anti-particle $\bar{\kappa}^0$, where the two antithetic particles have a strangeness of equal but opposite sign. Dirac has suggested that the antithetic neutrinos have magnetic moments which are equal but opposite in sign.

There is in principle an experimental method of distinguishing between the Dirac and Majorana theories, but the practical difficulties of carrying it out indicate that in work of this nature, the boundaries of discoverable knowledge may be being approached. It has been shown that some nuclei should decay with the emission of *two* beta particles. If in such a process two neutrinos are found to be emitted, then it is probable that the Dirac hypothesis would be the correct one. On the other hand the Majorana hypothesis would be valid if no neutrino should be detected, that is to say if the two potentially emitted neutrinos should each be the anti-particle of the other, and therefore would be mutually annihilated at the moment of emission. Double-beta decay should take place from the ground state of even–even nuclei. Such nuclei are $^{130}_{52}$Te, $^{238}_{92}$U, $^{124}_{50}$Sn, $^{100}_{42}$Mo and $^{48}_{20}$Ca. Unfortunately, the half-life of such a process can be calculated to be $10^{16}$–$10^{30}$ years. It is thus extremely unlikely that such an event will ever be observed, although attempts have been made to do so. It is therefore improbable that any decision can ever be made between the two hypotheses on this basis.

We have therefore seen that the facts which have been discovered about the fundamental particles do not admit of any simple explanation. It was pointed out in Chapter 1 that there is no *a priori* reason why natural phenomena should admit of any simple explanation, and there is also no reason why the observations concerning them should be incorrect because they are complex. There are, however, two considerations which must be borne in mind. In the first place it is possible that the development of more powerful particle accelerators may lead to the discovery of other primary particles. The properties of such particles might cause a drastic revision of our ideas about the nature of those particles which have already been described. Secondly, the proliferation of particles has led to more and more complex theories of the nature of matter. Even though it is unreasonable to expect any mechanistic analogue of the way in which fundamental particles behave, the mathematical correlation of their behaviour has become very involved. The use of nuclear quantum numbers such as that involving strangeness is not entirely satisfactory. It is possible to be reminded of the confused state of the theories concerning electromagnetic radiation in the days before relativity and quantum theory. It is therefore reasonable to suspect that there may be further theoretical advances which, while they are unlikely to be easy to understand, may be based on some further unifying assumption. The evidence which is now accepted as indicating the existence of objects which we visualize as particles may admit of some other and more general explanation. This may be found either in a shift of emphasis to bring their wave-like characteristics into more prominence, or in some other fashion which has not yet been formulated. The outline of particle properties given in this chapter is intended to indicate the present state of our knowledge regarding them, but none of the theories of the fundamental

properties of matter is immutable, and none may survive the discoveries
to be made in the future.

## REFERENCES

(1) HOFFMANN *The Strange Story of the Quantum* p. 225 (Dover Publications Inc., New York, 2nd Edition, 1959)
(2) BUNN *Chemical Crystallography* (O.U.P. 1961)
(3) TUTIN *The Atom* (Longmans, Green & Co. 1934)
(4) MARSHAK *Scientific American* **202** (No. 3) 99 (1960)
(5) YUKAWA *Proc. Phys. Math. Soc. Japan.* **17** 48 (1935)
(6) KEMMER *Proc. Roy. Soc.* **A166** 127 (1938)
(7) ANDERSON and NEDDLEMEYER *Phys. Rev.* **51** 884 (1937)
(8) LATTES, OCCHIALINI and POWELL *Nature* **160** 453 (1947)
(9) ROSSI *Scientific American* **189** (No. 3) 64 (1953)
(10) ROSSI *Scientific American* **201** (No. 5) 135 (1959)
(11) CARTWRIGHT, RICHMAN, WHITEHEAD and WILCOX *Phys. Rev.* **81** 652 (1951)
(12) CLARK, ROBERTS and WILSON *Phys. Rev.* **83** 649 (1951)
    DURBIN, LOAR and STEINBERGER *Phys. Rev.* **83** 646 (1951)
(13) MATTHEWS *Reports Progr. Phys.* **18** 452 (1955)
(14) ROCHESTER and BUTLER *Nature* **160** 855 (1947)
(15) BROWN *et al. Nature* **163** 82 (1949)
(16) ARMENTIERES, BARKER, BUTLER and CACHON *Phil. Mag.* **42** 1113 (1951)
(17) THOMPSON *et al. Phys. Rev.* **90** 1122 (1953)
(18) COWAN *Phys. Rev.* **94** 161 (1954)
(19) YORK, LEIGHTON and BJORNERUND *Phys. Rev.* **90** 167 (1953)
(20) BONETTI *et al. Nuovo cim.* **10** 1736 (1953)
(21) DEBENEDETTI *et al. Nuovo cim.* **12** 952 (1954)
(22) SMITH, HECKMAN and BARKAS U.C.R.L. Report 3289 (1956)
(23) FRY, SCHNEPS, SNOW and SWAMI *Phys. Rev.* **100** 448 (1955)
(24) WEIZSÄCHER *Z. Phys.* **96** 431 (1935)
(25) PRYCE *Reports Progr. Phys.* **17** 1 (1954)
(26) MAYER *Phys. Rev.* **75** 1969 (1949)
(27) CHAMBERLAIN, SEGRE, WIEGAND and YPSILANTIS *Phys. Rev.* **100** 947 (1955)
(28) CHAMBERLAIN *et al. Phys. Rev.* **101** 909 (1956)
(29) BRIDGE, CALDWELL, PAL and ROSSI *Phys. Rev.* **102** 930 (1956)
(30) BONDI *Reports Progr. Phys.* **22** 97 (1959). This review is a magnificently simple and explicit exposition of the relation between Newton's and Maxwell's laws and Einstein's relativity theory
(31) FERMI *Elementary Particles* (Yale University Press, 1951)
(32) PAIS *Phys. Rev.* **86** 663 (1952)
(33) DALITZ *Reports Progr. Phys.* **20** 163 (1957). The author wishes to record his indebtedness to Prof. Dalitz's article in writing this section

(34) GELL–MANN *Phys. Rev.* **92** 833 (1953)
(35) NISHIJIMA *Progr. Theor. Phys. Japan* **12** 107 (1954) **13** 285 (1954)
(36) PLANO *et al. Nuovo cim.* **5** 216 (1957)
(37) SORRELS, LEIGHTON and ANDERSON *Phys. Rev.* **100** 1457 (1955)
(38) BONETTI *et al. Nuovo cim.* **11** 210, 330 (1954)
(39) SIEMAN, SHAPIRO and STILLER *Phys. Rev.* **100** 1480 (1955)
(40) SCHEPS, FRY and SWAMI *Phys. Rev.* **106** 1062 (1957)
(41) COHEN, JUDD and RIDDELL *Phys. Rev.* **110** 1471 (1958)
(42) HUGHES *Phys. Rev.* **108** 1106 (1957)
(43) WEST *Reports Progr. Phys.* **21** 271 (1958)
(44) SENS *Phys. Rev.* **113** 679 (1959)
(45) PAULI *Nuovo cim.* **6** 204 (1957)
(46) LEE and YANG *Phys. Rev.* **105** 1671 (1957)
(47) MAJORANA *Nuovo cim.* **14** 171 (1937)
(48) SERPE *Physica* **18** 295 (1952)

# CHAPTER 4

# Chemical Structure

A CYNIC might be tempted to say that the principal difficulty which faces a scientist today is not a lack of recorded data, but an excess of it. Individual scientists tend to work in more and more restricted and specialized fields, and it is difficult for them to learn even the broad outlines of the work which is being carried out in fields far removed from their own. Progress does not take place at a uniform rate over the whole front of scientific investigation; this is as true of the development of techniques as it is of the acquisition of basic knowledge. Certain techniques may be developed to a stage of great refinement in the course of basic research, but then also have considerable potential value for more routine applications. Unfortunately, it often happens that the investigation for which the technique was developed is far divorced from another field in which it would also be of use. In such a case there is a considerable delay in making use of the method or the underlying principle involved, and effort may sometimes be wasted in rediscovering what is already known and recorded in unfamiliar journals.

The theory of the design of experiments themselves is a good example of the way in which valuable information was neglected. This subject was being studied by agriculturalists early in the present century. Research into plant breeding is essentially long term, and only one set of experiments can normally be carried out in each year; it is therefore of the greatest importance that the information gained from each such experiment shall be as complete as possible, and that all the sources of experimental error shall be evaluated with the greatest accuracy. Variances can arise from differences in the soil quality in different parts of the experimental plot, and from variations in aspect, drainage and so on. Such variables could produce differences within the yield from a single strain which might be greater than the differences between the various strains which were being evaluated. In order to enable strains to be compared, devices such as 'Latin square' designs were employed, which minimized the effect of the random variables. The interpretation of the quantitative differences between the growths in the various blocks of the Latin square design required the application of some statistical theory. The necessary mathematics was codified into techniques such as analysis of variance and tests of significance. This approach to an investigation in which there were a large number of possible variables which might effect the final result has a direct relevance to problems of reaction conditions which face the chemical engineer. For many years it was very uncommon to find these techniques used by chemists although they had been developed to a highly sophisticated state by the agriculturalists. One can only assume that this delay was not due to a desire on the part of chemists to make their work as difficult to evaluate as possible, but rather that chemists had no apparent need to read papers which dealt with improvements in the crop yield of wheat.

Chemistry is more closely allied to physics than it is to agriculture, in the sense that many chemists are familiar with the methods of physicists, and they have a broad general interest in the advances made in that branch of science; many physical techniques were adapted for chemical purposes very soon after their original discovery. The chemist relies almost entirely upon such methods in arriving at his interpretation of molecular structure and arrangement. There is a large area of work in which the activities of chemists and physicists overlap to such an extent that it is hardly possible to say what is chemistry and what is physics; in any case, the distinction is of no real importance. Both chemists and physicists are searching out new information about the composition of material things. It is hardly possible to define the proper domain of the chemist without using the tautology that he is concerned with the chemical properties of matter, while the physicist is concerned with the physical properties.

The structure and properties of matter on both the atomic and on the molecular scale is common ground for both sets of workers. The primary interest of the chemist is in the types of atom which are present in a given system, their relative positions in space and the reasons for the occurrence of a particular structure. Such considerations lead on to questions of bond types and bond lengths. This information enables persistent chemical groupings to be identified, and their stability to be studied in various situations. The physical methods which have been used to establish the nature and formation of such structural patterns often become diagnostic tools to identify them in routine analyses.

The way in which atoms are arranged in space is affected by every property of the atoms concerned. Our knowledge of the way in which such atomic parameters interact is still very incomplete It is seldom possible to predict molecular properties from 'first principles', although when a structure has been established it is often possible to 'explain' why that one occurs rather than another. The relative size of atoms is one important factor in determining their relative spatial distribution. The size of an atom is not in itself a simple concept; atoms are not elastic spheres with abruptly defined surfaces. The equilibrium separation between the centres of two atoms is the resultant of a complex system of attractive and repulsive forces, some of which may be derived from the general energy field in the neighbourhood of the atoms. A variety of different factors can influence such energy relations, and the dominant one will differ from structure to structure. In aromatic systems, the stabilizing effect of the electrons in $\pi$-orbitals is a dominating factor. The stability of such a system is usually a maximum when the atoms which form the aromatic system are co-planar. However, it will be shown in a later chapter that this is not the case in, for example, crystals of solid anthracene, in which the molecular neighbours each distort one another so that the molecules are not perfectly planar. This involves a loss of aromatic stability, but the gain in lattice energy apparently more than compensates for this.

It is usual to describe atomic systems as, for instance, 'planar' or 'tetrahedrally disposed' as if we knew that that was what the molecules were 'really' like. The evidence for the existence of such arrangements is, however, always indirect. Atoms cannot be felt or touched or seen and their relative arrangement cannot be determined in the same way as we perceive the arrangement of chairs round a table or of marbles in a box. So much evidence derived from very different sources has accumulated about molecular structure that we accept certain atomic patterns as being established facts. Such a molecular model is a satisfactory and useful one in practice. From it, predictions may be made and subsequently verified by experiment. It must, however, be remembered that atoms are certainly not occupying points distributed in space at fixed locations in a rigid geometrical lattice.

At any temperature above the absolute zero, atoms are always in motion. In a crystalline lattice they behave as if they were vibrating about certain mean positions. Not only are atoms in a structural group vibrating about mean positions within the group, but such a group may be undergoing rotational or translational vibrations relative to other atoms or groups. There are certain situations in which these group movements have a dominating importance even in the solid phase, but in discussing molecular structure it is usual in the first analysis to describe the atoms as if they were actually located at their apparent mean positions.

In most solid structures there is a high degree of short-range order, but there is not necessarily a correspondingly high degree of long-range order. Solids are seldom truly amorphous, but real crystals of finite size are never perfect. Systems such as amorphous carbon are sometimes regarded as being totally disordered, but in fact they consist of small regions in which the degree of order is high. These regions may contain a few hundred atoms or even less. The apparent lack of structure is due to the ordered areas being arranged in a disorganized way relative to each other. A similar situation obtains in fibres such as cellulose. Each individual long cellulose chain molecule passes through a number of regions in the fibre where there is a high degree of crystalline order. In between these micro-crystallites there are regions of lower order, and the structure as a whole may appear to be disorganized because of the random relative orientations of the crystalline regions.

In any solid, the areas of perfect crystallinity are usually small and the crystal exhibits irregularities for one or more of a number of different reasons. Some of the lattice points may be vacant at places where it would be expected that they should be occupied by a particular type of atom. This state of affairs is known as a lattice defect. A defect of this type occurs in ferrous sulphide in which the FeS phase is stable between 50 and 55 atomic percent of sulphur. The sulphur atoms form a close-packed array which is stable even if a few ferrous ions are absent. Chemical analysis has established formulae such as $Fe_6S_7$ and $Fe_{11}S_{12}$ for the composition of such iron deficient phases and it is perhaps unfortunate that ferrous sulphide has so often been used to illustrate the law of Fixed Proportions. Lattice points may also be vacant because atoms which originally occupied them have subsequently migrated to other parts of the crystal. If the migrated atom occupies an interstitial position close to the vacant site, it is known as a Frenkel defect; if the atom has migrated for a considerable distance, for instance to the surface of the crystal, it is called a Schottky defect.

In some cases, the presence of a very small number of foreign atoms may have profound effects upon the properties of the crystal. Alloy properties may be affected by the presence of foreign atoms in concentrations as low as 1 in $10^3$. The close-packed structure of the metals is considerably distorted by the presence of a comparatively few atoms of a different type, and a new crystal structure is then formed. The properties of semiconductors may be profoundly changed by the presence of impurities in the proportion of only 1 atom in $10^8$ even though the structural changes are inappreciable. The electrical properties of these compounds depend upon the behaviour of a small number of the total electrons in the system and a very small proportion of impurities can disturb the electronic energy level scheme, and have a profound effect upon the semi-conductor properties.

Apart from irregularities of these types, the way in which crystals are formed makes it unlikely that they will be perfectly regular. Lattices grow from a number of independent nuclei. As the crystal faces grow out from one such centre they meet the faces of other micro-crystals growing similarly. This results in the formation of a mosaic of micro-crystals whose faces do not join each to each in a perfectly ordered way. On the large scale, the crystal appears to be more or less perfect with well-defined faces, because the steps and distortions which form the mosaic are very small. A single micro-crystal growing from one nucleus may only extend for twenty or thirty atomic diameters before there is a dislocation caused by the interference from a face grown from another nucleus. The imperfections can in some cases be seen in electron microscope photographs of crystals. The lack of precise orientation one to another of the mosaic fragments is

6

sometimes sufficient to produce a detectable effect when X-rays are reflected from crystals.

Most of the methods which are used for determining the structure of chemical substances are founded upon an assessment of the average arrangement in a large number of structure units. A structure is identified if the relative positions of the component atoms, and their electronic states, are known. The only way in which these properties can be determined is by allowing radiation to interact with the structure, and then by interpreting the observed changes in the radiation. The principal method by which atomic positions are determined is by arranging that radiation of appropriate wave-length shall be diffracted by the regular arrangement of atoms in the lattice, and by then observing the directions and intensities of the diffracted beams. For this purpose, a crystal can be considered to be a three-dimensional grating from which radiation will be diffracted in a manner somewhat similar to that in which light is diffracted by a ruled two-dimensional grating. In order that diffraction may take place, it is necessary that the wave-length of the radiation shall be of the same order as the line spacing of the grating. In a three-dimensional crystal the distance between the lattice planes may be considered to correspond to the line spacing in a flat grating. Radiation of an appropriate wave-length may be either of a type which is usually thought of as 'wave-like', that is to say X-rays, or it may be radiation which is more commonly thought of as a stream of particles. Beams of electrons or neutrons have an associated wave-length which length is a function of the mass and velocity of the particles in the beam. The equation which connects these quantities is $\lambda = h/mv$.

X-rays, electron beams and neutron beams are the three principal types of radiation which have been used for such investigations. The diffraction or scattering of X-rays is chiefly due to their interactions with the extra-nuclear electrons of the atoms in the lattice and from the way in which the X-rays are diffracted, the electron density in the different regions of the crystal can be calculated. Atoms of elements of high atomic number have many extra-nuclear electrons, comparatively few of which are involved in bond formation, and the electron density in the inner closed shells is only distorted to a small degree by the electric fields due to other neighbouring atoms. The inner shells are distributed about each nucleus with approximately spherical symmetry and therefore the nuclei, which are the centres of mass of each atom, can usually be considered to be located near the 'centre of gravity' of each region of maximum electronic density. The nuclei of elements of low atomic number are surrounded by comparatively small numbers of electrons and a much higher proportion of the total number of electrons associated with each such nucleus is present in orbitals which are distorted due to bond formation. In the extreme case of hydrogen which has only one extra-nuclear electron, the electron density in the neighbourhood of the nucleus is naturally low. When a bond is formed between an atom of hydrogen and that of some other element, the density becomes even lower and more diffuse. If a covalent bond is formed between a hydrogen atom and another atom, the region of maximum electronic density near the hydrogen nucleus is located between the nuclei of the two atoms involved; the hydrogen nucleus is not, therefore, located at the centre of the local region of relatively high electronic density. If the bond has appreciable ionic character, the hydrogen atom is normally the positive pole of the resultant dipole. In such a case the electronic density in the neighbourhood of the hydrogen nucleus is so low that it gives no indication of the position of the proton. It is therefore difficult to assign a position to the hydrogen atom on the basis of electron density measurements. This difficulty is present to some extent whenever light elements are present in the lattice. As the atomic number of the atoms concerned increases, more precise location becomes possible. However, when a few lighter atoms are present together with a number of heavier elements, the location of the lighter atoms is particularly difficult; the diffraction from the high electron density round the heavy nuclei tends to 'swamp' that from the lower electron density around the light nuclei.

A beam of electrons is diffracted by regions of high electrostatic potential in the crystal, and these are not the same as the regions of high electronic density. The points of maximum electrostatic potential coincide with the positively charged nuclei, and the potential field is modified by the distribution of the extra-nuclear electrons. When a hydrogen atom forms a bond which has a large degree of ionic character, although the electron density in its neighbourhood is very low, the rate of change of electrostatic potential is very high. The effect of this upon the diffraction of the electron beam is easy to detect, and electron diffraction analysis has therefore considerable value under those conditions in which X-ray diffraction is of least use. It is, however, easier to locate heavier atoms than lighter atoms by the use of this technique because the absolute value of the potential depends upon the nuclear charge. This is, by definition, less for nuclei of low atomic number than for those of high atomic number. The ease of detection of any nucleus is expressed in terms of the 'scattering factor'. The difference in scattering factor is, however, considerably less as between light and heavy nuclei when electron diffraction is used than it is for X-ray diffraction.

A beam of neutrons is scattered in diamagnetic materials primarily by the interaction of the nuclei in the beam with those in the lattice. The variation in scattering factor for the different nuclei over the whole range of the periodic table is fairly small, and differs only in the ratio of approximately $1:3$. The difference does not primarily depend upon mass or atomic number, and the importance of this in determining the structure of, for example, the hydrides of the heaviest elements is referred to below.

Whatever radiation is used for structure determinations by means of diffraction analysis, it must be as monochromatic as possible. In this sense, monochromatic means that the wave-length of all the incident radiation is contained within a narrow band. It is seldom possible to obtain radiation all of which has identically the same wave-length. X-rays for diffraction measurements are usually produced by excitation of a copper target, from which radiation of four different wave-lengths is emitted. Within each of the four primary wave-bands, there is some 'fine structure', but the breadth of each band is sufficiently small for this to be disregarded in practice. Three of the bands can be almost completely filtered out by the use of suitable filters, and only that radiation which has a wave-length of 1·54 ÅU is allowed to emerge and strike the crystal target. Rather shorter wave-length radiation produced by the excitation of molybdenum is sometimes used.

For electron diffraction measurements, electrons emitted from a hot tungsten wire are accelerated by a voltage of 50–100 kV. The electrons then have a velocity which corresponds to a wave-length of 0·06–0·04 ÅU. This beam is focused by diaphragms and magnetic lenses (1).

Beams of neutrons can be obtained from suitable nuclear reactors ('atomic piles'). The neutrons emerge through a collimator and the beam undergoes primary diffraction by passage through a large crystal. A narrow beam of neutrons diffracted at a suitable angle is isolated, and this is used to bombard the sample. The narrower the beam which is selected, the more nearly monochromatic it is, and the less diffuse will be the diffraction from the sample. There is a practical limit to this, however, because the narrower the angle, the fewer the neutrons that will be contained within it, and therefore the fewer which will be observed after diffraction. The neutrons which are used have a velocity which corresponds to a wave-length of approximately 1·2 ÅU, and those which are diffracted from the specimen at various angles are detected with a boron trifluoride neutron counter (2), (3).

Whichever type of radiation is used, similar experimental data are obtained. In each case, the quantities which are measured are the angles at which diffraction takes place, and the relative amount of radiation, or 'intensity' associated with each angle. X-ray and electron intensities can be recorded on suitably sensitized photographic films or plates; this is more convenient than the rather laborious neutron-counting procedure. An outline of the interpretation of X-ray diffraction measurements is described in the following paragraphs; there is no difference in principle between this and the corresponding derivations of structure from electron and neutron diffraction measurements.

When radiation falls on matter which is regularly arranged on lattice points, the diffracted beams reinforce or interfere with each other so as to produce what may be described as 'light' or 'darkness'. Von Laue predicted in 1912 that the regular structural elements in a crystal would behave in this way and the first diffraction photograph was taken by Friedrich and Knipping in the same year. Structural information could only be gained from such photographs when monochromatic radiation was used and this was first done some ten years later by W. L. Bragg.

Diffraction photographs of a single crystal consist of an arrangement of dots or spots on a diffuse background. If the target material is a mass of small crystals which is rotated about an axis perpendicular to the direction of the incident radiation, the diffraction pattern consists of a series of parallel lines. Each line corresponds to a spot on the single crystal photograph, and describes the locus of the spot consequent upon the rotation of the photograph through 180°.

The fundamental equation upon which the interpretation of diffraction measurements depends, is the Bragg relation

$$n\lambda = 2d \sin \theta$$

This equation describes each condition which must be fulfilled when diffraction takes place if there are to be situations in which there is to be reinforcement of the diffracted beams. It is this reinforcement which is manifested as spots or lines on the photographs. In the equation, $d$ is the distance in the lattice between successive layers or planes of atoms of the same type and which have similar crystallographic environments, and $\theta$ is the angle of incidence of the radiation on the successive parallel lattice planes. A train of waves which is incident, for example, on the surface layer of the lattice, will be reinforced by another wave-train which is reflected from a layer below the surface when $2d \sin \theta$ is equal to an integral number multiplied by the wave-length of the radiation. This is similar to the state of affairs which obtains when light is diffracted from a two-dimensional grating. The light spots on the diffraction photographs form a two-dimensional representation of the three-dimensional lattice.

The electrons within the crystal structure from which the X-rays are diffracted may be formally considered to exist as standing waves within the crystal. The electron density at each point within the crystal is the resultant from the addition of the amplitude and phase of all the standing waves which specify the electron distribution. The two-dimensional spot pattern which is obtained is in itself an analysis of the characteristics of all these standing waves. Any particular spot corresponds to a resultant sinusoidal wave which describes the electron density within the crystal. The spots in a diffraction photograph are arranged above and below its centre. A spot near the centre of the photograph indicates a wave of electron density of long wave-length while a more distant spot corresponds to an imaginary density wave of shorter wave-length. The way in which the spot is located relative to the axis of the photograph indicates the direction within the crystal of the wave of electron density. If, for example, the spot is vertically above the centre of the photograph, it corresponds to a wave of electron density oriented vertically. That is to say, it indicates that in the crystal there are horizontal layers of high electron density, separated by regions of low density. The amplitude of the standing wave of electron density is proportional to the square root of the blackening of the photographic plate at the corresponding spot.

A Fourier *analysis* is a method of representing a complex periodic curve. The method involves the description of such a curve as being made up of a large number of superimposed sine curves of differing frequencies, phases and amplitudes. The diffraction photograph is a geometrical representation of such an analysis. In other words, the spots on the photograph represent the way in which the periodic variation of electron density throughout the crystal may be represented in terms of a number of sine curves. A Fourier *synthesis* consists of building up upon these sine curves a picture of the electron density over a given two-dimensional plane of the crystal, and then deducing the positions of the constituent atoms from the location of the regions of maximum density. A three-dimensional representation of the electron density may be then obtained by laying one above another a number of such two-dimensional contour maps like playing cards in a pack.

The principal difficulty in carrying out such a synthesis is that the photograph does not contain enough data for this to be done in a rigid mathematical fashion. In order to carry out such a synthesis, three pieces of data are essential. Two of these are the orientation of the wave relative to an axis of the crystal, and its amplitude. Both can be derived from the photograph. The third essential parameter is the phase of the wave, and this cannot be so derived. The phase indicates the amount by which a particular train of waves is 'out of step' with neighbouring trains. In order to resolve this difficulty, resort is made to a process of trial and error. Certain assumptions are first made about the probable structure. Such assumptions are usually made on chemical grounds; certain radicals or groups may be known or expected to be present, and their form or shape known from other measurements. A Fourier analysis is then made of the electron density in this trial structure, and this is compared with that shown in the photograph. The trial structure is then modified and improved, until by successive approximations a reasonably good agreement is obtained with the pattern which was obtained experimentally.

Various expedients may be employed to assist the process of trial and error. The 'heavy atom' method involves the substitution in the compound under investigation of a light atom by a heavy one. For example, in an organic compound it may be possible to replace a hydroxyl group by an atom of bromine or iodine without apparently appreciably altering the crystalline structure. The electron density due to the atom of high atomic number then dominates the structure. A diffraction photograph of the compound with the substituted atom can then be interpreted as if the lattice were composed of these heavy atoms alone. This may be done by what is known as a Patterson synthesis, which involves using the square of the amplitudes of the waves of electron density to build up a Fourier synthesis in which the atoms are taken together in pairs. The vectors between the pairs of heavy atoms are immensely greater than those between pairs of light atoms, or between light and heavy atoms. From this synthesis, the positions of the heavy atoms may be established. The relative positions of other groups can then be estimated on chemical grounds and a new Fourier analysis carried out and compared with the photograph.

Another technique which is used to assist the process of trial and error is known as 'isomorphous replacement'. The amplitudes present in two isomorphous crystals are compared. In isomorphous crystals of the type of use for this purpose, the compounds only differ in the nature of a single type of atom in the two lattices. The position of this substituted atom in each lattice may be determined from a Patterson synthesis based on the combined photographs. The most probable phase relationship may then be deduced from the two sets of data.

These methods of analysis have been applied to a large number of more or less complex organic structures as well as to many inorganic crystals. The process of analysis of very complicated substances is laborious and time-consuming. The preparation of crystals suitable for diffraction photographs is often technically very difficult. Sometimes the empirical formulae of the compounds has not been certainly established, as in the case of some of the vitamins which have been studied by X-ray diffraction; in other cases, their chemical formulae have been amended as a result of crystallographic analysis. In working out the trial Fourier analysis of complex substances, it is not practicable to carry out the mathematical operations except with the aid of a computer; it is fortunate that computer technology has kept pace with the needs of the crystallographer. One final point about the difficulty of precise interpretation of diffraction data should be noted. The photographs themselves are not perfect. The recorded diffraction spots have a finite size, and are not true points. They are not defined by perfectly sharp edges, but to some extent they merge into the background. This means that the estimation of their relative intensities which is necessary to establish the amplitude of the electron density waves, cannot be exact. As is so often the case with the interpretation of data, it is not possible to draw absolutely rigid conclusions, and a crystallographer must be prepared to use flair and intuition in deriving the structures. The phrase 'it was found by X-ray methods . . .' sometimes occurs in text-books, and it should be remembered that such a discovery may have involved years of trial and error. Diffraction methods are usually not rigid and formal means of determining structure.

Electron and neutron diffraction analysis are valuable ancillaries to the methods of X-ray diffraction. For both the two former methods it is usual to employ single crystals of the compound under investigation, and these must be at least 0·1 mm in diameter—it is preferable for the crystals to be somewhat larger than this. Electron diffraction analysis is of particular value because it is the only method by which results can be obtained when the material can only be provided in the form of a thin film. Diffraction takes place even if the film is only $10^{-6}$ cm thick.

An interesting series of results which has been obtained from the study of the diffraction of electrons concerns the carbon–hydrogen bond distances in organic compounds. It was suspected that in some compounds the bond length would differ from the accepted value of 1·09 ÅU. By the use of electron diffraction it has been shown to be $1·12 \pm 0·015$ ÅU in the heavy paraffins $C_{18}H_{38}$, $C_{28}H_{58}$ and $C_{30}H_{62}$ (4), and to be $1·14 \pm 0·01$ ÅU in hexamethylene tetramine (5). The latter value was confirmed by measurements using neutron diffraction from which a bond length of $1·13 \pm 0·02$ ÅU was calculated (6). This work exemplifies the advantage to be derived from both electron and neutron diffraction, because it would have been impossible to fix the position of the hydrogen atoms with this precision by X-ray diffraction methods.

There are a number of instances in inorganic chemistry in which it has been of value to determine the electrostatic potential gradient by means of electron diffraction. For example, the potential gradients in the face-centred cubic cell of metallic silver were studied. The potential surrounding the silver atom was shown by means of electron diffraction analysis to possess spherical symmetry, and it is therefore evident that no metal–metal bonds are formed. This is in accordance with accepted theories of metal structure in which the valency electrons enter a common 'conductivity zone' (7).

The experimentally measured curve of electrostatic potential in lithium oxide, $Li_2O$, does not agree with the 'pure' bonding curves which were calculated. It can therefore be deduced that the lithium–oxygen bonds are not wholly covalent, and that they have some ionic character (8).

The principal limitation to the use of neutron diffraction analysis is the expense of the equipment required. X-ray and electron diffraction cameras are both relatively cheap and are available commercially. Nuclear reactors are the only effective source of neutrons for diffraction experiments. In the early work on this type of analysis, the primary diffraction, from which the monochromatic beam of neutrons was selected, was achieved by a crystal of LiF, NaCl or $CaF_2$. In more recent work, the monochromator has consisted of crystals of metals such as copper or lead (9), and a 'monochromatic' flux of a few million neutrons per minute can be obtained in this way. A large bulk sample of the substance to be studied is necessary. If a powdered sample is used, it is typically in the form of a cylinder 2–3 cm high and 1 cm in diameter. The boron trifluoride neutron counter usually contains some $^{10}$B which leads to a higher counting efficiency. A typical counter is 5 cm in diameter and 50 cm long, and is placed 60 cm from the specimen. It is shielded to prevent the entry of stray neutrons, and it scans the arc of diffraction at, for instance, 5° of arc per hour. This slow scanning speed is necessary because of the low intensities of the diffraction peaks. The apparatus is thus both massive and expensive: observations require a large sample and take a long time to carry out.

The experimental observations of neutron diffraction are often difficult to interpret and the background scattering is usually high. There are a number of reasons for this. It may happen that an incident neutron is not diffracted by a nucleus, but forms a metastable addition compound with it from which it is subsequently ejected in a random direction. Many nuclei have a resultant spin which can be denoted by $I$. When the neutron reacts with such a nucleus, two transient states will be formed. These will have net spins of $I = +\frac{1}{2}$ and $I = -\frac{1}{2}$ respectively. The effect of this will be that part of the scattered neutron radiation will be coherent and produce diffraction effects, and part will be incoherent and will contribute only to the background scattering. Different nuclei of the same element will usually have different spin properties. Such different isotopic nuclei will be distributed over equivalent lattice points with a statistically random distribution and this will further increase the incoherent background scattering.

In spite of these disadvantages, there are a number of applications in which neutron diffraction is of particular value. Hydrogen nuclei have approximately the same scattering factor for neutrons as have the nuclei of the other elements, and they can therefore be located with a comparable precision, but unfortunately the incoherent scattering from them is very high. This is because the interaction between proton and neutron differs when they each have parallel spins from that which occurs when their spins are anti-parallel. The resultant incoherent scattering is particularly intense when powdered specimens are used, and if single crystals cannot be obtained, the deuterated compound is usually employed because there is less incoherent scattering from the neutron–deuteron interaction than from the neutron–proton interaction.

Neutron diffraction has been used to investigate a number of instances of suspected hydrogen-bond formation. For example, Pease and Bacon ( 10 ) have investigated single crystals of $KH_2PO_4$ by means of this technique, and have shown that the hydrogen atom in the O—H—O hydrogen bond appears to be considerably elongated along the 0-0 axis. They have put forward two alternative explanations of this observation. On the one hand, it may be due to thermal vibrations of the hydrogen atom along the O–O axis. On the other, it may be that there are two possible locations of the hydrogen atom, one of which is closer to one oxygen atom, and one to the other so that the measured diffraction is due to random occupation of these positions. It is of interest that below $-150°$ C, the crystal becomes ferro-electric, and when an electric field is applied, the hydrogen atoms appear to lie asymmetrically between the pairs of oxygen atoms. When the hydrogen bond in $KHF_2$ was investigated by Peterson and Levy (11), no such assymetry was observed. The diffraction work was carried out with a large single crystal, and the hydrogen atom was found to be located half-way between the fluorine atoms.

When uranium hydride was investigated, it was not possible to prepare a large single crystal and the measurements were carried out with $UD_3$ powder. No evidence for a bridge structure was found. Each atom of deuterium was located at the approximate centre of a deformed tetrahedron of uranium atoms. The mean U–D distance of $2·32$ ÅU was abnormally high. The compound was not salt-like, and no evidence of metallic U—U bonds was found. The same author also investigated $ThC_2$. In spite of the fact that by this method it is difficult to locate carbon in the presence of thorium atoms, it was found that the Th–C separation was approximately the same as the sum of their covalent radii. Even so, the compound shows some ionic properties.

Atoms of neighbouring atomic number are practically indistinguishable by X-ray diffraction techniques. X-ray diffraction is of little value for studying alloys of, for example, iron, cobalt and nickel. Owing to their differing nuclear properties, atoms of these metals can be distinguished by neutron diffraction, and the structures of their alloys determined in this way. A further limitation of X-ray analysis is that it is concerned with electron density, and the assumption must be made that the nucleus is at the centre of the surrounding electron cloud. The diffraction of neutrons takes place from the nuclei themselves, and it can be shown in this way that the latter are not, in fact, always symmetrically placed with reference to the surrounding electrons. In such a case, a lower symmetry state may be revealed by neutron diffraction than was apparent from the X-ray diffraction measurements.

The methods of structure analysis which have been described are used to determine how the component atoms of a structure appear to be arranged in space. The chemist is also concerned with finding out why they are arranged in one way rather than in another. Under certain conditions of temperature and pressure, a particular compound is formed with certain specific properties. The atoms are assembled together in such a way that the potential energy of the structure as a whole has a minimum value. In this structure, bonds of various types are formed between the atoms. In the course of the investigation of the stability of compounds, it is necessary to determine the types and energies of the bonds between the atoms of which they are composed.

The weakest bonds are formed when atoms are held together by Van der Waals forces. These forces do not operate in particular directions in space and are effective at distances of separation of a few Ångstrom units. Strong repulsive forces are effective at shorter distances of 1–2ÅU and their strength depends inversely upon a high power of the distance of separation. For any pair of atoms, there is an equilibrium distance at which the strength of the repulsive and of the attractive forces have equal and opposite signs and the potential energy of the structure is then at a minimum. The distance of separation of the atoms of inert gases in the solid state is determined in this way.

A second type of bond occurs in solid metals. In such phases, the atoms usually form a close-packed array similar to that found in a solid held together by Van der Waals forces. The attractive forces or bonds between the metal atoms are not directed in space. The valency electrons, that is to say those electrons which do not participate in the closed shells, are common to the structure as a whole, and they occupy a system of energy levels known as the conductivity zone.

Chemists are chiefly interested in a third type of bond structure. In this type, the forces between atoms result from the interactions of their valency electrons. Such bonds are usually described as if they had rigidly distinguishable characteristics. The term 'ionic bond' is used to denote a situation in which one or more electrons are regarded as being entirely transferred from one atom or group to another, so that each achieves a more stable electronic configuration. The bond is then formed between the atoms through the operation of electrostatic forces which are consequent upon the transfer of electronic charge from one atom to the other. In covalent bonds, electrons are contributed to the bond by two or more atoms. The electrons then exist in a bonding orbital which is common to the atoms or groups participating in the bond. In co-ordinate bonds, two bonding electrons are contributed to the bond orbital by a single atom or group. The electrostatic ionic bond is not directed in space, but covalent and co-ordinate bonds are so directed, and the bond angles correspond to certain characteristic derivatives of their associated wave-functions.

Few bonds are 'pure' in the sense that they are wholly ionic or wholly covalent or co-ordinate. Since X-rays are diffracted by the electronic zones around the nucleus, it would be expected that X-ray diffraction analysis could give an indication of how equally electrons are shared between two or more atoms forming a bond. The increase in electron density due to the presence of a pair of bonding electrons is, however, small in comparison with the general electron density around nuclei. Precise work of this nature by Cruickshank (13) on the electron distribution in anthracene has indicated the position of the $\sigma$-bonding electrons, but the effect of the $\pi$-orbitals is too diffuse to be detected. The electronic distribution and the bond types must therefore be studied by less direct methods.

Many of the more useful of these methods depend upon the behaviour of chemical compounds when they are placed in a magnetic field. In such a situation, the extra-nuclear electrons tend to arrange themselves so that their interaction with the magnetic field is at a minimum, but this arrangement is opposed by the thermal motion. All chemical substances except atomic hydrogen and the bare proton contain two or more electrons which either occupy closed shells or which occupy one or more bonding orbitals. In addition, there may be other electrons which are unpaired and contribute to a net electronic spin moment. Paired electrons do not contribute to such a moment, but in the presence of a magnetic field, they behave as if their planes of rotation became oriented. This involves an absorption of energy from the field, giving rise to the phenomenon of diamagnetism; it is independent of temperature. The interaction of the unpaired electrons with the magnetic field is temperature dependent, and it is known as paramagnetism. Almost all chemical compounds contain electrons in pairs or in closed shells in addition to any unpaired electrons which may be present. The measured magnetic moment will therefore be the resultant of two quantities. These are, firstly, the almost universal diamagnetic component, and secondly the paramagnetic component if unpaired electrons are present. In paramagnetic atoms, the unpaired electrons behave in some respects similarly to miniature magnets which seek to align themselves parallel to the external magnetic field. This alignment is opposed by the thermal motion and the paramagnetic component can therefore be isolated by making measurements of the moment at different temperatures. If this is done, the paramagnetism usually exhibits an inverse temperature dependence. If the value of the paramagnetic moment is proportional to $1/T$, the compound is said to obey the Curie law. The behaviour of some paramagnetic substances follows the Curie–Weiss law, and in such case the moment is proportional to $1/(T+\Delta)$. There is another type of paramagnetic behaviour, the effect of which is usually so small that it can be neglected in comparison with the paramagnetism which has been described above. This is known as Van Vleck, or temperature independent paramagnetism. It occurs when the energy levels into which the electrons may be promoted by the external magnetic field are separated from the ground state by an interval or energy increment which is small compared with $kT$. There are thus three components of the measured magnetic moment.

$$\chi_{meas} = \chi_P + \chi_D + \chi_{V.V}$$

The orientation of the atoms (or in some cases groups or molecules) which have unpaired electrons is not only opposed by the thermal motion, but the applied field may also be modified locally by the magnetic fields of neighbouring atoms or groups. This modification will always occur if each paramagnetic group is not contained within a magnetically dilute environment in which neighbouring paramagnetic groups are sufficiently separated for their effect on each other to be negligible. In such an ideal situation

$$\chi_P = N^2\mu^2/3RT$$

where $\mu$ is the magnetic moment of the electron. An unpaired electron of subsidiary quantum number $l$ gives rise to a magnetic moment which has the value $\sqrt{[l(l+1)]}.(eh/4\pi me)$. The quantity $(eh/4\pi me)$ has the numerical value $9.18 \times 10^{-21}$ in c.g.s. units, and it is known as the Bohr Magneton $(\beta)$. In order to calculate the effective magnetic moment $\mu_{eff}$ it is usual to ignore the small effect of $\chi_{V.V.}$ and the corrected moment $(\chi_{meas} - \chi_D)$ is substituted in the equation

$$\mu_{eff} = 2.84\sqrt{(\chi_{corr}.T)}$$

This treatment of the experimental results would give a simple measure of the number of unpaired electrons associated with each atom if it were not for various complicating factors. For example, the paramagnetic behaviour of a compound is affected by the energy relationships between the various Bohr orbits which the electrons can occupy. This can be expressed in terms of the spectroscopic ground state; it may also depend on higher states if their separation is small compared with $kT$. The behaviour of the electrons which give rise to paramagnetic behaviour is also affected by the symmetry and strength of the electric field which is associated with the immediately adjacent atoms or ligands.

The operation of these factors gives rise to a number of more or less well-defined types of paramagnetic behaviour. The typical or ideal from which all other types may formally be considered to deviate is known as the 'Rare Earth Type'. It occurs when the unpaired electrons, are well shielded from the field of the nucleus by inner shells of electrons and when the ground state is separated from the next higher state by a quantum of energy which is very much greater than the quantity $kT$. In such a case, the magnetic moment is given by the expression

$$\mu = g\sqrt{[J(J+1)]}$$

$g$ indicates a quantity known as the Landé splitting factor, and is equal to

$$1 + \frac{J(J+1)+S(S+1)-L(L+1)}{2J(J+1)}$$

$J$ is the resultant angular momentum of the unpaired electrons, and it is derived by combining the values of $L$ and $S$ in an appropriate way. $S$ is simply the number of unpaired electrons divided by two; the spin angular momentum is then $Sh/2\pi$. The orbital angular momentum is equal to $Lh/2\pi$, where $L$ is the vector sum of the subsidiary quantum numbers $l_1$, $l_2$, $l_3$. The way in which the spin angular momentum and the orbital angular momentum must be combined together to make up the resultant angular momentum $J$ is expressed in a set of generalizations known as Hund's Rules. However, in some circumstances, coupling together of the two momentum components may not take place. When the multiplet separation is small, that is to say when the difference in energy of the various $J$ levels is not large compared with $kT$, each reacts separately with the external magnetic field. In such a case

$$\mu = \sqrt{[4S(S+1)+2(L+1)]}$$

A particularly interesting situation arises when the multiplet separation has an intermediate value. Here the energy separation between the various levels is of the same order as $kT$. $L$–$S$ coupling takes place, and the electrons are distributed over the various $J$ levels. The distribution is a statistical one, and it accords with the generalization known as Boltzmann's law which has been found to apply in a number of similar cases, where particles are distributed between various energy levels. Such behaviour is found to occur in the molecule NO and in the trivalent cations of samarium, europium and plutonium. Samarium and plutonium have a similar electronic configuration—plutonium is the actinide analogue of the rare earth samarium. The way in which the measured magnetic susceptibility of their trivalent ions varies with temperature does not follow either the Curie law or the Curie–Weiss law and the susceptibility curve exhibits a shallow minimum. The case of trivalent samarium was discussed by Van Vleck (14) who derived a theoretical expression to account for this behaviour:

$$\chi = \frac{N \sum\limits_{J=L-S}^{J=L+S} [g_J^2 \beta^2 J(J+1)/3kT + \alpha_J](2J+1)\exp(-W_{J^\circ}/kT)}{(2J+1)\exp(-W_{J^\circ}/kT)}$$

The significance of the symbols used in this expression is set out in Appendix 4. 1. The evaluation of $\chi$ from this expression is not difficult, but it involves a large number of very tedious arithmetical operations. One of the quantities involved is the spin doublet screening constant $\sigma_2$. This can be considered to be a measure of the degree to which the nuclear charge is shielded by the closed shells of electrons underlying those that are not spin-paired. The value of this constant is not accurately known, but a reasonable estimate of its magnitude can be made.

It was stated above that plutonium is the actinide analogue of the rare earth samarium. This implies that in their trivalent ions, each has five unpaired electrons in an $f$ sub-shell, $4f^5$ in the case of samarium and $5f^5$ in the case of plutonium. The $Pu^{3+}$ ion would only behave in a similar way to $Sm^{3+}$, and its magnetic susceptibility/temperature curve would only exhibit a minimum if this configuration was present. No minimum would occur if the configuration were, for example, $5f^46d^1$. The measurement of the susceptibility of compounds such as $PuF_3$ and $PuCl_3$ was thus an important piece of evidence for the acceptance or rejection of the actinide hypothesis which involved the possession of five $5f$ electrons by the trivalent plutonium ion.

The shape of the curve, and the position and magnitude of the expected minimum were calculated for $Pu^{3+}$ from Van Vleck's equation. The most probable values of the screening constant were 57, 58 or 59, and separate calculations were made involving each of these values. The experimental measurements of the susceptibility showed a minimum, and its position was in good agreement with that calculated from values of the screening constant of 57 and 58 (15).

A number of other types of paramagnetism are known. In some cases, the orbital angular momentum appears to make no contribution to the magnetic moment. Paramagnetism of this nature is known as the 'spin only' type and is frequently found among ions of elements in the first transition period from titanium to copper. In such a case, the magnetic moment is expressed by

$$\mu = \sqrt{[4S(S+1)]}$$

There are two types of paramagnetism in which the spins of unpaired electrons appear to cancel each other out so that the residual moment is then less than would be expected from the number of unpaired electrons present. One of Hund's Rules stipulates that the multiplicity must be a maximum. This means that the number of available energy levels which are occupied by unpaired electrons must be as large as possible. The separation of the levels, that is to say the difference in energy between them, is affected by the field of neighbouring ligands. If this is very strong, the levels may become energetically so widely separated that it is no longer possible for an electron to acquire sufficient energy to occupy the highest levels. Electrons therefore become paired in lower levels, and the paramagnetic effect is thereby reduced.

The second situation in which the value of the susceptibility which would be expected on other grounds is not observed in practice is found in some ions of the second and third transition periods. Here, the $d$ electrons may be visualized as occupying very elliptical orbits. They behave as if for part of the time they were penetrating the inner closed shells and were coming under the influence of the intense electrostatic field of the nucleus. This is apparently manifested by the $S$ and $L$ vectors becoming aligned in opposite directions. In the case of an ion with four $d$ electrons, and in which $L = 2$, and $S = 1$, then if $L$ and $S$ are aligned in opposite directions, the effective moment will be zero. In such a case, even though four unpaired electrons are present, the ion will not exhibit paramagnetism.

From the examples given, it can be seen that measurements of magnetic susceptibility must be interpreted with considerable caution and they frequently do not provide an unequivocal answer to a problem of structure. The measured susceptibility may not exactly coincide with the value derived from any of the pre-supposed theoretical electronic configurations, and even a zero value for the paramagnetic effect does not necessarily indicate that all the valency electrons are involved in bonding orbitals. The difficulty of assigning the correct electronic configuration may be illustrated from further work carried out by Dawson and his colleagues (16). The reason for using examples derived from work on elements of the last period in the table, is that the electronic situation is here extremely complex, and that the difficulty of interpretation is particularly great.

The magnetic moment of tetravalent uranium in $UO_2$ was found by experiment to be 3·20 Bohr Magnetons. The moments expected for the various electronic possibilities were

| Configuration | Spectroscopic ground state | Moment (Bohr magnetons) | | |
|---|---|---|---|---|
| | | L–S coupling | Spin only | jj coupling |
| $5f^2$ | $^3H_4$ | 3·58 | 2·83 | 3·84 |
| $6d^2$ | $^3F_2$ | 1·63 | 2·83 | 1·96 |
| $5f^1 6d^1$ | $^3H_4$ | 3·58 | 2·83 | 3·74 |

The experimental result was interpreted as indicating that the electrons were either in the $5f^2$ configuration, or possibly the $5f^1 6d^1$. If this were true, then partial quenching of the orbital electrons must be occurring. This would involve the screening effect of the inner closed shells being considerably less effective than is the case in the corresponding members of the rare earth series. The uranium atom in $UO_2$ is not in a magnetically dilute environment, however, and it would be expected that in this situation, the fields of neighbouring ions would exercise a considerable influence on the observed moment. Since uranium dioxide is isomorphous with thorium dioxide, it is possible to make a wide range of solid solutions of $UO_2$ in $ThO_2$ which contains no unpaired electrons, and therefore acts as a magnetically inert diluent for $UO_2$. Other workers in the U.S.A. measured the magnetic moment of uranium in a range of such solid solutions. From these measurements, the values found could be extrapolated to find the value at 'infinite dilution', that is to say in an isolated $UO_2$ molecule (17). This value was close to that calculated for the 'spin only' moment, which is the same for each of the three possible electronic configurations. However, by considering the results as a whole, it was concluded that they indicated a $6d^2$ configuration.

It has also been found that the magnetic behaviour of fluorides is usually very similar to that of the corresponding oxide systems. Dawson therefore studied solid solutions of $UF_4$ in $ThF_4$ (18). The extrapolated value of the moment here appeared to indicate that only the $5f^2$ configuration was possible. He pointed out, however, that in tetravalent uranium there appeared to be only a small energy difference between the $5f$ and $6d$ levels and small changes in the environment might be sufficient to affect the electronic configuration. It is therefore obvious that statements about the electronic configuration of such compounds must be treated with considerable reserve.

Apart from difficulties in the interpretation of the observed results, magnetic susceptibility measurements suffer from an inherent disadvantage. The susceptibility measured is that of the bulk sample, and the magnetic properties of each single atomic species present contribute to the observed result. Very small quantities of ferrous impurities can give rise to an effect many times larger than that from the paramagnetism of the sample. The paramagnetic effect may however be used to give information about electronic configurations in another way. In this method, the compound containing the electrons with unpaired spins is placed in a magnetic field, and the electrons are then excited by high frequency electromagnetic radiation. An electron in any given energy state will only take energy from the radiation when $h\nu$ is equal to the energy necessary to promote the electron to a higher quantum level. At a particular frequency of the external radiation, such electrons will absorb energy from the field, but this frequency will in general be different for each atomic or ionic species. It will therefore be possible to make observations of the behaviour of each separate paramagnetic species in a mixture of different ions, and extensive purification will be unnecessary. Such techniques are referred to as resonance absorption methods. The theoretical principles which underlie them will now be discussed in more detail.

When an ion has one or more unpaired electrons, it will possess a resultant angular momentum $J$. When a crystal containing such an ion is placed in a strong constant external magnetic field, the angular momentum vector of each ion will take up a definite orientation relative to the field. Each possible orientation will have a particular energy associated with it. Only certain relative orientations will be possible; that is to say, the spatial orientations will be quantized. It can be shown that if the external magnetic field has a strength $H$, then the various permitted orientations will have energies equal to $Mg\beta H$. As before, $\beta$ is the value of the Bohr magneton, and $g$ is the Landé spectroscopic splitting factor, which has the value of $2 \cdot 0023$ for a free electron. $M$ is the magnetic quantum number of the electron. The

7

selection rules for orientation transitions allow $M$ to vary by $\pm 1$. The probability of transitions in either direction, that is to say either from $M$ to $(M+1)$ or to $(M-1)$, are equal. In the absence of an outside source of energy there will be more electrons in the level of lower energy, and the distribution of electrons between the levels of different energies will be in accordance with Boltzmann's law. More transitions will take place from the level containing the most electrons than from any other state. Since the level with most electrons is the lowest one, $\Delta M$ will most frequently be $+1$. If the sample is subjected to a beam of electromagnetic radiation, energy will be absorbed from the field if the radiation has such a frequency that transitions can take place. If the applied electromagnetic field is part of a tuned circuit, the effect of this absorption will be to damp the circuit. If the frequency of the tuned circuit is equivalent to the separation between levels, that is to say if

$$h\nu = g\beta\, H$$

where
$$\lambda = h\nu$$

then
$$H = hc/\lambda g\beta$$

Resonance absorption is found to take place if the magnetic field has a strength of 3–4000 gauss, and the electromagnetic field derived from microwave radiation has $\lambda = 3$ cm. The paramagnetic sample is usually placed in a cavity resonator or in a wave guide which is part of a tuned circuit. It is most convenient in practice to maintain a tuned circuit at a constant frequency, and to vary the strength of the magnetic field and the change in the reflected or transmitted power is then measured at the field strength at which resonance absorption occurs.

In order to obtain sufficient information about the magnetic properties for useful deductions to be made about the electronic configuration, two further parameters are varied during paramagnetic resonance absorption experiments.* Observations are made over a range of temperatures as in magnetic susceptibility work, and measurements are also made with the sample crystal oriented at different angles to the applied field. Paramagnetic crystals are anisotropic, that is to say the resonance peaks are affected by the relative orientation of the field and the crystal. This is primarily due to differences in the value of the splitting factor $g$. The effect of this is that each paramagnetic ion will give rise to an individual absorption spectrum.

This is not only of value when there may be traces of ferrous impurity in the sample. Most paramagnetic ions are derived from transition elements in which valency bonds can be formed by the outermost electrons without involving the inner incomplete shell, and it therefore happens that the most

* This technique is also referred to as Electron Spin Resonance or E.S.R.

interesting magnetic behaviour is exemplified by just those elements which are the most difficult to separate chemically from their neighbours in the periodic table. The rare earth elements are the most extreme example of this. A method which enables a study to be made of a particular ion without the necessity for separating it from its neighbours is therefore of great value. The quantity of material required in this work is very small; under favourable conditions it is possible to detect $10^{14}$ magnetic centres with $S = \pm \frac{1}{2}$ at room temperature (19). The only experimental limitation is that single crystals are necessary.

The resonance absorption spectra can be interpreted so as to yield information about the number of unpaired electrons associated with the ions being studied. In addition, it is possible to determine the symmetry of the electric field surrounding the ion in the crystal. From this it may be possible to make deductions about the types of bond between the paramagnetic ion and its neighbours. This symmetry is a function of the electron density around the ion. If the density is symmetrical, $\sigma$-bonding is probable; a lower symmetry is frequently consonant with the existence of $\pi$-bonding orbitals.

Resonance techniques can be used to derive information about organic free radicals, as well as about inorganic crystals. Free radicals have one valency electron with an unpaired spin, and they are therefore paramagnetic. When a dilute solution of triphenylmethyl radical is studied in this way (20), a single resonance absorption line is observed under low resolution. This corresponds to one unpaired electron. Under very high resolution eighteen groups of multiplets can be detected. This is interpreted as demonstrating that the unpaired electron which is formally associated with the methyl carbon atom, is in fact delocalized, and 'smeared' over the whole aromatic ring system. Similar work has been carried out with the negative naphthalene ion (21).

E.S.R. measurements may also be used to detect the presence of free radicals in systems in which there are no other atoms which are likely to have unpaired electrons associated with them. Free radicals have been shown by this means to be present in partially polymerized glycol dimethacrylate (22). Free radicals are believed to be produced in many substances when they have been irradiated with X-rays, and E.S.R. measurements indicate that when dimethyl mercury is irradiated in this way, $[C_2H_4]^+$ is probably produced (23). An interesting observation concerns the glow discharge of nitrogen in which an afterglow persists when the electric discharge has been switched off. If this glowing gas is rapidly condensed at $4°$ K, the resultant solid shows resonance absorption, which presumably indicates that free nitrogen atoms are present, and that it is the energy liberated in their recombination which gives rise to the glow (24). A further use of E.S.R. measurements has been to detect radiation damage suffered by substances irradiated in nuclear reactors by identifying the free radicals formed. High intensity irradiation may lead under certain circumstances to the production of ions which have unfamiliar valency states and these are often produced when a small proportion of transition element ions is present as an impurity in crystals such as those of silicon, and the alkali halides, hydrides and azides (25).

Not only do orbital electrons react with an external field, but in addition those nuclei which have a net resultant spin tend to align themselves so as to minimize the potential energy of the system. The nucleons (proton and neutron) have a spin quantum number $I$ which can have the value $+\frac{1}{2}$ or $-\frac{1}{2}$. This is interpreted as indicating that such particles have a spin which may be aligned in either of two anti-parallel directions. A spinning particle must have a spin angular momentum, $\mathbf{I}$, which can be expressed in terms of the spin quantum number:

$$\mathbf{I} = \{\sqrt{[I(I+1)]}\}(h/2\pi)$$

The angular momentum of the proton has been measured, and $I$ found to be $+\frac{1}{2}$. For the deuteron, $I = 1$; it is therefore reasonable to suppose that $I = +\frac{1}{2}$ for the neutron also, and that in the deuteron the spins of the neutron and of the proton are aligned in parallel. In general, all nuclei of odd atomic number will have a half-integral resultant spin, and those of even number must have an $I$ which is either zero or an integer. For any nuclei in which $I$ differs from zero, there will be a magnetic moment associated with the angular momentum. Even–even nuclei with even $Z$ and even $N$ have a resultant zero spin and therefore no magnetic moment— $^{12}C$ and $^{16}O$ are among the commonest nuclei in this class.

The magnetic moment of the proton is given by the expression

$$\mu_p = g_p M\mu_N$$

where $M = \sqrt{[I(I+1)]}$   $g_p$ is a splitting factor similar to the Landé factor referred to above, and which for the proton has the value $5\cdot58490$. $\mu_N$ is the nuclear magneton $(he/4\pi m_p c)$ which is equal to $5\cdot0493 \times 10^{-24}$ erg gauss.

For any nucleus, $M$, the magnetic quantum number, will have a range of possible values from $+m$ to $-m$. The energy difference between them will depend upon the strength of the external field, and in fact the spacing of these levels varies linearly with the field strength. In the absence of such a field all the levels will be degenerate and there will be no splitting. The situation is visualized as being one in which the values of the magnetic quantum number correspond to permitted inclinations of the axis of the spinning nucleus to the direction of the applied field. The energy levels then correspond to the resultant of the magnetic dipole in the field direction at each of the possible inclinations.

For any nucleus in which $I$, the spin quantum number, is equal to $\frac{1}{2}$, the energy difference between any two adjacent sub-levels is given by the equation

$$h\nu = g_p\mu_N H_0$$

where $H_0$ is the strength of the applied magnetic field. From this equation it can easily be shown that for such a nucleus in an applied external field of $10^4$ gauss, the corresponding frequency $\nu$ is 42·6 Mc/sec. which is equivalent to a high frequency radio wave. In a similar manner to that in which the electrons were distributed between the various energy levels, the nuclei will also occupy the two possible levels. They will be distributed between them in the way predicted by Boltzmann's law, and the effect of this is that at room temperature there will be about $3\frac{1}{2}$ more nuclei in every million in the upper level than in the lower. In order to detect the resonance behaviour of this small excess, fairly large samples, of the order of 1 cc in volume, are necessary.

In a nuclear magnetic resonance spectrometer, the sample is contained within a magnetic field of the order of $10^4$ gauss. A split coil is connected to an R.F. oscillator, and is so placed that the induced field is at right angles to the axis of the magnetic field. A detector coil is placed at right angles to each of these two energizing fields, and this is used to detect the small voltage which is induced by the transitions between the two levels. After amplification, this voltage may be observed on the tube of an oscilloscope. In practice, the strength of the magnetic field is slowly increased until at a strength corresponding to the high frequency oscillation, the system comes into resonance.

Nuclei in which $I$ is greater than $\frac{1}{2}$ possess a quadrupole moment in addition to their dipole moment. The asymmetrical charge distribution gives rise to two positive and two negative magnetic centres or poles. Such a quadrupole will react with the electric field gradient whose presence is due to the overall electron distribution within the molecule of which the particular nucleus is a component. When the nucleus is a dipole ($I = \frac{1}{2}$), the resonance absorption peak is sharply defined. In the case of a nuclear quadrupole ($I > \frac{1}{2}$) the resonance peak may be broad, and have a considerable fine structure exhibiting a number of subsidiary peaks.

The reason for this behaviour is that the quadrupoles precess in the electric field gradient, and the precession displaces the nuclear spin levels. For isolated nuclei, in which $I > \frac{1}{2}$, in strong magnetic fields, the energy levels are given by the expression (26)

$$W = -\frac{M\mu_N H_Z}{I} \cdot \frac{eQ[3M^2 - I(I+1)]}{4I(2I+1)} \cdot \frac{\partial^2 V}{\partial_{Z^2}}$$

Here $M$ is a quantum number which can have values of $+1$, 0, and $-1$, $V$ is the electrostatic potential at the nucleus due to all charges outside it.

This formula implies that the magnetic interactions are stronger than the electric interactions, and that the latter may be expressed as a perturbation on the former. In liquids or gases, the Brownian movement tends to reduce all such intermolecular electric fields to an average value of zero. The broadening of the resonance line is therefore seldom observed in molecules which have complete rotational freedom. The first time that nuclear quadrupole resonance was observed for any nucleus was in 1950 when the nuclei involved were $^{35}Cl$ and $^{37}Cl$ in 1 : 2 dichloroethane (27).

The quadrupole nuclei have been likened to built-in probes by which the charge distribution at points within a molecule may be assessed (28). This charge distribution can give valuable information about chemical bond types, and in particular about the proportions of ionic and covalent character in a bond. The use of N.Q.R. in this way has been reviewed by Orville-Thomas (29).

Another nuclear magnetic resonance phenomenon is of particular interest to chemists. It has been defined by Wertz as follows (30):

At a time when physicists were busy comparing gyromagnetic ratios of various nuclei, and expressing these to seven or more significant figures, several disquieting papers appeared. It was reported that in compounds of phosphorus, nitrogen and fluorine, the resonant frequency for a particular nucleus depended on the compound in which it was present. The effect was called the 'chemical shift' because physicists could think of no stronger term of damnation for an effect which was making insignificant several digits in their nuclear moment data.

Such an effect is observed because the applied external field $H$ is modified by the field of the internuclear electrons. The magnetic field, $H_0$, actually experienced by the nucleus can be expressed as follows:

$$H_0 = H(1-\sigma)$$

or
$$\sigma = \frac{H_0 - H}{H}$$

where $H$ is taken as the resonance maximum for a reference substance. In compounds of cobalt, $\sigma$ may be as high as 2%. Different ligands give rise to different values of $\sigma$. The appearance of more than one resonance peak for two different atoms of the same element in a single compound was first reported for $[NH_4][NO_3]$ in 1950 (31). The sample consisted of an aqueous solution of ammonium nitrate in 2M manganese sulphate. The nitrogen resonance peak was split into two peaks with a separation of 1·6 kc in 3300 kc. Samples of ammonium acetate and of nitric acid were subsequently observed to exhibit peaks which corresponded to each of the two respective peaks which had been observed in ammonium nitrate.

The chemical shift is of particular importance in protonic compounds.

When the resonance lines observed for more acidic protons are compared with those for less acid protons, $\sigma$ is seen to decrease. This indicates a reduction in the extra-nuclear electronic shielding. Observations have been made on the nuclear magnetic resonance spectra of systems in which a chemical exchange reaction is occurring. For example

$$H_a A + H_b B \; \underset{\longleftarrow}{\longrightarrow} \; H_b A + H_a B$$

If the exchange is slow, two well separated proton resonance lines are observed. If it is rapid, only a single sharp line is apparent. For inter-mediate reaction velocities, a single broadened line occurs. A number of solutions of strong acids have been studied in this way, and from such measurements, the dissociation constant of $HNO_3$ has been calculated to be 22, and that of $HClO_4$ to be 38 (32).

The resonance absorption peak may be resolved into a number of lines for another reason, in addition to the chemical shift, or diamagnetic shielding as it is sometimes called, and in many instances, under very high resolution, considerable fine structure has been observed; the principal peaks are seen to be split into a number of minor peaks. This behaviour is due to what is known as electron-coupled spin interaction. The orientation of the magnetic dipole of one nucleus affects the orientation of the electrons which form the bond between that nucleus and a neighbouring nucleus, and the change of electronic orientation is transmitted to the second nucleus. Thus, one nucleus has a small polarizing effect upon its neighbour via the bonding electrons. The effect of this electron coupling is usually very small, but in some compounds, however, it may be as large as that of the chemical shift. The nuclear magnetic resonance spectrum of the ethanol molecule is often quoted as an example of the succession of effects which are observed as the resolution becomes progressively higher. Under low resolution a single resonance absorption peak is observed. As the resolution becomes higher, the effect of the diamagnetic shielding becomes apparent. Three proton resonance peaks appear, due to the differing proton environments in $-CH_3-$, $-CH_2-$, and $-OH$ respectively. As the resolution is further increased, more and more fine structure of the primary peaks can be detected. These are caused by the progressive manifestation of the effects due to successively weaker electron coupling. The full scheme for ethanol has been calculated to consist of thirty-seven lines or peaks. (Eight from $-CH_3$, twenty-five from $-CH_2-$, and four from $-OH$). Most of these have been actually observed; such observations require very refined equipment. Three of the four $-OH$ lines have been detected; their separation is 0·030 gauss in 7050, which is equivalent to 125 c/s in 30 Mc/s. The lines which have not yet been observed have been calculated to be separated by as little as 0·1 c/s.

Observations of this type may be used directly to give information about molecular structure. For example the primary peak due to $^{31}P$ has been observed in $H_3PO_3$ and $H_3PO_2$. In the former compound, this peak can be resolved as a doublet, and in the latter as a triplet. This is interpreted as indicating that in $H_3PO_3$, one proton is directly bonded to the phosphorus atom, while in $H_3PO_2$, two protons are bonded in this way (33).

This technique has been developed in order to assist in the solution of chemical structure problems by classifying the type of absorption spectra which are to be expected in various circumstances. This is done by comparing the relative magnitudes of the chemical shift and the spin-coupled effect. Neighbouring letters of the alphabet are used for nuclei for which the two effects are of comparable size (34). The symbol $AB_2$ is used to describe a system containing two equivalent nuclei, but in which the $AB$ chemical shift is not large compared with the $AB$ coupling constant. Various atomic combinations have been comprehensively indexed in this fashion, and the general type of spectrum to be expected in each case has been calculated. The acid hydrates are among the systems whose characteristic spectra have been interpreted according to this scheme. The observations appear to confirm that the water which is bound into the molecule occurs as $[H_3]^+$ rather than as $H_2O$ in $HNO_3.H_2O$, $H_2SO_4.H_2O$, and $HClO_4.H_2O$ (35). A similar structure is found in the dihydrate of chloroplatinic acid which appears to be $[H_3O]_2^+[PtCl_6]$ (36).

An interesting example of the use of the fine structure to provide information about the course of a chemical reaction is afforded by the use of N.M.R. to study keto-enol transformations. The change to the enol form increases the number of identifiable protons. If each separate absorption peak can be identified, and they do not overlap to any great extent, the area under each can be found graphically. From this measurement, the fraction existing in each form can be calculated. This has been done for 2:4 pentane dione (37).

Nuclear magnetic resonance measurements have been used to calculate the number of dislocations in apparently flawless crystals. It has already been pointed out that crystals contain many lattice imperfections; the dislocations cause large field gradients. From the intensity of the absorption peaks to which these give rise, estimates of their numbers can be made (38).

This brief account has set out some of the more modern methods of structure analysis, and the way in which they may be used has been indicated. It is obvious that it is essential to discover how atoms are arranged, and what is the nature of the bonds between them before it is possible to deduce why they are arranged in one way rather than another. However, none of those which have been discussed wholly supersede the older methods. Spectroscopy is still of prime importance in order to determine bond lengths and angles, force constants, and vibration frequencies. Infra-red, ultra violet and Raman spectroscopy may be referred to as classical methods for making such measurements, but in the Ostwald sense of the word classical and not in the pejorative sense. Of these three spectroscopic methods, Raman spectroscopy has been developed most recently but by now it has a long and respectable history behind it. As well as providing basic information about the structure of fairly simple compounds, it can be used in complex situations, such as the determination of bond angles and force constants in polyatomic silicon compounds (39). Equilibria such as the inter-halogen exchange

$$PBr_3 + PCl_3 \rightleftharpoons PBr_2Cl + PBrCl_2$$

may be followed by Raman spectroscopy (40).

When a new technique is developed, the whole known range of chemical compounds is available to be studied by its use. As has been seen in the preceding pages, such new techniques can often produce new information about well known and comparatively simple compounds. But the importance of a particular tool of research must not be judged by the volume of the published papers to which it gives rise in the years immediately following its adoption. Much of the information found with its aid serves only to confirm the general correctness of the way in which deductions are made from it. The experiments in many cases establish the technique rather than provide major advances in knowledge. However, the number of unsolved problems relating to simple compounds, as well as those presented by the most complex substances, require the application of all possible means of structure determination before even a partial solution of the outstanding questions is achieved.

*Appendix* 4.1

Van Vleck's expression for the variation of the susceptibility of trivalent samarium ions with temperature is:

$$\chi = \frac{N \sum_{J=L-S}^{J=L+S} [g_J^2 \beta^2 J(J+1)/3kT + \alpha_J](2J+1) \exp(-W_{J^\circ}/kT)}{(2J+1) \exp(-W_{J^\circ}/kT)}$$

where

$N$ = Avogadro's number

$g_J$ = $[1 + J(J+1) + S(S+1) - L(L+1)]/[2J(J+1)]$

$\beta$ = $eh/4\pi mc$ = $9 \cdot 18 \times 10^{-21}$ erg gauss$^{-1}$

$\alpha_J$ = $\dfrac{\beta^2}{6(2J+1)} \left[ \dfrac{F(J+1)}{h\nu(J+1;J)} - \dfrac{FJ}{h\nu(J;J-1)} \right]$

$F(J)$ = $1/J[(S+L+1)^2 - J^2][J^2 - (S-L)^2]$

$$W_{J^\circ} = W_J - W_{J_{\min}}$$

$$\frac{1}{e}\Delta\nu(J_{\max} - J_{\min}) = \pm \frac{5\cdot 82(2L+1)}{n^3 l(l+1)(2l+1)} \cdot (Z - \sigma_2)^4 \mathrm{cm}^{-1}$$

$\sigma_2$ = the spin doublet screening constant

## REFERENCES

(1) VAINSHTEIN *Quart. Rev.* **XIV** 105 (1960)
(2) BACON and THEWLIS *Proc. Roy. Soc.* *A***196** 50 (1949)
(3) BACON *Neutron Diffraction* (O.U.P., 1955)
(4) VAINSHTEIN, LOBATSCHEV and STASOVA *Kristallografiya* **3** 452 (1958)
(5) LOBATSCHEV *Trudy Inst. Krist., Akad. Nauk S.S.S.R.* **10** 167 (1954)
(6) ANDERSEN *Acta Cryst.* **10** 107 (1957)
(7) BRILL, GRIMM, HERMANN and PETERS *Ann. Phys.* **34** 393 (1939)
(8) VAINSHTEIN and DVORIANKIN *Kristallografiya* **1** 626 (1956)
(9) BACON and LONSDALE *Reports Progr. Phys.* **16** 1 (1953)
(10) PEASE and BACON *Proc. Roy. Soc.* *A***220** 397 (1953) *Nature* **173** 443 (1954)
(11) PETERSON and LEVY *J. Chem. Phys.* **19** 1416 (1951) **20** 704 (1952)
(12) RUNDLE *J. Amer. Chem. Soc.* **73** 4172 (1951)
(13) CRUICKSHANK *Acta Cryst.* **10** 504 (1957)
(14) VAN VLECK *The Theory of Electric and Magnetic Susceptibilities* Chap. IX (O.U.P., 1932)
(15) DAWSON, MANDLEBERG and DAVIES *J. Chem. Soc.* 2047 (1951)
(16) DAWSON and LISTER *J. Chem. Soc.* 2181 (1950)
(17) TRZEBIATOWSKI and SELWOOD *J. Amer. Chem. Soc.* **72** 4504 (1950)
(18) DAWSON *J. Chem. Soc.* 2889 (1951)
(19) OWEN *J. Inorg. Nuclear Chem.* **8** 430 (1958)
(20) WEISSMAN and SOWDEN *J. Amer. Chem. Soc.* **75** 503 (1953)
(21) (*a*) TUTTLE, WARD and WEISSMAN *J. Chem. Phys.* **25** 189 (1956)
    (*b*) TUTTLE and WEISSMAN *J. Chem. Phys.* **25** 189 (1956)
(22) FRAENKEL, HIRSHON, and WALLING *J. Amer. Chem. Soc.* **76** 3606 (1954)
(23) GORDY and McCORMICK *J. Amer. Chem. Soc.* **78** 3243 (1956)
(24) COLE, HARDING, PELLAM and YOST *J. Chem. Phys.* **27** 593 (1957)
(25) ORTON, AUGINS and WERTZ *Phys. Rev.* **119** 1691 (1960)
(26) POUND *Phys. Rev.* **79** 655 (1950)
(27) DEHRNELT and KRUGER *Naturwiss.* **37** 111 (1950)
(28) DAILEY *J. Phys. Chem.* **57** 490 (1953)
(29) ORVILLE-THOMAS *Quart. Rev.* **XI** 162 (1957)
(30) WERTZ *Chem. Rev.* **55** 847 (1955)
(31) PROCTOR and YU *Phys. Rev.* **77** 817 (1950)
(32) HOOD, REDLICK and REILLY *J. Chem. Phys.* **22** 2067 (1954)
(33) GUTOWSKY, McCALL and SLICHTER *J. Chem. Phys.* **21** 279 (1953)

(34) POPLE, SCHNEIDER and BERNSTEIN *High Resolution Nuclear Magnetic Resonance* (McGraw-Hill, New York, 1959)
(35) RICHARDS and SMITH *Trans. Faraday Soc.* **47** 1261 (1951) **48** 675 (1952)
(36) SMITH and RICHARDS *Trans. Faraday Soc.* **48** 307 (1952)
(37) JARRETT, SADLER and SHOOLERY *J. Chem. Phys.* **21** 2092 (1953)
(38) POUND *J. Chem. Phys.* **57** 743 (1953)
(39) KREIGSMANN *Z. anorg. Chem.* **299** 138 (1959)
(40) DELEVAULLE and BRIDOUX *Compt. rend.* **248** 1342 (1959)

# CHAPTER 5

# Solutions of Electrolytes

ONE OF THE characteristics of an ionic crystal is the orderly way in which
the constituent ions are distributed over the imaginary lattice points.
Within a volume bounded by dislocations, the degree of order has both
short-range and long-range characteristics. The general basis of this
orderly arrangement is that the nearest neighbours of any one ion are
other ions which bear the opposite electrostatic charge. In any liquid phase
there is little long-range order, because of the constant random molecular
movement. However, when the liquid phase consists of an electrolyte
dissolved in an ionizing solvent, considerable short-range order is present.
Throughout the solution, ionic nearest neighbours tend to bear opposite
electrostatic charges.

In addition to this physical order, local ordered regions of a different
type are present. These are caused by two types of interactions between
solvent and solute. In the first place, small strongly polarizing cations
attract the solvent dipoles, and a sheath of solvent molecules forms round
each cation. This sheath is neither fixed nor well defined, because the
solvent molecules are in constant movement, but the pattern is generally
maintained. Secondly, under certain conditions there is an electronic
interaction between solvent and solute, and complex ions are formed
through the formation of co-ordinate bonds between the negative portion
of the solvent dipoles and the acceptor cations. Such complex ions can
contain a variety of electron donating groups in addition to, or in place of,
the solvent molecules or ions. These groups, which may be either anionic
or electrically neutral are known as 'ligands'. The bonds which they form
are not primarily electrostatic, although the most common situation is one
in which a metal cation is surrounded by anionic ligands. The stability of
the system is enhanced by some or all of the unfilled electronic levels of the
metal atom being utilized to form bonding orbitals, even though the net
electronic structure is not necessarily that of an inert gas. Ions of the
transition metals have an incomplete inner shell of electrons which may be
either the $d$ or the $f$ shell; all transition metal ions are normally complexed
in solution and may co-ordinate so many negatively charged ligands that
the stable complex is itself an anion.

The smallest cation is the hydrogen ion, and its polarizing power is very
great. Its co-ordination number is 1; only the $1s$ shell is available for

bonding, and this can accept a single pair of electrons from a donor. In water, a free proton is invariably complexed to form $[H_3O]^+$. Water is the most widely used solvent, and for many years chemistry has been dominated by the behaviour of aqueous solutions in which the most important ions are $[H_3O]^+$ and $[OH]^-$ produced by the self ionization of the solvent. In classical or Arrhenius terms, a substance which on dissolution in water increases the concentration of hydrion is known as an acid, and one which increases the concentration of hydroxyl ion is known as a base. In aqueous solution, these are reasonably satisfactory working definitions, and, indeed, the Arrhenius definition of an acid can be extended to any protonic solvent, that is to say to any solvent which gives rise to a solvated hydrogen ion on self-ionization. However, the characteristic property of a base in a non-aqueous solvent cannot be made to depend upon the presence of hydroxyl ion, and must be related to the nature of the anion which is derived by self-ionization from the particular solvent.

The terms 'acid' and 'base' are not exact definitions of particular classes of chemical compounds in the same way as the word 'hydrocarbon' has a precise meaning. A compound is either a hydrocarbon or it is not; it does not matter whether it is in solution, or whether it is in the solid, liquid or vapour phase. If it is a hydrocarbon it remains a hydrocarbon, but the terms 'acid' and 'base' do not describe an inherent property of any compound. They describe the way in which a given compound behaves when dissolved in a particular solvent, and the terms must be carefully defined before they can be applied to systems in general.

In non-aqueous solvents, there are reactions which appear to be entirely analogous to the familiar 'acid + base = salt + water' reaction of aqueous chemistry, with the difference that the left-hand reactants are not the familiar acids and bases. The common factor in the reaction is often the production of a molecule of the solvent from the two original reactants. It appears to be logical in such a situation to regard the original reactants as acid and base respectively with reference to the particular solvent system. A consequence of this is that the acid/base neutralization reaction in water is only one of a wide range of analogous reactions in a variety of solvents.

The first extension of the terms acid and base to describe the behaviour of various ionic compounds in solvents other than water was made independently by Brønsted (1) and by Lowry (2) in 1923. Their definition was only applicable to solutions in protonic solvents. It groups together all those systems in which there is an exchange of a proton, or, in other words, transfer of a hydrogen ion. An acid is defined as a substance which can give up a proton to some other ionic species. It therefore follows that a Brønsted base is an ionic species which can accept a proton. The loss of a proton from the original compound involves the existence of a negatively charged ion which is known as the conjugate base of the acid; it is a base because by definition it can accept a proton to form the original acid. The following are examples of acids and their conjugate bases:

| Acid | Conjugate Base | | Proton |
|---|---|---|---|
| $HClO_4$ | $\longrightarrow$ $[ClO_4]^-$ | + | $H^+$ |
| $CH_3$—COOH | $\longrightarrow$ $[CH_3$—COO$]^-$ | + | $H^+$ |
| ⟨benzene⟩—OH | $\longrightarrow$ $\left[$⟨benzene⟩—O$\right]^-$ | + | $H^+$ |

These examples are of systems which Arrhenius would have recognized as acids. There are similar systems which he might not have so recognized:

$$[(CH_3)_3NH]^+ \longrightarrow [(CH_3)_3N]+H^+$$
$$[Al(H_2O)_6]^{3+} \longrightarrow [Al(H_2O)_5(OH)]^{2+}+H^+$$

The Brønsted bases which can accept a proton, and thereby become conjugate acids are usually negative ions or neutral molecules, but there is no reason why a positively charged ion should not be so described as is the case with the $[Al(H_2O)_5(OH)]^{2+}$ ion in the example above. The following are examples of Brønsted bases and their conjugate acids:

| Proton | | Base | | Conjugate Acid |
|---|---|---|---|---|
| $H^+$ | + | $[OH]^-$ | $\longrightarrow$ | $H_2O$ |
| $H^+$ | + | $[SO_4]^{2-}$ | $\longrightarrow$ | $[HSO_4]^-$ |
| $H^+$ | + | $[HSO_4]^-$ | $\longrightarrow$ | $H_2SO_4$ |
| $H^+$ | + | $[CH_3O]^-$ | $\longrightarrow$ | $CH_3OH$ |

An ion such as $[HSO_4]^-$ must be described either as a conjugate acid or as a base depending upon the reaction in which it is taking part.

Since the definition of acids and bases in the Brønsted and Lowry sense depends upon the transfer of a proton, water must be described as both acid and base.

| Acid | | Base | | Conjugate Acid | | Conjugate Base |
|---|---|---|---|---|---|---|
| $H_2O$ | + | $H_2O$ | $\longrightarrow$ | $[H_3O]^+$ | + | $[OH]^-$ |

This type of self-ionization or 'auto-protolysis' is a common feature of many polar solvents. When it occurs, equal quantities of conjugate acid and conjugate base are formed. The former is sometimes referred to as 'lyonium', and the latter as 'lyate'.

The Brønsted–Lowry definition of acids and bases enables a comparison to be made between the relative strengths of the members of each class. When a Brønsted acid is in solution in an ionizing solvent, the proton which is available for donation by the acid is solvolysed. That is to say, it reacts with the solvent, just as in water the proton forms the hydroxonium ion $[H_3O]^+$. The strength of an acid in a given solvent, that is to say its ability to yield protons, will depend upon the extent to which the solvent can accept protons, or in other words its basicity. The solvent must be polar. If an acid dissociates in some way in the absence of a polar solvent, the 'acid' is not displaying acid-like behaviour. According to the Brønsted–Lowry definition, acidic properties are only manifested in the presence of a substance which can accept a proton, and this must be a polar compound.

Liquid ammonia is a more basic solvent than water; that is to say, protons are more readily accepted in ammoniacal than they are in aqueous solution. Carboxylic acids which are weak acids when dissolved in water are fully ionized in liquid ammonia solution. All carboxylic acids therefore appear to have approximately the same strength in liquid ammonia and are as strong as the common mineral acids. This behaviour is referred to as the 'levelling effect' of a very basic solvent. Such solvents are of no value for comparing the strength of acids, since their readiness to accept protons is so great that virtually complete ionization of all acids is attained.

Water is a strong enough base to exert a levelling effect on the strong mineral acids. Its basicity is sufficiently high for all such acids to be almost completely ionized in aqueous solution. When such acids are dissolved in less basic solvents, differences in their ionization behaviour become apparent. For example, the strengths of sulphuric and hydrochloric acids may be compared by contrasting their behaviour when dissolved in anhydrous formic acid. In this solvent, the first ionization of sulphuric acid is complete while hydrochloric acid is only partially ionized (3). On the other hand, hydrochloric acid is fully ionized in methanol solution, but nitric acid is only partially ionized in this solvent (4). By carrying out a number of such comparisons, acids may be arranged in order of strength. The strengths of bases may be estimated by the reverse of this procedure, that is to say, by dissolving a single acid in various basic solvents. The solvent in which a particular acid appears to be strongest, and is therefore most highly ionized, must be the most ready acceptor of protons, and is therefore the strongest base. There is no rigid point of demarcation between bases and acids and it is equally true to say that the solvent which is the most ready acceptor of protons is the weakest acid in the series.

Formic acid, for example, can be regarded as a weak base because it will accept protons from sulphuric acid, but does not readily do so from hydrochloric acid. On the other hand, in aqueous solution it must be regarded as a fairly strong acid because of the readiness with which its proton is accepted by water.

Some Brønsted acids are so weak that they are virtually not dissociated at all in water and a base stronger than hydroxyl is necessary to accept their protons. For instance fluorene is insoluble in water. It will however, react with the amide ion which is present in liquid ammonia to form a conjugate base

Such reactions have been studied by observing the deeply-coloured solutions which are formed by the ionized conjugate bases (5).

Similarly, very weak bases can only be studied in solution in strong acids; sulphuric acid is a convenient solvent for this purpose. It freezes at $10 \cdot 36° C$, it has a low vapour pressure at room temperature, and it is liquid over a wide temperature range. Its cryoscopic constant is three times as large as that of water, and it is therefore easy to follow apparent ionic dissociations by measurements of the depression of the freezing point of sulphuric acid solution. Gillespie (6) has studied the behaviour of a number of bases in this solvent. These include monobasic amines, ketones, nitro compounds, and ethers; the latter accept a proton to form a cation which has the general formula

$$\left[ \begin{array}{c} R \\ R' \end{array} \!\! >\!\! O\!\!-\!\!H \right]^{+}$$

Nitro compounds are extremely weak bases, since they are not completely ionized even in solution in an acid as strong as sulphuric acid.

Determinations of the relative strengths of acids have considerable practical importance. An example of the use of such information is the selection of the most appropriate acid/solvent system when it is necessary to carry out a reaction which is catalysed by the hydrogen ion. A number of methods for comparing the effectiveness of various acid solutions for this purpose have been proposed. The Hammett scale (7) is based upon certain acid–base indicators which may be referred to as $In$. These are partially converted by acid solvents ($SH$) to their conjugate acids ($In$H) and the ratio of the resultant two coloured forms of the indicator is measured spectrophotometrically. The Hammett acidity function $H_0$ is then defined as

$$H_0 = pK_{BH^+} - \log \left( C_{BH^+}/C_B \right)$$

where $(C_{BH^+}/C_B)$ is the measured ratio of the coloured forms of the indicator. At infinite dilution in aqueous solution, $H_0$ is equal to the pH. The function may be regarded as a measure of the ability of a solution to convert a neutral basic molecule into its conjugate acid. Hammett claims that this method of assessing the acid-forming ability of a solvent can be applied to a wide range of media from formic acid (dielectric constant, 50) to anhydrous sulphuric acid ($\Delta = 110$). This range of dielectric constants includes that of water ($\Delta = 79$) but not that of ethyl alcohol ($\Delta = 24 \cdot 2$) or of hydrogen cyanide ($\Delta = 123$).

A more recent method of assessing the acid-forming power of solvents has been put forward by Grunwald (8). This system correlates activities, while the Hammett scale is directly concerned with concentrations. Reference solvents are used; these are mixtures of ethanol and water which cover a range of dielectric constants from 24 to 79. The scale is based upon the degree of ionization of carboxylic acids and substituted ammonium and anilinium compounds in these reference solutions.

The surrender of a proton is the property which is common to all compounds which are contained within Brønsted and Lowry's definition of acids. Lewis considered that this property was only a particular instance of a wider range of phenomena. In aqueous solutions, the proton, which is bare of electrons, becomes bound to some other atom or group through the agency of a hitherto unshared pair of electrons. Lewis extended this concept, and he described as an acid any species which could accept a pair of electrons to complete an octet (or, in the case of hydrogen, to obtain a pair of electrons). In this situation, he described any donor as a base:

| Lewis acid | | Lewis base | | Adduct |
|:---:|:---:|:---:|:---:|:---:|

Lewis acids can therefore be defined as those chemical substances which can accept electrons; these substances are described as 'electrophilic'. Conversely, Lewis bases are described as 'nucleophilic'.

In some circumstances, positive ions may be Lewis acids:

$$Li^+ + O\!\!<^{Me}_{H} \longrightarrow \left[Li\!-\!O\!\!<^{Me}_{H}\right]^+$$

$$Ag^+ + NH_3 \longrightarrow [Ag(NH_3)]^+$$

There is little formal difference between these reactions, and the more familiar reactions such as

$$H^+ + O\!\!<^{Me}_{H} \longrightarrow [Me(OH_2)]^+$$

$$H^+ + NH_3 \longrightarrow [NH_4]^+$$

Whether a given compound is an acid or a base is thus largely a question of how the terms 'acid' or 'base' are defined and the definition may be framed so as to include a narrow or a wide range of substances. The definition is not a matter of mere semantics. It can be used to demarcate various groups of compounds in a way which is convenient in the context in which a discussion of their properties is being made. The Brønsted–Lowry definition includes only those solvents which undergo self-ionization to form a solvated proton. However, when discussing the many liquids which do not possess an available proton but which undergo self-ionization, it is convenient to describe them in terms of the concepts used by Lewis. There is a further definition of acids and bases which is of value in describing certain systems (10). This definition states the formal assumptions of Lewis in more general qualitative terms, and defines an acid as a solute which increases the concentration in solution of the cations contributed by the solvent. Similarly a base increases the concentration of the anions characteristic of the pure solvent.

A large part of inorganic chemistry as well as an appreciable part of organic chemistry is the chemistry of aqueous solution. Water is cheap, plentiful and both liquid and stable over a convenient range of temperatures. It is non-toxic, a good solvent with a high ionizing power ($\Delta = 79$) and has a reasonably high cryoscopic constant. The study of chemistry has largely been dominated by the relation of water to other chemical compounds. However, it has long been realized that many interesting reactions which cannot be carried out in water, may be studied in non-aqueous solution. Franklin (11) published the results of experiments using liquid ammonia in 1898, and Walden reported some of the solvent properties of liquid sulphur dioxide in the following year (12). Of all the non-aqueous ionizing solvents, these are the two which have been most extensively investigated.

Liquid ammonia has the property of dissolving considerable amounts of the alkali metals. This phenomenon has been known for nearly a hundred years (13). The solutions are coloured, and their precise composition is still not certainly known, but it is now generally accepted that the solute consists of ammoniated metal cations together with free electrons. The conductivity of such solutions is similar to that of metals. For example, the conductivity of a saturated solution of sodium in ammonia at $-33°$ C is of the same order as that of liquid metallic mercury at $0°$ C. Solutions in liquid ammonia of some of the alkaline earth metals may also be prepared, and unstable solutions of aluminium have been made by cathodic reduction (14). The nature of these solutions has been extensively discussed by Symons (15). They have been used in preparative chemistry as powerful reducing agents. They will reduce metal complexes; by this means the Ni(II) cyano complex is first reduced to the Ni(I) compound and finally to a complex in which the nickel is in the zero valency state (16).

$$[Ni(CN)_4]^{2-} \longrightarrow \{[Ni(CN)_3]_2\}^{4-} \longrightarrow [Ni(CN)_4]^{4-}$$

Lead is reduced by solutions of sodium to a plumbide which may contain the anion $[Pb_9]^{4-}$ (17).

$$Pb \xrightarrow{\ Na\ } Na_4Pb_9$$

The solutions also have the property of reducing preferentially isolated benzene rings. This behaviour was used in the synthesis of 19-nortestosterone which was the first biologically active astrogen to be synthesized (18)

Liquid ammonia exhibits slight autoprotolysis,

$$2NH_3 \rightleftharpoons [NH_4]^+ + [NH_2]^-$$

a solvated proton and the ammine anion being formed. In liquid ammonia solution, ammonium salts are acids, and the amides of alkali metals behave as bases. Such compounds respectively correspond to acids and bases on any of the definitions which have been discussed above. The analogy to aqueous acids and bases is an extremely close one. Solutions of alkali metal amides in liquid ammonia turn phenolphthalein pink, and they precipitate the ions of heavy metals as amides in a similar way to that in which heavy metal hydroxides are precipitated by aqueous alkalis. Solutions of ammonium salts in liquid ammonia liberate hydrogen when treated with metals. A particularly interesting analogy is that of the amphoteric nature of zinc amide. An ammonozincate $K_2[Zn(NH_2)_4]$ is formed when zinc amide is dissolved in a solution of potassium amide in liquid ammonia, and corresponds to the zincate formed in aqueous solution when zinc hydroxide is dissolved in an excess of caustic soda.

Examples of other solvents which exhibit autoprotolysis are:

$$2CH_3COOH \rightleftharpoons [CH_3COOH_2]^+ + [CH_3CO.O]^-$$

$$3HF \rightleftharpoons [H_2F]^+ + [HF_2]^-$$

$$2H_2SO_4 \rightleftharpoons [H_3SO_4]^+ + [HSO_4]^-$$

$$2H_2SO_4 \rightleftharpoons [H_3O]^+ + [HS_2O_7]^-$$

$$2HCN \rightleftharpoons [H_2CN]^+ + [CN]^-$$

In the hydrogen cyanide system, for example, salts which can give rise to free cyanide ions behave as bases (19). Acetic acid has actually been used as a solvent for acid/base titrimetry using coloured internal indicators (20).

The work of Gillespie on solutions in sulphuric acid has been referred to above. He maintains that self-dissociation is very extensive in the sulphuric acid system, and by measuring their transport numbers he showed that $[H_3SO_4]^+$ and $[HSO_4]^-$ have unusually high mobilities. Gillespie suggests that this can only be explained by postulating a process of proton transfer, in which a proton moves along a chain of solvent ions (21). In sulphuric acid solution, the hydrogen sulphates of potassium, silver, sodium, lithium, barium and strontium are strong bases. Disulphuric acid is a weak electrolyte, while sulphuryl chloride forms a non-conducting solution. Acetone and acetic acid are strong bases. Nitro compounds are fairly strong bases, as is water, the ionization of which is not complete in sulphuric acid solution.

When the solvent does not contain an ionizable proton, acids and bases are often conveniently defined in accordance with the ideas of Lewis. A large number of such systems have been studied, and it is only possible to quote a few examples to show the wide variety of acid/base reactions which are possible. Molten mercuric bromide ionizes according to the equation (22)

$$2HgBr_2 \rightleftharpoons [HgBr]^+ + [HgBr_3]^-$$

In such solutions, HgO has been shown to behave as a weak acid, while thallous bromide is a strong base (23).

A number of ionizing solvents are known which contain chlorine. Iodine chloride, for example, undergoes self-ionization to give $[I]^+$ and $[ICl_2]^-$ ions (24). In selenyl chloride solution (25), pyridine and similar compounds such as quinoline and isoquinoline exhibit a base-like behaviour. The ionization apparently proceeds according to the following equation:

$$C_6H_5NSeOCl_2 \longrightarrow [C_6H_5NSeOCl]^+ + Cl^-$$

In nitrosyl chloride, NOCl, a number of nitrosyl compounds containing complex anions may be titrated as acids with the sparingly soluble base $(CH_3)_4NCl$. Such compounds include $NO[FeCl_4]$, $NO[AlCl_4]$, $NO[BF_4]$ and $[NO]_2[SnCl_6]$. When a solution of $NO(FeCl_4)$ in NOCl is electrolysed, NO is evolved at the cathode, and $Cl_2$ at the anode (26). In arsenic trichloride solution, tellurium tetrachloride behaves as an acid, and can also be titrated conductimetrically with tetramethyl ammonium chloride. The 'neutralization' of the 'acid' tellurium tetrachloride gives rise to two compounds which have been isolated. These are probably the 'acid salt', $[N(CH_3)_4][AsCl_2][TeCl_2]$ and the 'normal salt' $[N(CH_3)_4][TeCl_6]$ (27).

Fluorsulphuric acid undergoes a self-ionization which is really an example of auto-protolysis.

$$2F.SO_3H \rightleftharpoons [F.SO_3H_2]^+ + [F.SO_3]^-$$

However, the fluorine ion dominates the chemistry of reactions in this solvent. The transition metal fluorides $AuF_3$ and $TaF_5$ behave as acids in fluorsulphuric acid solution, while basic behaviour is exhibited by non-metal fluorides such as $AsF_3$, $SbF_3$, $BrF_3$ and $IF_5$ (28).

The non-protonic solvents which have been most extensively investigated are $N_2O_4$, $BrF_3$ and $SO_2$. Dinitrogen tetroxide ionizes in a two-stage process. The molecule itself is probably a resonance hybrid, of which the two principal canonical forms are:

$$\overset{O}{\underset{-O}{>}}N^+{-}N^+\overset{O^-}{\underset{O}{<}} \quad \text{and} \quad \overset{O^-}{\underset{O}{>}}N^+{-}N^+\overset{O}{\underset{O^-}{<}}$$

The first stage of the ionization results in the formation of the ions $[NO_2]^+$ and $[NO_2]^-$. An oxygen atom transfer then takes place, so that the net products of the dissociation are $[NO]^+$ and $[NO_3]^-$. The brown colour of the liquid is due to the dissociation of the dinitrogen tetroxide into a small number of molecules of $NO_2$. If a strong acceptor of electrons is present, the only products which are observed are those resulting from the first stage of the dissociation. For instance, two insoluble white compounds are precipitated when $BrF_3$ is poured into dinitrogen tetroxide. These have the formulae $[NO_2]^+[BF_3NO_2]^-$ and $[NO_2]^+[N(OBrF_3)_2]^-$. In the presence of nitric acid, the second stage of the ionization appears to go to completion. If $BrF_3$ is poured into a solution of nitric acid in dinitrogen tetroxide, the only compound which can be isolated is $[NO]^+[BrF_4]^-$ (29).

$BrF_3$ is an exceedingly powerful fluorinating agent, in which the ions $[BrF_2]^+$ and $[BrF_4]^-$ are present. Many compounds will dissolve in bromine trifluoride, and a complex fluorine-containing anion is usually present in the solutions. Simple fluorides such as potassium fluoride form tetrafluorobromites such as $KBF_4$. Antimony pentafluoride appears to form $[BrF_2]^+[SbF_6]^-$ which is an acid in the bromine trifluoride system, and can be titrated with silver tetrafluorobromite according to the equation

$$Ag[BrF_4] + [BrF_2][SbF_6] = Ag[SbF_6] + 2BrF_3$$

The similarity of this reaction to an acid/base titration in aqueous solution is at once apparent.

Sulphur dioxide is the aprotonic solvent to which most attention has been paid. In this system, it is not easy to characterize the acid/base relationship. In liquid sulphur dioxide solution, sulphites certainly act as bases (30). It has been suggested (31) that the self-ionization of the solvent proceeds according to the equation

$$2SO_2 \longrightarrow [SO]^{2+} + [SO_3]^{2-}$$

However, no compound has been found which exhibits acidic properties in sulphur dioxide solution. It might be thought that thionyl chloride should behave as a strong acid in this system, but in fact it is a weak electrolyte. The ions produced by this compound in solution are probably $[SOCl]^+$ and $Cl^-$ (32).

It is appropriate at this stage to consider why so much attention has been paid to the properties of systems in solution in non-aqueous solvents. There are a number of reasons for this. In the first place, the study of such systems can throw light on the properties of ionized solutes in general. If theories of conductance are to have general validity, they must apply to non-aqueous as well as to aqueous solutions. Modern theories of conductance relate the limiting conductance to the effective size of the ions, to the viscosity of the solution, and to various terms which relate the residual association in ion pairs to the dielectric constant of the solvent. These ideas have been developed by Onsager and Fuoss (33), and although the theory is still in a comparatively primitive state, it certainly shows a qualitative agreement with the results of a large number of conductance measurements in aqueous solution. In some cases, experimental measurements are in good quantitative agreement with the predictions of the theory. For instance, Fuoss and his co-workers have managed to obtain the necessary parameters for their equation to be used to calibrate aqueous potassium chloride conductance cells to an accuracy of $\pm 0.013\%$ (34). In addition to the measurements which they have made on aqueous solutions, they have investigated systems of mixed solvents in which water is one component of the mixture. They have also studied a number of solutions in non-aqueous solvents, and have made accurate measurements of the conductance of solutions of quaternary ammonium salts in phosphorus oxychloride (35) and of solutions in antimony trichloride (36), acetamide (37), and in the new reagent tetramethylene sulphone (sulpholane) (38).

A second use of non-aqueous solvent systems is to enable analytical estimations to be made which cannot be carried out in aqueous solutions. An example of this is a method for determining acetylenic hydrogen. When a mono-substituted acetylenic compound reacts with silver perchlorate, hydrogen ions are liberated. The reaction can be carried out in methanol solution, and a standard solution of tris-(hydroxymethyl)-methylamine can be used as a base for the titration of the hydrogen ions. In this case, screened thymol blue is used as an indicator (39). The levelling effect of strongly nucleophilic solvents can be used to perform titrations with compounds which have an inappreciable acid reaction in water (40). In some cases, the progress of the titration can be followed by the use of coloured acid/base indicators. In this way, 4-amino-4-nitroazobenzene can be used for the titration of phenols in solution in pyridine (41). It may sometimes be necessary to use potentiometric or amperometric methods, as is the case when amides are titrated with perchloric acid in acetic anhydride solution (42). The establishment of their equivalent is a useful guide in characterizing aldehydes and ketones. If such a compound is converted to its 2:4-dinitrophenylhydrazone, the reaction product may be dissolved in pyridine and titrated as a weak acid with tetrabutylammonium hydroxide, and the equivalent weight calculated from the resultant titre (43). A more familiar example of the use of a non-aqueous solvent in an analytical determination is the estimation of water itself by means of the Karl Fischer reagent which consists of iodine and sulphur dioxide in methanol solution.

Non-aqueous solvents may be used as media in which to prepare compounds which are not stable in solution in water. The hydroxyl ion is a strongly complexing ligand, and in its presence it is impossible to form complex co-ordination compounds of a variety of other ligands, particularly when these ligands themselves are not stable to hydrolysis. Reference has already been made to some co-ordination complexes which may be prepared in this way. The method is particularly valuable for the preparation of complexes containing a metal in its zero valency state. The preparation of such a stable complex of nickel has already been described, and analogous compounds of cobalt (0) (44) and of palladium (0) (45) of the general formula $K_4[M(CN)_4]$ have been isolated from liquid ammonia solution. A compound of iridium (0), $[Ir(NH_3)_4]$ is formed by the use of potassium in liquid ammonia solution to reduce bromopentam-minoiridium in which the metal is complexed in the trivalent state (46). An ammono-platinum (0) compound may be prepared in a similar way (47)

$$[Pt(NH_3)_4]Br_2 + 2K \longrightarrow [Pt(NH_3)_4] + 2KBr$$

Many complex fluorides such as $AgAuF_4$ can be prepared in bromine trifluoride solution. An interesting series of salts is available when reactions are carried out in a mixed solvent of bromine trifluoride and dinitrogen tetroxide (48a). Examples of such reactions are

$$PBr_5 + N_2O_4 + BrF_3 \longrightarrow [NO_2][PF_6]$$
$$SnF_4 + N_2O_4 + BrF_3 \longrightarrow [NO_2]_2[SnF_6]$$
$$B_2O_3 + N_2O_4 + BrF_3 \longrightarrow [NO_2][BF_4]$$
$$Au + N_2O_4 + BrF_3 \longrightarrow [NO_2][AuF_4]$$

This series of reactions appears to indicate that in the presence of $BrF_3$ the dissociation of dinitrogen tetroxide does not proceed beyond the first stage, and it is possible that the reactant species is nitryl fluoride, $NO_2F$. More recently, a better method for the preparation of this type of compound has been found to be the reaction between fluorides such as $PF_5$ which are Lewis acids, and a mixture of anhydrous nitric and hydrofluoric acids. Extremely pure salts of $[BF_4]^-$, $[PF_6]^-$ and $[SiF_6]^-$ have been made by using esters of nitric acid for this purpose, but oxidising fluorides such as $AsF_5$ cannot be used because of their explosive reaction with nitric esters (48b). Considerable interest attaches to these salts as nitrating agents for aromatic compounds, because in many such reactions, the attacking species is the $[NO_2]^+$ ion (48c).

If a mixture of bromine trifluoride and nitrosyl fluoride is used as a solvent, nitrosyl compounds are formed (49).

$$V_2O_5 + NOCl + BrF_3 \longrightarrow [NO][VF_6]$$

If uranium is dissolved in mixtures of nitrosyl chloride and dinitrogen tetroxide, the products vary with the composition of the solvent. When the tetroxide contains only a trace of nitrosyl chloride, the product is $[UO_2][NO_3]_2 \cdot N_2O_4$, and in 99% nitrosyl chloride it is $[NO][UO_2Cl_3]$. Uranium does not react with pure dinitrogen tetroxide, but with pure nitrosyl chloride, $[NO][UCl_6]$ is formed (50). Complex chlorides may be obtained from solutions in molten chloride systems. For example $[POCl_2][SbCl_6]$ has been isolated from molten antimony trichloride (51).

There are a number of compounds which can only be isolated from aqueous solution as their hydrates. The anhydrous compounds can often be obtained from non-aqueous solvents; if the chosen solvent is volatile it may then be evaporated from the solvated crystal at a low temperature. It often happens that the properties of anhydrous salts which are prepared in this way differ from those of their more familiar hydrates. Anhydrous copper nitrate has been prepared by reacting copper with a mixed solvent of dinitrogen tetroxide and ethyl acetate. From this mixture, solvated crystals of $Cu(NO_3)_2 \cdot N_2O_4$ have been separated, and the tetroxide removed by evaporation at $85°$ C. The compound is volatile in a vacuum at $200°$ C, and the vapour has been found to be monomeric ($52$). The molecule has been studied in the gas phase by means of electron diffraction and the results have been interpreted as indicating that one nitrate group is covalently bonded to the copper atom through an atom of oxygen with a Cu–O distance of $1 \cdot 98$ ÅU. The other nitrate group is bonded in a different way through its nitrogen atom; the Cu–N distance is also $1 \cdot 98$ ÅU ($53a$). This behaviour and structure differs considerably from what might have been expected from the properties of the compound in its hydrated state.

The anhydrous tetranitrate of zirconium has also been prepared. An excess of dinitrogen pentoxide was distilled on to anhydrous zirconium tetrachloride at $-220°$ C, the mixture heated to $30°$ C and the excess oxides of nitrogen removed by vacuum distillation, followed by sublimation of the complex *in vacuo*. The infra-red spectrum indicated the presence of nitrato groups, and no lines indicative of the presence of nitrate ions were observed ($53b$). The behaviour of zirconium nitrate in aqueous solution is described in Chapter 6.

A very wide variety of ligands are known to form complexes with the transition elements. The ions of transition elements have an electronic structure in which one or more *d*-orbitals are either occupied by electrons or are available for occupation. There are a number of theories which have been put forward to describe the manner in which such orbitals are occupied, and the effect which this has upon the properties of the resulting complex compound.

Sutton has listed the principal attributes of a satisfactory theory of complex formation ($54$). In his view, it is necessary to explain, among other things

(i) The stability of the complex in terms of its free energy or heat of formation.
(ii) Its oxidation/reduction characteristics.
(iii) Its stereochemistry.
(iv) Its physical properties, such as the spectrum and magnetic properties associated with it.

The theoretical treatment of complex formation has been approached from two standpoints. The first is the electrostatic or crystal field theory which was first put forward by Bethé (55) and developed also by Van Vleck (56). The effect of the ligand is considered to be a distortion of the electron orbitals which are associated with the central atom. This distortion is considered to be caused either by the negative charge on the ligand, or by the negative end of the dipole which results when an uncharged ligand approaches a positively charged ion. The alternative approach is known as the method of molecular orbitals; Van Vleck was also one of the early proponents of this theory (57). Here the available orbitals are considered to be occupied by the electrons associated with both the ligand and the central atom. Griffith and Orgel (58) consider that these two views are complementary and that they are both part of a wider and more comprehensive scheme which they call 'ligand field theory'. Pauling (59) has taken up a typically individualistic approach to the problem. He discusses the formation of the complexes in terms of the type of valence bond (ionic or covalent) which may formally be considered to exist between the ligand and the central atom or ion. His approach to this and similar problems has recently been criticized. Just as Niels Bohr was described by Hoffman as a vital catalyst whose intuition enabled significant advances to be made in physical theory, so has Pauling's intuition acted as a great stimulant to chemical thought. However, his earlier contributions to our knowledge of the chemical bond have not always been capable of development in the light of more recent experimental data.

In all the interpretations of the mechanism of complex formation, the basic electronic picture is very similar. An ion of a transition element whose $d$-orbitals are not completely filled, can have up to five of them available for occupation. When the distribution of the six ligands is equivalent to their being situated at the apices of a regular octahedron, the five orbitals can be regarded as falling into two groups. The three orbitals which are generally denoted by $d_{xy}$, $d_{yz}$, and $d_{xz}$ are more stable than the two orbitals $d_{x^2-y^2}$ and $d_{z^2}$. The maximum electron density associated with the former is situated between the ligands; this type of orbital is known as '$t_{2g}$'. In the latter type, the maximum electron density is situated near the ligands themselves; these orbitals are referred to as '$e_g$'. It is necessary to stress that the relative energies associated with $t_{2g}$- and $e_g$-orbitals are not the same under all conditions of ligand symmetry. In particular, if the co-ordination is fourfold, with ligands at the corners of a plane square, the energies of the $t_{2g}$-orbitals lie between those of $e_g$-orbitals with higher and lower energy.

According to the electrostatic theory, two modes of distribution of the available electrons are possible in an octahedral complex. In the first case, the orbitals are filled by electrons in such a way that the process conforms with Hund's law of maximum multiplicity. All the orbitals, (both $t_{2g}$ and $e_g$) are occupied singly before any orbital is occupied by an electron pair. It is, of course, a consequence of Pauli's exclusion principle that the maximum number of distinguishable electrons which can be contained in a single orbital is two. The second situation involves maximum multiplicity occurring at first only for the $t_{2g}$-orbitals. These levels will become filled with electron pairs before any electron is accommodated in the $e_g$ levels. These may be considerably higher energetically than the $t_{2g}$ levels. Which method of occupying the available orbitals is adopted depends upon the strength of the ligand field. When this is weak, maximum multiplicity occurs, and all possible levels tend to be occupied by at least a single electron. When the ligand field is strong, the electrons tend to form pairs with anti-parallel spins in the orbitals of lowest energy. The relative strengths of some common ligands is

$$[CN]^- > [NO_2]^- > NH_3 > H_2O > [F]^- > [Cl]^- > [Br]^- > [I]^-$$

The strength of the ligand depends upon its polarizability and not upon its electronegativity. This is because its perturbing effect on the electronic orbitals of the central ion depends not so much upon its surface charge, as upon the degree to which this charge can approach the central atom; this is a function of its polarizability, or, qualitatively speaking, the extent that the charge can be deformed in order that it may penetrate to the vicinity of the metal atom.

The development of the molecular orbital theory leads to a similar conclusion, that is to say with strong ligands some orbitals are filled with pairs of electrons while others are empty, and with weak ligands, as many orbitals as possible tend to be at least singly occupied. These situations are referred to by Griffith and Orgel as 'high spin' and 'low spin'. They prefer these terms to more conventional descriptions such as 'spin free' and 'spin paired', and they consider that 'ionic' and 'covalent' are very inappropriate descriptions of any electronic situation which exists within the complex. When the bonds within a complex are directed towards the apices of a regular octahedron ('octahedral complexes') the low-spin state is that in which the electrons tend to be paired in orbitals of lower energy.

This system of distributing the electrons into orbitals is in general agreement with the experimental measurements of the magnetic susceptibility and with the spectra of complex-containing compounds. It is less easy to reconcile the thermodynamic data with the theory. It has not, for example, yet been possible to explain the experimental finding that the heat of formation of the bivalent aqueous ions of the first transition series, increases from calcium to zinc in a more or less regular manner.

One of the experimental facts which must be explained by any comprehensive theory is that the formation of a complex sometimes results in the stabilization of an unusual valency state of the central atom. Complexes containing the metals of the eighth group in the zero valency state are very common, and reference has already been made to some examples of this behaviour. In the production of certain compounds of this type, the ligand itself may act as the reducing agent, as in the following reaction (60):

$$Na_2[PtCl_4] + 2KOH + 5PPh_3 \longrightarrow$$
$$[Pt(PPh_3)_4] + 2KCl + 2NaCl + Ph_3PO + H_2O$$
$$(Ph = phenyl)$$

It is unusual for such a complex of an atom in its zero valency state to be prepared directly from the metal in its elemental form, but this occurs in the preparation of tetrakis (dichloromethylphosphine) nickel from the metal and dichloromethylphosphine (61).

Some of the most unusual complexes are those in which the metal apparently exists in a negative valency state. There can be little doubt about the existence of iron in the $-2$ state in (62)

$$[Fe\ en_3]^{2+}\ [Fe(CO)_4]^{2-} \qquad (en = ethylenediamine)$$

It has been stated that manganese exists in the $-3$ state in (63)

$$MnH_3(CO)_4$$

but this type of compound is discussed further in the next chapter when the properties of rhenium and technetium are being considered.

The complexes which are most stable to oxidation or reduction tend to be those in which the central metal atom attains one of its extreme oxidation states, either the highest or the lowest. Compounds in which the central metal atom displays low valency states tend to be volatile. The metal carbonyls are an example of this, but the generalization is not true when the complex contains the less electro-negative ligands. In the low valency state complexes, it is usual for the electron spins to be paired, and for the Effective Atomic Number of the metal atom to have attained that of the next higher inert gas.

In general, the ligands which enter into complex formation are those which contain $\pi$-orbitals. Such orbitals are made up from atomic $p$- or $d$-orbitals, or they may be hybridized $pd$-orbitals as in aromatic ligands. The ligand orbitals themselves may be full, or alternatively they may be partially vacant. If they are not full, the valency electrons of the central transition metal atom (which principally occupy $d$-orbitals) can react with the ligand $\pi$-orbitals and enter into molecular orbitals of low energy. Chatt (64) describes this as a process of 'feeding back' electrons via the molecular orbitals from the $d$-orbitals of the metal to the $\pi$-orbitals of the ligand group. He points out that this process of feed-back appears to be very effective, and he instances the case of the cobalt (0) compound $Co[(CO)_3(NO)]$. (NO) is a three-electron donor, and (Co) a two-electron donor. It has been calculated that if the electrons were 'transferred' to the metal atom from the ligand, and then shared between the bonds, the dipole moment of this complex should be 4·3 D. It has been found to be

0·43 D (65), and this presumably indicates that the electronic charge is 'smeared' over the whole complex and is not localized in bonds.

If the $\pi$-orbitals in the ligand system are completely filled, they are no longer available to the valency electrons of the central metal atom. These electrons can therefore only enter $d$-orbitals which are of higher energy than the $\pi$-orbitals, and in addition are anti-bonding and not bonding orbitals. Such electrons are readily removed by oxidation, and high valency states are likely to arise. These states also frequently occur if the ligand is of a type which has a 'lone pair' of electrons, as is the case in $H_2O$. The lone pair becomes localized at the end of the dipole which is directed towards the metal atom, whose valency electrons will thereby be repelled and easily removed by oxidizing agents.

The formation of complexes and some of the experimental observations about solution chemistry have been discussed so far only in terms of the products of the reactions, and of the structure of the resultant compounds. It is more difficult to study either the mechanism of such reactions, or the route by which the atoms rearrange themselves to form the products which can be isolated. One of the experimental difficulties is the speed at which ionic reactions proceed. For example, a reaction involving proton transfer is completed particularly rapidly. Virtually every reaction between a proton donor and a proton acceptor results in protonation of the acceptor. It has been stated (66) that if solutions of a (protonic) acid and a base could be mixed instantaneously, chemical equilibrium would be reached within about $10^{-6}$ sec. Such a rapid reaction rate is consonant with the small size, the consequent mobility, and the electron hunger of the bare proton. It is only comparatively recently that the nature of oxidation and reduction reactions in solution has been questioned, and that the means of investigating their mechanisms and their reaction rates have become available.

Oxidation reactions in solution are of three types:

(a) those in which one electron is lost, for example, $Fe^{2+} \longrightarrow Fe^{3+}$
(b) those in which more than one electron is lost, for example, $Sn^{2+} \longrightarrow Sn^{4+}$
(c) those in which a compound oxidized ion is formed, for example, $U^{4+} \longrightarrow [UO_2]^{2+}$

Type (a) most commonly occurs among transition elements, type (b) among those elements which precede a transition series, and type (c) is common in many parts of the periodic table.

The simplest type of electron transfer is that which takes place between the ions of two valency states of the same metal existing together in a solution.

$$M^{x+} + M^{y+} \rightleftharpoons M^{y+} + M^{x+}$$

This can be studied if the ions in one or other of the valency states have been formed from a radio-active isotope of the element M. The first instance recorded in the literature of such a study was carried out by Hevesy and Zechmeister in 1920 (67). They observed the reaction

$$Pb^{4+} + Pb^{2+} \ \rightleftharpoons \ Pb^{2+} + Pb^{4+}$$

Where the electron transfer occurs, as is more usual, between ions derived from two different elements, it is usual first of all to study the kinetic reaction rate. A plausible intermediate through which the reactants may pass is then postulated, and it may sometimes be possible to find chemical evidence for the existence of such an intermediate. For example, it is claimed that when $[Co(CN)_5]^{3-}$ is oxidized by $[Fe(CN)_6]^{3-}$ it has been possible to isolate the intermediate bridged state $[(NC)_5Co^{3+}\cdot NC\cdot Fe^{2+}(CN)_5]^{+6}$ (68).

This compound is typical of the transient intermediates which have been put forward to explain the mechanism of electron transfer. One of the basic reasons for thinking that such an intermediate is involved in the majority of these reactions is that in most cases the rate law is found to be of the first order with respect to both the reactants. It is believed that there are two limiting types of these intermediaries, and that all those which are formed can be classified as falling somewhere between these limits. In the first type, the transfer of electrons takes place directly between the central metal atoms whose co-ordination shells are 'in contact' (the compact type). In the other type, electron transfer takes place across a bridging ligand which is common to the co-ordination shell of both metal atoms (the extended type).

Although the reactions are generally found to obey a first order law, the rates of reaction differ widely, even when the same metal atom is surrounded by different ligands. An example of this from the compact type of reactions demonstrates the great change in reaction rate which can be made by even a small change of the co-ordinating ligands (69).

| System | $mole^{-1}\ sec^{-1}$ |
|---|---|
| $[Cr\ dipy_3]^{2+} + [Co(NH_3)_6]^{3+}$ | 7·1 |
| $[Cr\ dipy_3]^{2+} + [Co(NH_3)_5Br]^{3+}$ | $1\cdot6 \times 10^4$ |
| (dipy = dipyridyl) | |

An example of a similar situation in the case of an extended type is (70)

| | |
|---|---|
| $Cr^{2+} + [Cr(NH_3)_5F]^{2+}$ | $2\cdot7 \times 10^{-4}$ |
| $Cr^{2+} + [Cr(NH_3)_5I]^{2+}$ | 5·5 |

There may be some form of bridging even when the reaction is among those which are formally considered to be of the compact type. For example,

Taube (71) has shown that the oxidation $[MnO_4]^{2-} \rightarrow [MnO_4]^-$ is accelerated by the presence of cations of the alkali metals, the rate of reaction increasing from lithium to caesium. It has been suggested that in this case a bridged intermediate such as $[O_3MnO—Cs—OMnO_3]^{2-}$ may be formed.

When one of the ligands is an unsaturated or an aromatic organic compound, the mechanism of the oxidation is of great interest when it is of the extended type. For example, when divalent chromium is oxidized by complexes of the general formula $[Co(NH_3)_5 \text{ org}]^{2+}$ in which 'org' represents an organic ligand, the rate of reaction is considerably greater when the organic ligand is fumarate than when it is, for instance, succinate (72). This is consistent with the view that the organic ligand forms a bridge, and the system of conjugated double bonds assists the process of electron transfer:

$$\left[ (NH_3)_5Co—O \underset{O}{\overset{}{\diagup}} C—CH{=}CH—C \underset{OH}{\overset{O}{\diagdown}} O—Cr(H_2O)_5 \right]^{4+}$$

The process of electron transfer seems to be similarly assisted by the inorganic azide ligand. The rate of reaction in the $Cr^{2+} \rightarrow Cr^{3+}$ reaction is considerably faster when an azide ligand is present than it is when the ligand is the thiocyanato group (73). This is to be expected if bridge formation takes place, since the azide group would form a symmetrical bridge $[Cr—N{=}N{=}N—Cr]^{4+}$. The asymmetrical thiocyanato group could only form the unstable $[CrSCN]^{2+}$ complex.

There seems to be no doubt that in redox reactions in solution, the course of the reaction may be profoundly affected by the nature of the ligands involved. Even in the absence of a complex which can be isolated, the ions are usually complexed by the solvent itself, and the rate of reaction can therefore be affected by the nature of the solvent. The reaction usually takes place at a measurable rate, whether a bridge is formed or not.

A practical consideration which has given considerable impetus to the investigation of transition metal complexes is the increasing interest in the separation and purification processes known as solvent extraction and liquid–liquid extraction. There are two different types of metal-solvent interaction which can take place in the course of these extractions. In the first type, the extracting solvent can become a ligand in the co-ordination shell of the metal ion, and it complexes in this way the metal ions which dissolve in it. Further ions are therefore extracted from the original solvent in order that the partition coefficient, in terms of the uncomplexed ion, may be maintained. In this way, uranyl nitrate is extracted as the dihydrate into organic esters such as tributylphosphate. Two molecules of the ester become co-ordinated to the uranium atom. In the second type, the extracting solvent reacts with the original solution to form a pair of ions which are soluble in the former. Thus, a solution of ferric chloride in aqueous hydrochloric acid will extract into diethyl ether. This results from the solubility in this ether of the two ions $[Et_2OH]^+$ and $[FeCl_4]^-$. Extractions of this type are often extremely specific, and by suitable adjustments of the concentrations, oxidation states and acidities, an effective separation may be made between very similar metals. The process is also suitable for large-scale process work, and it has been developed extensively to meet the requirements of the Nuclear Energy programme. It can not only be used for the separation of chemically similar metals of which one has inacceptable nuclear properties, but also for the separation of radio-active fission products, since the process can be easily controlled remotely from behind shielding. An example of such a process is the separation of niobium from tantalum. This is extremely difficult to carry out by any other chemical method. In the process used, the fluorides of the metals are dissolved in aqueous hydrofluoric acid, and are extracted into ketones such as 'hexone' (isobutyl methyl ketone) (74). The tantalum is extracted into the organic liquid, while the niobium remains in the aqueous phase.

## REFERENCES

( 1 )  BRØNSTED *Rec. Trav. chim.* **42** 718 (1923)
( 2 )  LOWRY *J. Soc. Chem. Ind.* **42** 43 (1923)
( 3 )  HAMMETT and DEYRUP *J. Amer. Chem. Soc.* **54** 4239 (1932)
( 4 )  DEYRUP *J. Amer. Chem. Soc.* **56** 60 (1934)
( 5 )  (*a*) CONANT and WHELAND *J. Amer. Chem. Soc.* **54** 1212 (1932)
       (*b*) MCEWEN *J. Amer. Chem. Soc.* **58** 1124 (1936)
( 6 )  (*a*) GILLESPIE *et al. J. Chem. Soc.* 2473, 2493, 2504, 2516, 2532, 2537, 2542 (1950)
       (*b*) GILLESPIE and LEISTEN *Quart. Rev.* **8** 40 (1954)
( 7 )  (*a*) HAMMETT and DEYRUP *J. Amer. Chem. Soc.* **54** 2721 (1932)
       (*b*) PAUL and LONG *Chem. Rev.* **57** 1 (1957)
( 8 )  GRUNWALD *J. Amer. Chem. Soc.* **73** 4934 (1951)
       (*b*) GRUNWALD and BERKOWITZ *J. Amer. Chem. Soc.* **73** 4939 (1951)
       (*c*) GUTBENZAHL and GRUNWALD *J. Amer. Chem. Soc.* **75** 559, 565 (1953)
( 9 )  LEWIS *Valence and Structure of Atoms* (Chemical Catalog. Co., New York, 1923)
(10 )  CADY and ELSEY *J. Chem. Educ.* **5** 1425 (1928)
(11 )  FRANKLIN and KRAUSS *J. Amer. Chem. Soc.* **20** 820 (1898)
(12 )  WALDEN *Ber.* **32** 2862 (1899)
(13 )  WEYL *Ann. Phys.* **121** 601 (1864)
(14 )  McELROY, KLEINBERG and DAVIDSON *J. Amer. Chem. Soc.* **72** 5178 (1950)

(15) SYMONS *Quart. Rev.* **XIII** 99 (1959)
(16) (*a*) EASTES and BURGESS *J. Amer. Chem. Soc.* **64** 1187 (1942)
    (*b*) WATT, HALL, CHOPPIN and GENTIL *J. Amer. Chem. Soc.* **76** 373 (1954)
(17) ZINTL, GOUBEAU and DULLENKOPF *Z. Phys. Chem.* **154** 1 (1931)
(18) BIRCH *J. Chem. Soc.* 367 (1950)
(19) JANDER and SCHOLZ *Z. Phys. Chem.* **192** 163 (1953)
(20) HIGUCHI, FELDMAN and RHEM *Analyt. Chem.* **28** 1120 (1956)
(21) GILLESPIE and WARIF *J. Chem. Soc.* **204** (1953)
(22) JANDER and BRODERSEN *Z. anorg. Chem.* **261** 261 (1950)
(23) (*a*) JANDER and BRODERSEN *Z. anorg. Chem.* **262** 33 (1950)
    (*b*) *Idem Angew. Chem.* **62** 264 (1950)
(24) (*a*) SPANDAU and BRUNNECK *Z. anorg. Chem.* **270** 201 (1952)
    (*b*) *Idem Z. anorg. Chem.* **278** 197 (1955)
(25) JACKSON and SMITH *J. Amer. Chem. Soc.* **62** 544 (1940)
(26) SEEL and NOGRADE *Z. anorg. Chem.* **269** 188 (1952)
(27) GUTMAN *Monatsh.* **83** 159 (1952)
(28) WOOLF *J. Chem. Soc.* 433 (1955)
(29) SPRAGUE, GARRETT and SISLER *J. Amer. Chem. Soc.* **82** 1059 (1960)
(30) JOHNSON, NORRIS and HUSTON *J. Amer. Chem. Soc.* **73** 3052 (1951)
(31) JANDER and ULLMANN *Z. Anorg. Chem.* **230** 405 (1937)
(32) JANDER and WICKERT *Z. Phys. Chem.* **A178** 57 (1936)
(33) (*a*) FUOSS and ONSAGER *J. Phys. Chem.* **61** 688 (1957)
    (*b*) FUOSS *J. Amer. Chem. Soc.* **79** 3301 (1957)
    (*c*) FUOSS and KRAUSS *J. Amer. Chem. Soc.* **79** 3304 (1957)
    (*d*) FUOSS *J. Amer. Chem. Soc.* **80** 5059 (1958)
    (*e*) FUOSS *Proc. Nat. Acad. Sci. U.S.A.* **45** 807 (1959)
    (*f*) FUOSS *J. Amer. Chem. Soc.* **81** 2659 (1959)
    (*g*) FUOSS and ACCASCINA *Electrolytic Conductance* (Interscience Publishers, New York, 1959)
(34) LIND, ZWOLENIK and FUOSS *J. Amer. Chem. Soc.* **81** 1557 (1959)
(35) (*a*) GUTMANN and BAAZ *Monatsh.* **90** 239 (1959)
    (*b*) BAAZ and GUTMANN *Monatsh.* **90** 256, 276, 426 (1959)
(36) JANDER and SWART *Z. anorg. Chem.* **299** 252 (1959)
(37) JANDER and WINKLER *J. Inorg. Nuclear Chem.* **9** 39 (1959)
(38) BURWELL and LANGFORD *J. Amer. Chem. Soc.* **81** 3799 (1959)
(39) BARNES *Analyt. Chem.* **31** 405 (1959)
(40) BACKE–HANSEN *Med. Norsk. Farm. Selsk.* **17** 282 (1955)
(41) TAKIURA and TAKINO *J. Pharm. Soc. Japan* **74** 971 (1954)
(42) WIMER *Analyt. Chem.* **30** 77 (1958)
(43) (*a*) SENSABAUGH, CUNDIFF and MAKUNAS *Analyt. Chem.* **30** 1445 (1958)
    (*b*) CUNDIFF and MAKUNAS *Analyt. Chem.* **30** 1447, 1450 (1958)
(44) HUBER and BARTENSTEIN *Naturwiss.* **13** 300 (1952)
(45) BURBAGE and FERNELIUS *J. Amer. Chem. Soc.* **65** 1484 (1943)
(46) WATT and MAYFIELD *J. Amer. Chem. Soc.* **75** 6178 (1953)
(47) WATT, WALLING and MAYFIELD *J. Amer. Chem. Soc.* **75** 6175 (1953)

(48) (a) EMELEUS and WOOLF J. Chem. Soc. 1050 (1950)
     (b) KUHN Canad. J. Chem. 40 1660 (1962)
     (c) OLAH, KUHN, and FLOOD J. Amer. Chem. Soc. 83 4571 (1961)
(49) (a) WOOLF J. Chem. Soc. 1053 (1950)
     (b) SHARPE and WOOLF J. Chem. Soc. 798 (1951)
(50) ADDISON R.I.C. Lectures, monographs and reports, No. 2 (1960)
(51) MASCHKA, GUTMAN and SPONER Monatsh. 86 52 (1955)
(52) ADDISON and HATHAWAY J. Chem. Soc. 344 (1958)
(53) (a) PORTER, SCHOONMAKER and ADDISON Proc. Chem. Soc. 11 (1959)
     (b) FIELD and HARDY Proc. Chem. Soc. 76 (1962)
(54) SUTTON J. Inorg. Nuclear Chem. 8 23 (1958)
(55) BETHÉ Ann. Physik 3 133 (1929)
(56) VAN VLECK Phys. Rev. 41 208 (1932)
(57) VAN VLECK J. Chem. Phys. 3 807 (1935)
(58) GRIFFITH and ORGEL Quart. Rev. XI 381 (1957)
(59) PAULING The Nature of the Chemical Bond (Cornell University Press, 1950)
(60) MALATESTA and ANGOLETTA Atti. Accad. naz. Lincei, Rend. Classe Sci. fis. mat. nat. 19 34 (1955)
(61) QUIN J. Amer. Chem. Soc. 79 3681 (1957)
(62) HUBER Metal Carbonyls F.I.A.T. review of German Science
(63) HURD, SENTALL and NORTON J. Amer. Chem. Soc. 71 1899 (1949)
(64) CHATT J. Inorg. Nuclear Chem. 8 515 (1958)
(65) GRIFFITHS and OWEN Proc. Roy. Soc. A226 96
(66) SCHWARZENBACH and MEIER J. Inorg. Nuclear Chem. 8 302 (1958)
(67) HEVESY and ZECHMEISTER Ber. 53 410 (1920)
(68) HAIN and WILMARTH J. Amer. Chem. Soc. 83 509 (1961)
(69) ZWICKEL and TAUBE Discuss. Faraday Soc. 29 73 (1960)
(70) OGARD and TAUBE J. Amer. Chem. Soc. 80 1084 (1958)
(71) TAUBE Chem. Soc. Special Publ. 13 57 (1959)
(72) SEBERA and TAUBE J. Amer. Chem. Soc. 83 1785 (1961)
(73) BALL and KING J. Amer. Chem. Soc. 80 1091 (1958)
(74) WERNING, HIGHIE, GRACE, SPEECE and GILBERT Ind. Eng. Chem. 46 644 (1954)

## CHAPTER 6

# The Periodic Table and the Recent Chemistry of some Metals

THE CHEMICAL properties of some of the elements and their compounds are described in the remaining three chapters of this book. It is not yet possible to provide a comprehensive mathematical picture of the energy relationships which exist between atoms and molecules, and it is necessary to undertake experiments in order to establish the chemical and physical properties of compounds. In particular, stability in a given environment can only be predicted in the most general terms—in many cases we do not know whether there is any way in which a postulated compound can be prepared or isolated. In studying the chemical properties of matter, we are still at the stage at which it is necessary to prepare the widest possible range of compounds and to determine and classify their behaviour. The quantity of recorded data is already very great, and it is necessary that it should be classified in a rational and ordered way before the underlying patterns can be identified. A useful classification not only facilitates the handling of the data, but can also make a contribution to the theoretical understanding of the way in which chemical combination takes place.

The study of chemistry would have been infinitely more complicated if the chemistry of each element had been found to be entirely unrelated to that of every other element, and if no pattern or periodicity of properties had been detected within the range of known elements. The existence of such a pattern was appreciated in the middle of the nineteenth century, by which time so much chemical data had been obtained that it was essential for this to be codified in some way if further advances were to be made.

Such a classification could not be made until the nature of elements was clearly appreciated, and until there was an accepted differentiation between elements and compounds. It also had to await sufficient advances in chemical methods and techniques for the properties of the elements themselves to be reasonably well characterized. It must be remembered that at this early stage of chemical development, no more was known of the structure of matter than that it was of the nature of elements that they could not be further sub-divided by chemical means, and that the atoms of any one element were chemically identical, and differed chemically from the atoms of every other element. The nature of this difference was not known, and the only atomic property which was established as being peculiar to each

119

element was the relative atomic weight of its atoms. It is fortunate that it was realized that this was an important atomic property, and that it suggested that a basic method of arrangement of the elements was to place them in order of ascending relative atomic weight. Other properties of the elements might have been used to classify them—density, melting point, boiling point or relative frequency of occurrence in the earth's crust.

The principle of using an atomic property in order to achieve a logical arrangement leading to a periodic pattern is so familiar to modern chemists that it is not easy to appreciate that this was not at once accepted when it was first proposed. When Newlands made such an arrangement, and detected the periodic pattern which he described as a law of octaves, not only did his scheme receive little support, but the scepticism of his contemporaries was so great that it was suggested that he should look for further regularities by arranging the known elements in alphabetical order. Dobereiner's law of triads was looked on as a fortuitous arrangement of no great significance. It was in the context of this climate of scientific opinion that Mendeleef considered that the evidence in favour of a logical periodic classification of the elements was so strong that it was necessary to postulate the existence of elements as yet undiscovered where this was essential in order to preserve the periodic form of his table. It was his successful prediction of the nature of these unknown elements which played a large part in gaining acceptance for his table as a contribution to the theoretical understanding of chemistry instead of merely being a useful generalization which might be due to no more than coincidence.

The importance of Mendeleef's periodic hypothesis was not only that it conferred a logical basis for the classification of the known facts of chemistry, but that it directed the attention of chemists and physicists to a necessary line of research. It made it reasonable to speculate about a possible rational relationship between the atoms of the various elements; that is to say, whether the difference between the atoms of any one element and those of any other had a quantitative and not merely a qualitative basis. Such a quantitative relationship implied that there was an atomic structure, and it had the further implication that if such a structure could be studied experimentally, atoms could no longer be regarded as indivisible in a physical if not in a chemical sense.

The possibility of 'splitting the atom' was therefore latent in the periodic table of Mendeleef. It is remarkable that such a grouping of the elements, based upon purely chemical considerations, should have anticipated so accurately the 'physical' grouping which became conceivable after the discovery of the electron. The 'Bohr Atom' described very elegantly, if only qualitatively, how the electronic shells accorded with the periodicity of chemical properties. The periodic table of Mendeleef remains the most convenient method of grouping the chemical elements. The inert gases, which were not known to Mendeleef, took their place without difficulty in the table and it has been modified to accept the triads in Group VIII, the lanthanides, and the actinides. The modifications made necessary by the recognition of the transition elements has, however, done away with much of the original simplicity of the table. The importance of this new complexity has often been exaggerated. While the distribution of the electrons between the various quantized energy levels is of the greatest practical importance, it is not possible to indicate this in a simple and useful table. Within the various series of transition elements, the energy levels of the 'orbits' are such that these do not become occupied in a regular manner in passing from element to element. Not only this, but as has been pointed out in an earlier chapter, within certain compounds of transition elements, the distribution of electrons between quantum levels may differ from that in the elements in their ground states. Any exact correspondence cannot be expected between the chemical behaviour of any lanthanide, and that of the actinide which is formally analogous with it on the basis of the total number of electrons in excess of that possessed by the next lower inert gas.

Thus, the periodic table of Mendeleef was not only a convenient codification of knowledge, but it also embodied a potential advance in our knowledge of the structure of matter. The convenience remains, but what was then an advance has now become an accepted part of chemical history. No further theoretical progress is likely to be made as a result of any attempt to 'modernize' the table or by writing it in circular form, or upon pyramids or cones in order to relate in more detail the positions occupied by the various types of transition element. In spite of this, there is still considerable discussion about the best or most correct way of representing Mendeleef's periodic hypothesis in tabular form. As will be seen later in this chapter, the transition elements in the higher periods have only a formal resemblance to the typical elements of the group to which they are usually assigned. Such elements have a sub-shell which is not 'filled by electrons', that is to say the quasi-stable sub-shell is not 'made up to the inert gas configuration'. It is not easy either to show in tabular form the principal chemical interrelationship between such elements or to avoid grouping together elements with little similarity of properties. Much ingenuity is still being exercised in designing tables which purport to set out these relationships in a more precise fashion. For instance, it was suggested by one author ( 1 ) in 1959 that the table should be spread out in vertical groups based on the electron shells that are actually being filled, adding a third $(c)$ sub-group for filling $f$ shells in addition to an $(a)$ sub-group for filling $s$ and $p$ shells, and a $(b)$ sub-group for $d$ shell filling. This suggestion was criticized by another writer (2) who rightly said: 'Most tables defy verbal description, and their connexion with basic concepts is obscure.' Indeed, this was amplified by the first writer (3) who said:

'A periodic table is not a law in itself, but a way of tabulating (or making generalizations about) facts which are related to more fundamental principles.'

The periodic *hypothesis* was an imaginative generalization of the greatest value to the advance of chemistry. It produced order out of an apparently random distribution of chemical properties over the known elements. The periodic *table* is at best an *aide-mémoire* regarding a situation about which any broad generalization cannot be true in detail. There is very little real value, for instance, in basing a table on transition alloy behaviour. This has been attempted by constructing a circular table with titanium, zirconium, hafnium and thorium forming a spoke in an otherwise blank semicircle (4). It is better to retain the conventional table as a general guide, and to study the chemistry of the individual elements without worrying too much about how the elements may be fitted into a table which cannot accurately show all similarities and relationships.

One of the difficulties which is inherent in any comparison of the chemical properties of elements or compound is to decide what is normal and what is aberrant. Throughout the whole history of chemistry, there has been a marked tendency for some properties to be described as typical, and for others to be described as anomalous. This may in some cases be a useful approach, provided that the words do not imply any sense of 'rightness' or 'wrongness'. The simplest and most easily comprehended example may reasonably be described as typical, while those examples which differ from the general pattern may be called anomalies. Such anomalies are in no sense irregularities; if their existence upsets a convenient theory, then so much the worse for the theory. The behaviour of matter is conditioned by many interacting forces and their combination produces a rational disposition of the matter which is subjected to them, even if our limited knowledge makes the result unexpected on prima facie grounds. The use of the periodic table as a basis of classification has involved the description of elements, whose electronic structure is within four electrons of the nearest inert gas, as typical; the temptation to describe the remainder as anomalous has happily so far been resisted. The resemblances between elements in the same vertical group (or sub-group) of the table are in many cases very marked, but equally there are many differences of great theoretical and practical importance. The periodic resemblances which can be accounted for by the successive filling of the electronic energy levels are superimposed upon the linear increase in atomic number whose periodic influence is very much less marked. The net effect is that while there is a broad periodicity and a general gradation of properties within a group or sub-group, compounds of particular elements show properties which differ from those which might be predicted by a simple process of analogy based on the behaviour of similar compounds of elements in the same group.

Because of this failure of the elements in any one group of the periodic table to form a precise series of homologous compounds, it is possible to learn from the compounds of each individual element something of the way in which matter behaves when in chemical combination. Unfortunately for the teacher, the number of elements is inconveniently large for all their individual points of interest to be included in an elementary syllabus. However, it is possible that it would be more valuable to increase the number of elements with the chemistry of which students became familiar, rather than that so much time should be spent in inculcating the impractical details of obsolescent chemical manufacturing processes, often to the exclusion (or at least with the partial eclipse) of the principles which the process was originally selected to illustrate. Considerable advances have been made during the last twenty years in the chemistry of those elements whose properties are less generally known. In the following paragraphs are described some of the points of interest in the chemistry of a selection of such elements. In many cases, there is as yet no detailed quantitative explanation of many of the differences in the behaviour of elements in the same group or sub-group although they may often be accounted for in a general qualitative way.

The metal gallium, which was discovered by Lecoq and Boisbaudran in 1875, was shown to have many of the properties predicted by Mendeleef for eka-aluminium whose existence was not known when the periodic hypothesis was formulated. In spite of the consequent historical interest of this element and the length of time for which its compounds have been characterized, its chemistry had not been extensively studied until about 1940. At this time three main problems in gallium chemistry were known to be outstanding—the structure of the dihalides, the gallium–oxygen system and the nature of the volatile hydride.

The typical electrovalency of gallium is 3, and the trihalides $GaCl_3$, $GaBr_3$ and $GaI_3$ were well known. However, a series of compounds were known which had the formulae $GaCl_2$, $GaBr_2$ and $GaI_2$ although it was expected that the subsidiary valency of gallium would be 1; monovalent gallium halides were, in fact, unknown. The dihalides were found to be diamagnetic, and since this indicated that they contained no electrons with unpaired spins, it was apparent that the simple formula could not describe their structure. Two possible alternative structures were suggested, each of which were equivalent to the doubled formula $Ga_2X_4$. The alternatives were:

$$X_2\text{—}Ga\text{—}Ga\text{—}X_2 \quad \text{and} \quad Ga^I[Ga^{III}X_4]$$

Since the monovalent halides were unknown the first of these two formulae was considered to be the more probable. However, in 1955 the phase diagram of the gallium/iodine system was constructed (5) and eutectics were found which corresponded to the phases GaI and $(GaI_2)_x$. This indicated a strong probability that a monovalent gallium ion could exist in a halide system, and considerably strengthened the case for the formula $Ga[GaX_4]$. Observations on the Raman spectrum of the halides also supported this (6), as did X-ray diffraction measurements (7). Corbett and Macmullan, who had investigated the gallium/iodine phase diagram produced conventional chemical evidence for the existence of the monovalent ion by reducing gallium dichloride with gallium metal in the presence of aluminium trichloride. The gallium absorbed during the reaction was found to be within 0·1% of that required by the equation

$$Ga[GaCl_4] + 2Ga + 4AlCl_3 = 4Ga[AlCl_4]$$

Since $[AlCl_4]^-$ is a well-known monovalent ligand, it seemed very probable that in both $Ga[GaCl_4]$ nad $Ga[AlCl_4]$, one gallium atom was monovalent (8).

Gallium dichloride (gallium gallichloride) is soluble in benzene. The monovalent gallium ion appears to be strongly solvated by this solvent. If the solution is allowed to crystallize, a rather stable benzene complex of the gallichloride separates out. A similar complex is formed by gallium aluminochloride. These benzene complexes are not isomorphous with the electronically similar silver perchlorate–benzene complex. This is because of a fundamental difference between ions such as $Ga^+$ and those such as $H^+$ and $Ag^+$. In $Ga^+$, the $s$-orbital is occupied by the inert pair of electrons, and the lowest acceptor orbital is a $p$-orbital. This is also the case for monovalent ions of the Group III metals indium and thallium. Since the donor orbital in benzene is a $\pi$-orbital no distortion of electronic levels is necessary when the monovalent ions of Group III metals interact with benzene; the complex can have a high degree of symmetry with the cation lying on the benzene axis, that is to say in the plane of the benzene $\pi$-orbital. When the Group I metals form a complex with benzene, the $s$-orbital is available for bonding, and in forming the complex there has to be considerable charge promotion, and the cation must take up a postion of lower symmetry (9). The solution of the gallium gallichloride complex in benzene was used in another way to demonstrate the existence of the $Ga^+$ ion; if hydrogen sulphide is added to the solution, part of the gallium is precipitated as what appears to be monovalent gallium sulphide contaminated with chlorine (10). Finally, the ions have been characterized in a number of compounds of the general formula $[Ga\ Lig_4]^+[GaX_4]^-$ where Lig indicates a monodentate ligand and X is Cl or Br (11).

The information about the oxide system of gallium was in a confused state for many years, although it was known that the system was similar to the aluminium/oxygen system. For instance, in each case the $M_2O_3$ compounds showed polymorphism, and when these compounds were hydrated, gels were formed. The phases in an oxide system of this type are primarily controlled by the way in which the close packing of the larger oxygen ions is distorted or polarized by the smaller metal ions. The difference between the oxide phases of the two metals illustrates the disturbing effect of the increased atomic volume which is superimposed upon the periodic similarity.

The gallium/oxygen system was exhaustively studied by three workers in the U.S.A. (12) who observed five forms of $Ga_2O_3$:

(I) An $\alpha$-$Ga_2O_3$ which had a hexagonal lattice and which was similar to $\alpha$-$Al_2O_3$.

(II) The most stable form, $\beta$-$Ga_2O_3$. This form results when any form of $Ga_2O_3$ or its hydrates is heated in air above $1000°\,C$. The X-ray diffraction pattern of $\beta$-$Ga_2O_3$ is somewhat similar to that of $\beta$-$Al_2O_3$.

(III) A $\gamma$ form. This did not appear to resemble $\gamma$-$Al_2O_3$, although its full structure was not worked out, but it was quite distinct from the other forms of $Ga_2O_3$.

(IV) A $\delta$ form which had a body-centred cubic structure. This can be prepared by dissolving the metal in nitric acid, and evaporating the solution. The residue must then be heated to $250°\,C$ to decompose the nitrate, and further heated at $200°\,C$ for 12 hr. This form is metastable. It corresponds to the rare earth oxide C-type structure, and is analogous to $Mn_2O_3$, $In_2O_3$ and $Te_2O_3$. The unit cell is, however, larger than would be expected for this type of structure; the $Ga^{3+}$ ion is very small, and it can probably only be accommodated in a body-centred cubic structure if there is considerable strain in the lattice.

(V) A form only stable in the high temperature range $525$–$870°\,C$. This can be formed by heating $\delta$-$Ga_2O_3$. Its structure is not known, but its X-ray pattern is clearly defined. If heated above $870°\,C$ inversion to $\beta$-$Ga_2O_3$ takes place with a considerable emission of heat.

At present, experimental chemists can only observe and report the structure of phases in systems of this type, and study the nature of the transitions between them; it is impossible to give a fundamental theoretical explanation of the precise causes of the observed facts.

The hydrated oxides of gallium are also dissimilar to those of aluminium. Roy and his co-workers found one monohydrate entirely analogous to one of the hydrated aluminas (diaspore) but could not identify any phase which resembled, for example, boehmite. A metastable trihydrate had been reported earlier (13), but this was not confirmed. There were only two phases in the phase diagram, $\beta$-$Ga_2O_3$ and $Ga(OH)_2$ and these were separated by an univariant line at $300 + 5°$ C. The $Ga^{3+}$ ion is slightly more acidic than $In^{3+}$ and its hydrolysis is governed by the formation of $(GaOH)^{2+}$ ions (14).

The third feature of gallium chemistry which gave considerable difficulty in interpretation was the existence of the volatile hydride $Ga_2H_6$. It can be formed by the following series of reactions (15). Trimethyl gallium mixed with hydrogen is subjected to a glow discharge and a colourless viscous liquid is formed. This has the formula $Ga_2H_2(CH_3)_4$, and decomposes above $130°$ C according to the equation

$$3Ga_2H_2(CH_3)_4 = 4Ga(CH_3)_3 + 2Ga + 3H_2$$

However, gallium hydride, together with a triethylamine compound of trimethyl gallium, is formed when the viscous liquid $Ga_2H_2(CH_3)_4$ reacts with triethylamine at room temperature:

$$3Ga_2H_2(CH_3)_4 + N(C_2H_5)_3 = 4Ga(CH_3)_3 N(C_2H_5)_4 + Ga_2H_6$$

The theories of the structure of this compound have been closely connected with those concerning the hydrides of boron. Since these will be considered in a later chapter, we will only refer here to the bridged formula which is now generally accepted (16):

$$\begin{array}{ccccc} H & & H & & H \\ & \diagdown & | & \diagup & \\ & Ga & & Ga & \\ & \diagup & | & \diagdown & \\ H & & H & & H \end{array}$$

The work of Longuet-Higgins on these compounds was also developed in the U.S.A. where the compound dimethyl gallium borohydride was studied (17)

$$\begin{array}{ccccc} CH_3 & & H & & H \\ & \diagdown & | & \diagup & \\ & Ga & & B & \\ & \diagup & | & \diagdown & \\ CH_3 & & H & & H \end{array}$$

and the wave-mechanical interpretation extended (18).

In the majority of its compounds, gallium behaves as a typical Group III element. For instance, the trifluoride can be obtained by heating the metal in hydrogen fluoride gas; it is isomorphous with ferric fluoride. $(NH_4)GaF_4$ is isomorphous with $(NH_4)AlF_4$. Gallium forms two nitrides, $Ga_3N$ and $GaN$ (19). Salts are formed with all the strong acids, and the sulphate forms alums. Heteropoly-ions containing gallium such as $(Co(NH_3)_5H_2O)(GaO_6Mo_6O_{15})$ have been prepared (20).

Less is known about the Group III metal indium. Many features of indium chemistry resemble those of thallium as well as those of gallium. The univalent state is not very stable and appreciable disproportionation of the univalent ion takes place in aqueous solution.

$$3In^+ \longrightarrow 2In + In^{3+}$$

and this state is only stabilized in complexes when the inert pair of electrons may be donated to the orbitals of the complex.

The basic chemistry of the element is reasonably well established. The metal is soft and is stable in air at ordinary temperatures, although it burns to the oxide when heated. The nitride has been prepared by heating $(NH_4)_3InF_6$ to 600° C. This compound, InN has the wurtzite structure, and is probably a covalently-bound giant molecule (21). The trihalides are all known and with the exception of $InI_3$, they are all dimeric in the vapour phase (22). Indic salts are formed with all the oxyacids, and the sulphate forms both alums and double sulphates. Indium resembles thallium in that they both form complex sulphides.

The problems of indium chemistry chiefly arise from the occurrence and stability of the lower valency states. 'Divalent' halides are believed to be analogous to the corresponding gallium compounds and to have the general formula $In(InX_4)$. However, when indium metal reacts with mercurous or mercuric halides, compounds of empirical formula $InX$ and $InX_2$ are formed. When the halogen is chlorine, a compound $In_2Cl_3$ can also be isolated. This appears to be $In_3(InCl_6)$. When the halogen is iodine, the compounds $InI$ and $InI_2$ seem to have the simple formulae (23). The polarographic reduction of indic ions in the presence of a high concentration of chloride ion indicates that $(InCl_2)^+$ and $(InCl_4)^-$ can exist in aqueous solution (24). When solutions of indic chloride are shaken with metallic indium, they acquire reducing properties. This behaviour was investigated quantitatively by shaking indic perchlorate with indium metal, filtering the suspension, and titrating the filtrate with a ceric salt. From this, equilibrium constants for the formation of both $In^+$ and $In^{4+}$ were calculated, and it was shown that these can only exist in very low concentrations in aqueous solution (25). In spite of these observations, the conditions necessary for the existence of indium in a valency state lower than three are still largely unknown, and considerable further work is required in order to clarify the situation.

The relation of the fourth group metal germanium to the third group metal gallium is similar to that of carbon or silicon to boron. Germanium and some of its compounds are semi-conductors; the electronic properties of such substances are considerably modified by the presence of impurities in concentrations as low as 1 part in $10^7$. For this reason, many compounds of germanium have been investigated as possible intermediates in purification processes, and in particular, studies have been made of the preparation and properties of many volatile compounds which can be purified by distillation.

Germanium has two valencies, 2 and 4, the divalent compounds being generally less stable than the quadrivalent. For example, when the difluoride is heated above 350° C, it disproportionates to the metal and the tetrafluoride. Disproportionation of the dichloride commences at $75°$ C, and the dibromide and the diiodide behave similarly. The dihalides are considerably less volatile than the tetrahalides.

Sidgwick (26) attributed this to co-ordination by a donor, and he considered that in these compounds there is no inert pair of electrons. He suggested that the chloride should be formulated

$$
\begin{array}{c}
\text{Cl} \\
\text{Ge} \diagdown \quad \text{Cl} \\
\text{Cl} \rightarrow \text{Ge} \diagup \quad \text{Cl} \\
\text{Cl} \rightarrow \text{Ge} \diagup \\
\text{Cl} \ldots
\end{array}
$$

but he rejected the alternative formulation which is analogous to that adopted for palladous chloride

$$
\text{Ge} \underset{\text{Cl}}{\overset{\text{Cl}}{\diagdown\!\diagup}} \text{Ge} \underset{\text{Cl}}{\overset{\text{Cl}}{\diagdown\!\diagup}} \text{Ge} \underset{\text{Cl}}{\overset{\text{Cl}}{\diagdown\!\diagup}}
$$

When the disulphide is heated in air, it is converted to $GeO_2$ and sulphur dioxide is given off. $GeO_2$ is the stable oxide of germanium, and it can be hydrated to a hydroxide $Ge(OH)_4$ which resembles silicic acid. A definite monohydrate has not been isolated, but evidence has been found for the existence of 'pentagermanoic acid' $H_2Ge_5O_{11}$. This has been detected as a result of X-ray diffraction analysis and also on the basis of a phase diagram derived from a study of the vapour pressure of hydrated germanic oxide (27).

The tetrafluoride is a colourless fuming gas which will not attack dry glass. The tetrachloride is a fuming liquid at room temperature, and the compound is stable up to $950°$ C. It is soluble in many organic solvents, but it is rapidly hydrolysed by water. It is unaffected by hot concentrated sulphuric acid, and also insoluble in concentrated hydrochloric acid; no compound of the type $H_2MCl_6$ is formed as is the case with the tetrachlorides of the Group IV metals tin, lead and titanium. The tetrabromide is similar to the tetrachloride; the tetraiodide is a solid which melts at $144°$ C.

When germanium tetrachloride vapour is mixed with an inert carrier gas, heated to $900-1000°$ C, and suddenly cooled, a solid brown subchloride $(GeCl)_x$ is formed. This is insoluble in all solvents, but it is decomposed by alkali with the evolution of hydrogen. When it is heated to $500°$ C in a vacuum, it disproportionates to tetrachloride, dichloride and germanium metal. If the heating is carried out at a higher pressure, only the tetrachloride and the metal are formed. Thermal decomposition of

$(GeCl)_x/GeCl_2$ mixtures leads to the production of $Ge_2Cl_6$ which is soluble in benzene, and which dissolves in alkali with the evolution of hydrogen (28).

Partial hydrolysis of the tetrachloride does not result in the formation of a volatile oxychloride as is the case with silicon tetrachloride; only polymers of the approximate composition $Ge_2O_3Cl_2$ are obtained (29). $GeHCl_3$ is prepared by the action of hydrogen chloride on germanium sulphide at a low temperature; it readily loses HCl to form the dichloride even at $-30°C$ (30). It also differs from the analogous silicon compound in that the oxychloride is not formed by passing $GeHCl_3$ over silver oxide (31). When quadrivalent germanium is dissolved in 6–9M hydrochloric acid, a variety of chloro-complexes is formed (32). These include

$$[Ge(OH)_xCl_{(5-x)}]^-  \quad \text{and} \quad  [Ge(OH)_xCl_{(6-x)}]^{2-}$$

in which $x$ lies between 3 and 4. Under these conditions, tin forms only $[SnCl_5]^-$ and $[SnCl_6]^{2-}$. In solution in liquid hydrogen chloride, germanium tetrachloride does not behave as an acid, although hexachlorogermanates have been prepared (33). The tetracyanide can be prepared by reacting the tetraiodide with silver cyanide in solution in benzene (34).

The monoxide has been prepared by the action of carbon dioxide on germanium metal at 700–900°C; the carbon dioxide is reduced to the monoxide (35). The dioxide can be formed by heating the metal or the disulphide in air. It occurs in two crystalline forms which corresponds to the quartz and rutile forms of silica and is soluble in hot water to form an acid weaker than $H_2S$. The disulphide is precipitated by hydrogen sulphide from a solution of the tetrachloride in 6N hydrochloric acid; it is not precipitated if the pH is greater than 2. It is hydrolysed in moist air with the evolution of hydrogen sulphide.

A few members of the series of homologous germanium hydrides are known; these include $GeH_4$ and $Ge_2H_6$. Germane can be prepared in 75% yield by reduction of an acidic aqueous solution of germanium hydroxide with sodium borohydride; less than 1% of digermane is formed in this reaction, and only a trace of germanium metal is precipitated. Stannane can be prepared by the analogous reaction with stannic hydroxide, but plumbane cannot be prepared in this way (36). Tetra- and penta-germanes have been identified among the products of the reaction of 10% HCl on magnesium germanide (37a, b). The germanium alkyls are colourless pleasant-smelling liquids which are stable to air and to water in which they are not soluble. They have the general formula $GeR_4$, where R = methyl, ethyl or n-propyl. Similar aryls are known in which R = phenyl, tolyl, etc. Germanium tetra-ethyl is an exceedingly stable substance; for example, it is not attached by fuming nitric acid unless sulphuric acid is present.

More recently, the mono-, di-, and tri-germanes have been prepared by the reduction of aqueous alkaline germanate solutions. The mono-germane was separated by fractional distillation *in vacuo*, and subjected to a high voltage A.C. discharge in an ozoniser. The higher germanes which were then formed were separated by gas-liquid chromatography; those up to and including nona-germane were identified by infra-red and mass spectroscopy (*37c*).

The higher germanes are examples of a group of interesting compounds which contain two or more germanium atoms bonded to each other. Hexamethyldigermane was prepared in 74% yield by reducing tri-methyl germanium bromide with molten potassium (*38*). Hexa-ethyldigermane is stable in air and can be distilled under atmospheric pressure at 265° C. Hexaphenyldigermane is also stable in air. It is only oxidized by very strong oxidizing agents, and it is insoluble in boiling aqueous sodium hydroxide which does not affect it in any way. A higher homologue, octaphenyltrigermane is also reported to be stable to air and moisture (*39*). The same authors also state that if diphenyl germanium chloride in solution in xylene is treated with sodium, a solid is formed which has the composition $(Ge(C_6H_5)_2)_n$. This melts at 294° C, and from the elevation of the boiling point of benzene in which the compound is dissolved, $n$ can be shown to equal 4 within 0·5%. The authors suggest that in this compound, a four-membered ring is formed:

$$(C_6H_5)_2Ge—Ge(C_6H_5)_2$$
$$(C_6H_5)_2Ge—Ge(C_6H_5)_2$$

Another curious polymer, which is also soluble in benzene, is formed when $C_6H_5GeCl_3$ is boiled together with potassium in solution in xylene under an atmosphere of carbon dioxide. This is a stable white amorphous solid; the depression of the freezing point corresponds to the formula $(Ge(C_6H_5))_6$. On bromination, 8 bromine atoms are taken up per molecule (40). At first sight, this behaviour indicates a structure comprising a chain:

$$\begin{array}{cccccc}
C_6H_5 & C_6H_5 & C_6H_5 & C_6H_5 & C_6H_5 & C_6H_5 \\
| & | & | & | & | & | \\
Ge—Ge=Ge—Ge=Ge—Ge
\end{array}$$

It is, however, curious that the chain should consist of 6 germanium atoms rather than 2, 4 or 8. It is tempting to suggest that an 'aromatic' ring is formed and that one bond is broken on bromination.

$$\begin{array}{c}
C_6H_5 \\
| \\
C_6H_5—Ge^{\diagup Ge\diagdown}Ge—C_6H_5 \\
| \qquad\qquad \| \\
C_6H_5—Ge\diagdown_{Ge}\diagup Ge—C_6H_5 \\
| \\
C_6H_5
\end{array}$$

A very large number of alkyl germanium halides are known. These have the general formula $GeCl_3X$, where $X = -C_5H_{11}$, $-C_5H_{10}Cl$, $-C_6H_{13}$, $-C_6H_{11}F_2$, $-C_6H_{12}Cl$, $-C_7H_{15}$, iso-$C_8H_{17}$ and $-C_{10}H_{21}$ (41).

A wide variety of solid compounds have been prepared and their semi-conductor properties studied. For example, in the G.E.C. laboratories in the U.S.A. (42), compounds of the general formula $A^{II}B^{IV}X_2^V$ have been studied in which

$$A = \text{Zn, Cd}$$
$$B = \text{Si, Ge, Sn}$$
$$X = \text{As, P}$$

Similar compounds have also been prepared in Germany. These compounds have a chemical as well as a physical interest. For example, in a similar series whose semi-conductor properties were studied, why can $Li_5GeAs_3$ be prepared, but apparently $Li_5GeP_3$ cannot? (43).

Germanium is a typical Group IV element which shows many resemblances to the Group IV elements carbon and silicon in the two short periods in the periodic system. Zirconium is a member of Group IV; but here two of the valency electrons occupy d-levels and not p-levels as in carbon, silicon and germanium. It is an early member of a transition series. In the fourth group, the transitional elements become more basic in character as the atomic weight increases from titanium to thorium. Valencies of 2, 3 and 4 are possible, but the lower valencies become less stable as the atomic weight increases. In the 'typical' series, the divalent state, in which two electrons form an inert pair, becomes more stable as the atomic weight increases. Titanium has marked acidic properties, and exhibits all three possible valencies. Thorium is predominantly basic and tetravalent. Much of the interest in the chemistry of zirconium lies in the fact that it exhibits properties which are intermediate between those of titanium and those of thorium.

Zirconium metal is very inert. The only mineral acids by which it is attacked are hydrofluoric acid and aqua regia. The carbide has been known since 1896 (44), and is prepared in an electric furnace from carbon and zirconium dioxide. It conducts electricity and is hard enough to scratch quartz. The nitride, $ZrN$, also conducts electricity; it has the sodium chloride structure, which is unusual for a nitride. In contrast to this behaviour, thorium is never trivalent, and forms the nitride $Th_3N_4$.

Zirconium hydride can be made by reducing the oxide with a 10% excess of magnesium chips at 900° C in an atmosphere of hydrogen; the hydride is left behind when the excess of magnesium is distilled off. It may be used to prepare the metal, which remains when the hydride is heated in vacuum (45); zirconium hydride thus differs markedly from the volatile hydrides of the typical elements. It resembles $ThH_4$; they both have the same deformed fluorite lattice structure.

The oxide $ZrO_2$ is trimorphic and has no structural resemblance to the dioxides of the typical elements. For example, the monoclinic baddeleyite has a complex structure in which each zirconium atom is surrounded by 7 oxygen atoms at distances varying from 2·04 to 2·22 ÅU (46). The tetrahalides are not stable in the presence of moisture, although they are not so readily hydrolysed as are those of titanium. Since transition elements are electron deficient in the sense that the inner $d$ shell is incompletely filled, their ions will tend to accept the $(OH)^-$ donor and become hydrolysed. Zirconium tetrachloride is attacked by hydroxyl ion even in the presence of concentrated hydrochloric acid. As is often the case, the fluoride of the highest valency state of the metal is the halide which is most stable to hydrolysis. $ZrF_4$ forms a trihydrate from which the monohydrate is formed at 100° C. Hydrolysis to zirconyl fluoride and zirconium oxide only occurs above 300° C (47). Zirconium tetrachloride forms complexes with diethyl phthalate and other esters; hafnium tetrachloride behaves similarly. These compounds are stable in dry, but not in moist air. When added to water, the ester separates as an oil. These complexes have not been characterized as exact 1 : 1 stoicheiometric compounds (48). When a solution of zirconyl chloride, $ZrOCl_2 6H_2O$ is treated with pyridine in solution in alcoholic hydrogen chloride, pyridinium chlorozirconate is formed. The yield is quantitative. From this complex, zirconium alkoxides can be prepared and those which have so far been characterized have the formula $Zr(OR)_4$ where R = ethyl, isopropyl, butyl, or sym-isobutyl. They are made by suspending the complex in a mixture of benzene and the appropriate alcohol, and by then passing ammonia into the suspension (49).

The salts of the oxy-acids are as readily hydrolysed as are the chlorides, bromides and iodides. Neither the sulphate nor the nitrate can be crystallized from water. The zirconium ions are complexed in the presence of strong acids such as perchloric, nitric, hydrochloric and sulphuric; in each case, equilibrium is only attained slowly. At low acidities, polynuclear hydrolysis products are formed, and at higher acidities a variety of complexes are formed (50) such as:

$$[Zr(NO_3)_2(H_2O)_4]^{2+}$$
$$[Zr(OH)_2(NO_3)(H_2O)_3]^+$$
$$[Zr(OH)_2(NO_3)_2(H_2O)_2]^{2+}$$
$$[Zr(OH)_2(NO_3)_4]^{2+}$$

The preparation of the anhydrous nitrate was described in Chapter 5. Double sulphates are formed with divalent metals such as magnesium. Magnesium zirconium sulphate, $MgSO_4 . Zr(SO_4)_2$ is prepared by heating together zirconium nitrate and magnesium sulphate heptahydrate in sulphuric acid of specific gravity 1·79. The double salt is soluble in a small quantity of cold water, but is hydrolysed when a dilute aqueous solution is heated (51).

Zirconium forms a basic benzoate, whose structure resembles that of basic beryllium acetate. However, since the covalency maximum of zirconium is 6, the formula of this compound is $(ZrO)_4O(O.CO.C_6H_5)_6$.

Zirconium resembles germanium in that it also possesses interesting semi-conductor properties. In many ways, the recent developments in the chemistry of both these elements have proceeded along similar lines. In each case, there has been an exhaustive examination of potentially interesting compounds which exhibit semi-conducting properties, and many compounds have been prepared in the search for useful purification intermediaries. As an example of the systematic preparation of potential semi-conductors, and the way in which composition affects such properties, work carried out in Australia by McTaggart and his co-workers may be cited (52). This investigation concerned the zirconium chalcogenides; a chalcogenide is the compound of a metal with sulphur, selenium or tellurium. Zirconium chalcogenides were prepared which had the limiting formulae $ZrX_3$, $ZrX_2$, $Zr_2X_3$ and $ZrX$ ($X = S$, Se or Te). All such compounds or phases could be reduced by excess alkali metal to zirconium, and throughout the series, sulphur would replace selenium or tellurium, and selenium would replace tellurium. There was no evidence for mixed phases containing more than one chalcogenide element; this may be due to the difficulty of forming a regular close-packed lattice with chalcogenide ions of different sizes. Many of these phases were oxidized in air; the effect ranged from surface oxidation to pyrophorism. The eventual oxidation products were zirconium oxide and the chalcogen oxide. Reaction with chlorine led to the formation of $Zr(iv)$ chloride, for example:

$$ZrTe_3 + 8Cl_2 = ZrCl_4 + 3TeCl_4$$

They did not react readily with water, possibly because the surface layer became coated with insoluble hydroxide complexes. They did, however, react violently with nitric acid to form zirconium oxide.

The $ZrX_3$ series of compounds is formed by the direct combination of the elements and are monoclinic. The $ZrX_2$ series is formed by the degradation of $ZrX_3$ compounds at $900°C$. It is probable that the stoicheiometric compounds $ZrS_2$ and $ZrSe_2$ can be formed, but the 'divalent' phase is stable down to a composition $ZrX_{1.7}$. The $ZrTe_2$ compound has not been prepared, and the only tellurium compound in this series which was isolated was $ZrTe_{1.7}$. The crystal structures of many of these compounds is of great interest in that they include a wide variety of different defect structures. For example, on the basis of crystal density determinations and X-ray diffraction analysis, a molecular formula of $Zr_{1.12}Te_{1.90}$ has been assigned to the $ZrF_{1.7}$ phase. The lattice appears to contain an excess of metal ions

10

and to be defective in non-metal ions. The lattice of $Zr_2S_3$ can be described as being of the sodium chloride type with systematic defects. There are a small number of defects in the metal lattice, restricted to one sixteen-fold set, while there are randomly distributed vacancies in the sulphur lattice. The structure of the monosulphide, whose composition may vary from $Zr_5S_8$ to $Zr_9S_8$ is of particular interest. The stoicheiometric phase ZrS also forms a sodium chloride type lattice, but one-quarter of both the metal and the non-metal sites are vacant. This structure is similar to that found in NbO (53), TiO (54) and VO (55).

The different phases have very different electronic properties. This is manifested by their colour, specific resistivity and the type of conduction, as is shown in the table.

This range of phases or compounds is a further example of a complex situation in which it is not possible at present to predict the pattern of behaviour. This must be found by experiment, and a subsequent attempt made to show how the current theories may be reconciled with the observed phenomena.

Electronic Properties of the Zirconium
Chalcogenides ($ZrX_y$)

X = Sulphur

| $y$ | Colour | Specific resistivity | Type of conduction |
|---|---|---|---|
| 2·95 | Orange | 2,000,000 | N-Semi |
| 2·00 | Brown-violet | 10 | N-Semi |
| 1·50 | Black | 0·08 | N-Semi |
| 1·00 | Dark grey/black | 0·006 | Metallic |

X = Selenium

| $y$ | Colour | Specific resistivity | Type of conduction |
|---|---|---|---|
| 3·05 | Black/purplish | 20,000 | N-Semi |
| 1·95 | Dark grey-green | 0·10 | N-Semi |
| 1·50 | Black | 0·007 | N-Semi |
| 1·00 | Very dark grey | 0·004 | Metallic |

X = Tellurium

| $y$ | Colour | Specific resistivity | Type of conduction |
|---|---|---|---|
| 2·90 | Lustrous/Black | 0·0004 | Metallic |
| 1·70 | Dark purple-brown | 0·001 | Metallic |
| 1·50 | Black | 0·0016 | Metallic |
| 1·00 | Black | 0·001 | Metallic |

In zirconium, the $d$ sub-shell has only just started to fill, while in the manganese sub-group it is half filled. Formally, manganese, technetium and rhenium are placed in the same group of Mendeleef's periodic table as the halogens. There is some similarity in the formulae of the anions in which the two respective series of elements take part, but otherwise there is little chemical justification for including them in the same group; the protagonists of revised tables can make a good case for revision here, but the extended table due to Thomsen and Bohr demonstrates this situation satisfactorily although the inclusion of the $f$ series is not very successfully contrived. The chemistry of manganese, the first element with a half-filled $d$ shell, is well known, but that of its congeners is less familiar, and their comparative chemistry is typical of the behaviour of elements near the middle of $d$ transition series.

Rhenium exhibits all possible valency states from 0–7, and it is possible that it may also be able to gain an electron to form an anion. It exhibits the general tendency for the higher valent states in a transition element sub-group to become stabilized as the atomic weight increases. Manganese forms no compound in which it is present in a pentavalent state, and the heptavalent oxide $Mn_2O_7$ loses oxygen at $0°$ C, while $Re_2O_7$ may be distilled unchanged at $300°$ C. The heptavalent compounds of rhenium are colourless in contrast to the highly-coloured heptavalent manganese compounds such as $KMnO_4$. Contrariwise, the divalent state of manganese is very much more stable than that of rhenium. The reason for this is by no means certain. It has been said (56) that the stability of divalent manganese is due to the difference between the third and second ionization potentials being greater than is the case with rhenium. Even if this is true in the condensed phase, it is a re-statement of the problem rather than an explanation of the underlying cause.

Rhenium metal itself is rather unreactive. It has the very high melting point of $3180°$ C, second only to tungsten ($3400°$ C). The heptoxide is formed when the metal is heated in air. No true carbide is formed, and carbon has a very limited solubility in rhenium. Phosphides are, however, known.

The heptavalent state is very stable. Perrhenic acid, $HReO_4$, can be formed by dissolving the oxide in water. The potassium salt can be distilled under a pressure of 1 atm at 1370° C (57), whereas $KMnO_4$ begins to lose oxygen when heated above 200° C. The perrhenates of many mono-, di-, and trivalent bases are well known. A series of salts of which there are no manganese analogues, is derived from the hypothetical acid $H_3ReO_5$, *meso*-perrhenic acid, and its solid salts can be made by fusing rhenium metal or $ReO_2$ with an alkali hydroxide in air or alternatively in aqueous solution by adding an excess of base to a solution of normal perrhenate. The salts are yellow, but they turn red when they are heated. If the solid salts are dissolved in neutral water, they are at once hydrolysed to the normal perrhenate.

It was thought for a long time that there were no heptavalent halides of rhenium. This was surprising in view of the tendency of most elements to exhibit their highest valency state in combination with fluorine. However, in 1960, Fried and his colleagues showed that the heptafluoride could readily be prepared by treating $ReF_6$ with fluorine at 400° C, and under several atmospheres pressure (58). They made a detailed examination of the compound, and were able to record its infra-red spectrum. They put forward a number of reasons for supposing that previous reports of the properties of $ReF_6$, between which there were considerable disparities, in fact referred to mixtures of $ReF_6$ and $ReF_7$. The oxyfluoride, $ReO_3F$ may be prepared by acting on the oxychloride with anhydrous HF, followed by sublimation *in vacuo*. It is a yellow solid, melting at 147° C, but it decomposes at 164° C. This low stability is surprising when it is contrasted with that of the other heptavalent compounds of rhenium, but even so, it is considerably more stable than the corresponding manganese compound (59). $ReOF_4$ and $ReO_2F_2$ have also been claimed to exist, but later work has not confirmed this, and has substituted in their place $ReOF_5$ and $ReO_2F_3$ (60).

Oxygen in heptavalent rhenium compounds is readily replaced by sulphur. Hydrogen sulphide converts the perrhenate ion to the thio-perrhenate ($ReO_3S$). The heptasulphide is a black amorphous powder which is not very stable.

The hexavalent state of rhenium resembles that of manganese, but it is somewhat less stable than the latter. The trioxide is prepared by heating the heptoxide with metallic rhenium at 300° C. On further heating, it disproportionates without loss of oxygen (61*a*).

$$3ReO_3 = Re_2O_7 + ReO_2$$

The trioxide does not easily dissolve in the common bases, and rhenates must be prepared by fusion of rhenium dioxide/perrhenate mixtures. In aqueous solution, the green rhenates also readily disproportionate to

Re(vII) and Re(IV). The hexafluoride can be prepared by fluorinating the metal with chlorine trifluoride. The hexachloride has also been prepared, and is thermally stable in an atmosphere of chlorine or nitrogen (61b).

Although examples of the pentavalent state of rhenium are known, they are not very numerous. The sodium salt of the hypothetical hyporhenic acid $HReO_3$ has been made by fusing sodium perrhenate with $ReO_2$ and sodium hydroxide in the absence of air. It was found to be insoluble in water, and it appears to be diamagnetic. Since the $(Re)^{5+}$ ion should be associated with two electrons with unpaired spins, sodium hyporhenate almost certainly has a complex structure. It readily disproportionates to Re(IV) and Re(vII) ions. The pentafluoride was prepared in the course of work designed to prepare carbonyl–rhenium fluorides. When $ReF_6$ was acted on by $WF_6$ and $W(CO)_6$, $ReF_5$ was formed. It was well characterized as a yellow-green solid which melted with some decomposition at 48° C, and which was decomposed by moist air but not by dry air. Disproportionation is complete at the boiling point (240° C) in air or at 180° C *in vacuo* (62).

$$2ReF_5 = ReF_4 + ReF_6$$

When $Re_2O_7$ is heated with chloroform in a sealed tube, $ReCl_5$ is formed (63). When this reacted with bis-cyclo-pentadienyl sodium, it was expected that a compound of the ferrocene type would be formed which would be paramagnetic, but the reaction product was found to be a yellow, crystalline diamagnetic solid which melted at 161° C. It was stable to water, but not to air. Measurements of the nuclear magnetic resonance showed a subsidiary proton peak which had a large chemical shift and this was interpreted as indicating that a diamagnetically shielded proton was directly bound to the rhenium atom. The compound therefore appeared to be bis-cyclo-pentadienylrhenium hydride $(C_5H_5)_2ReH$. It behaved as a base, in that in dilute hydrochloric acid solution it would accept a proton and form the cation $[(C_5H_5)_2ReH_2]^+$. Alkali liberated the original hydride. Salts could be precipitated by large anions such as $[Cr(NH_3)_2(SCN)_4]^-$ (64).

The tetravalent state of rhenium is very stable. $ReS_2$ is the most stable sulphide, and it can be formed by heating the heptasulphide to 350° C *in vacuo*. $ReO_2$ is also stable and it can be prepared by reducing the heptoxide with hydrogen at 300° C. Rhenites can be formed by fusing the dioxide with alkalis. Three series of rhenites are formed in this way, corresponding to the anions $(ReO_3)^{2-}$, $(ReO_4)^{4-}$ and $(ReO_5)^{6-}$ (65).

The tetrafluoride is a pale blue powdery solid which is made by pyrolysis of the pentafluoride at 240° C. It is immediately hydrolysed by water (66). There is no evidence for the existence of $ReCl_4$, but stable complexes of the general formula $M_2(ReX_6)$ are known. The hexachloro-, hexabromo- and hexaiodo- compounds may be prepared by reducing perrhenates in aqueous solution, but the hexafluoro compound must be made in the absence of water. The hexaiodide undergoes a curious reaction; when a 20% aqueous solution is shaken with ether, all the rhenium, $\frac{5}{6}$ of the iodine, but no alkali metal pass into the ethereal phase. The rhenium which is extracted in this way has been shown to be tetravalent, and the reaction is presumably (68)

$$K_2ReI_6 + H_2SO_4 = K_2SO_4 + HI + HReI_5$$

Both the tetrabromide and the tetraiodide have been prepared. The latter has not been made by direct combination of the elements, but by reducing perrhenic acid with hydrogen iodide. On evaporation to dryness, $ReI_4$ remains. It is unstable and slowly loses iodine *in vacuo* even at room temperature, decomposing more rapidly on heating. On heating in a sealed tube at 350° C, the loss of iodine goes only as far as the formation of the tri-iodide; the iodine may be separated by dissolution in carbon tetraiodide in which $ReI_3$ is insoluble. If the tetraiodide is heated to constant weight in a stream of nitrogen, the monoiodide is formed (67). The tetrabromide can be prepared by a method analogous to that used for the tetraiodide, using hydrogen bromide as the reductant. When this compound is heated in oxygen at 100–120° C colourless, volatile perrhenyl bromide is formed, $ReO_3Br$ (69).

No $Re^{3+}$ cation is known, and the trivalent state of rhenium is very readily oxidized. In the anions which have the general formula $[ReX_4]^-$ the trivalent state is to some extent stabilized by the presence of an octet of valency electrons. The oxide $Re_2O_3$ has been prepared by precipitation with alkali hydroxide from a solution containing trivalent rhenium in a complex anion. It is very readily oxidized, and does not appear to be stoicheiometric. The trichloride and the tribromide are formed in disproportionation reactions. Thus, when $Ag_2[ReCl_6]$ is heated, a mixture of $ReCl_5$ and $ReCl_3$ is formed instead of the tetrachloride. The trichloride is left if the pentachloride is distilled away. $ReCl_3$ is not a salt and it may well be $Re_2Cl_6$.

A divalent rhenium ion is formed in solution when, for instance, complex chlorides of tetravalent rhenium disproportionate.

$$5Re(\text{iv}) \longrightarrow 3Re(\text{ii}) + 2Re(\text{vii})$$

The trichloride will dissolve in a solution of sodium cyanide, and it may then be reduced quantitatively to rhenium(i) cyanide with sodium amalgam (69). The cyanide ion has been used by several workers as a ligand with which to stabilize lower valency states of rhenium.

There has been considerable controversy over the question of whether a rhenide ion can exist, that is to say whether rhenium can adopt a $(-1)$ oxidation state. It was reported in 1952 that when potassium perrhenate in solution in ethylenediamine is reduced by potassium, a white solid is produced which contained Re⁻ together with potassium hydroxide (70). In the next year, a crystalline hydrate of Li⁺Re⁻ was reported (71). In 1959, solutions containing the 'rhenide' ion were re-examined using nuclear magnetic resonance methods (72), and the results were interpreted as indicating the presence of a rhenium–hydrogen bond in rhenide solution. The evidence for the existence of the ( − 1) oxidation state of rhenium is as yet by no means conclusive.

The study of the chemistry of rhenium dates from the recognition of its X-ray spectrum in 1925; it had already been predicted by Mendeleef that such an element which he called dvi-manganese was necessary to complete his periodic table. Several claims had also been made for the discovery of the next lighter element in the sub-group, the eka-manganese of Mendeleef. Noddack and Tacke (73) (Fräulein Tacke afterwards became Frau Noddack) considered that they had found evidence for its existence in the same year as that in which they identified rhenium; they named it 'masurium'. Their claim has never been substantiated, and in the light of our present knowledge it is almost certain that they were mistaken. It is probable that very small quantities of this element occur naturally on earth, derived from the spontaneous fission of $^{238}U$, but it is unlikely that any detectable quantity of primordial material remains. The half-life of the most stable known isotope of technetium ($^{98g}Te$) is $2 \cdot 12 \times 10^5$ years, which is short compared with accepted estimates of $10^8$–$10^9$ years for the age of the earth. It is not believed to exist in the sun (74) but its existence has been reported in type $S$ stars (75) and this is of great interest because of the bearing it has on cosmological theories, and theories of stellar processes.

It is now generally accepted that the first separation of the element was carried out by Segré in 1937 (76). His starting material was a plate of molybdenum which had been bombarded in the Berkeley cyclotron for some months with a strong beam of deuterons. Two months after the end of this bombardment, Segré commenced a separation, and isolated tracer quantities of the new element on a rhenium carrier. Milligram quantities of the element became available after 1945 as a by-product of the chemical process by which plutonium was extracted from the fuel elements from nuclear reactors. In 1958 comparatively large-scale production started in the Fission Product Pilot Plant at the Oak Ridge National Laboratory where it was planned to produce 650 g per year of $^{99g}Tc$ which is derived from the meta-stable $^{99m}Tc$, which has a half-life of 6h (77). Technetium is usually separated from the other fission products by precipitation as the sulphide. This is then dissolved in ammoniacal hydrogen peroxide, and the solution evaporated to dryness. The resultant mixture of ammonium pertechnetate and ammonium sulphate is heated at 500–600° C in hydrogen, which reduces the pertechnetate to the metal (78).

Metallic technetium resembles rhenium in many ways. Its structure is based on hexagonal close packing. It may be dissolved in both dilute and concentrated nitric acid, concentrated sulphuric acid and in aqua regia, but it will not dissolve in hydrochloric acid of any strength (79).

The highest oxide of technetium, $Tc_2O_7$, is formed when the metal is burnt in oxygen. It is volatile, as is $Re_2O_7$, but it has a wider liquid range than the latter. It melts at $119 \cdot 5°$ C, and is stable up to $260°$ C. Its crystal structure has a low symmetry, and it is not isomorphous with $Re_2O_7$ (80). $Tc_2O_7$ is a strong oxidizing agent, and it is reduced by organic vapours including that of stop-cock grease. It is soluble in water. If an aqueous solution of $Tc_2O_7$ is evaporated, anhydrous pertechnetic acid separates out as long red-black crystals. Pertechnetic acid is a strong acid, and a number of salts have been isolated; these include ammonium, potassium, caesium and silver pertechnetates. The alkali metal and ammonium salts (which are colourless) are isomorphous with the perrhenates. The phenyl-arsinium and nitron salts are insoluble. The $[TcO_4]^-$ ion is stable over a much wider pH range than is the permangante ion. In neutral aqueous solution it inhibits the corrosion of soft iron. Mild carbon steels can be protected by less than 50 p.p.m. of technetium in the form of pertechnetate ion in aerated distilled water at temperatures up to $250°$ C. The minimum concentration at which protection has been observed corresponds to only $3 \times 10^{12}$ atoms of technetium per square centimetre of metal. No such inhibition of corrosion is conferred by the presence of the perrhenate ion (81).

The corresponding sulphide, $Tc_2S_7$, is precipitated by hydrogen sulphide from 2–4N hydrochloric or sulphuric acid solutions of the metal (82). When $Tc_2S_7$ is heated, it decomposes to amorphous $TcS_2$. Pertechnetyl chloride can be prepared by adding 12M hydrochloric acid to a solution of potassium pertechnetate in 18M sulphuric acid. When the final solution is shaken with carbon tetrachloride, chloroform or hexane, the pertechnetyl compound is extracted into the organic phase (83).

The only stable hexavalent technetium compound which has been prepared is technetium hexafluoride (84). Great difficulty was experienced in preparing any pentavalent compound. $Ag_2(TcCl)_6$ cannot be isolated because the $[TcCl_6]^{2-}$ ion is not stable to hydrolysis and the pentachloride cannot therefore be prepared by an analogous reaction to that in which $ReCl_5$ is prepared by heating $Ag_2[ReCl_6]$. Similarly, although when $Re_2O_7$ is heated with carbon tetrachloride, rhenium pentachloride is formed, the analogous reaction with $Tc_2O_7$ leads to the formation of blood-red $TcCl_4$. There is, however, some evidence that the pentavalent state can be stabilized by the fields of the ligands in complexes. The thiocyanate group probably has this effect (85). This ligand has frequently been used in both manganese and rhenium chemistry to form complexes which are used in the spectrophotometric determination of the elements.

In the presence of the thiocyanate ion, heptavalent rhenium is reduced to the yellow Re( v ) thiocyanato complex; the reduction takes place at a slow rate in 3–5M sulphuric or hydrochloric acid solutions. Heptavalent manganese is more vigorously reduced to Mn( ii ) without any intermediate colour formation. The reaction with heptavalent technetium is more complex than that with either of the other two elements. Several highly-coloured complexes are formed, and the maximum absorption occurs at 5130 ÅU. This behaviour enables technetium to be determined quantitatively in the presence of manganese and rhenium, since the manganese thiocyanate does not absorb in the visible part of the spectrum, and that of rhenium has its maximum absorption peak at 4300 ÅU. Potentiometric titrations seem to indicate that an unstable pentavalent technetium complex is present in the solution, and that this is analogous to the pentavalent rhenium compound. The pentavalent state of technetium may also be stabilized by the ditertiary arsine (86).

$$\text{\chemfig{*6(-(-As(CH_3)_2)(-As(CH_3)_2)----)}}$$

—As(CH$_3$)$_2$
—As(CH$_3$)$_2$

If this ligand is represented by the symbol D, a tervalent technetium compound $[Tc(D)_2Cl_2]ClO_4$ can be prepared which is oxidized by chlorine to a brown compound, which is probably the 8-co-ordinated complex of pentavalent technetium $[Tc(D)_2Cl_4]ClO_4$. A similar reaction takes place with the analogous tervalent rhenium complex.

It does not seem to be possible to prepare the simple tetravalent cations such as $Tc^{4+}$, $[Tc(OH)]^{3+}$, $[TcO]^{2+}$ or $[TcO_2(OH)]^+$ in aqueous solution, and this valency state is only found in complex anions. Solid tetravalent technetium compounds are well known. $TcO_2.2H_2O$ is precipitated from aqueous solution when the pertechnetate ion is reduced with metallic zinc in the presence of hydrochloric acid. The anhydrous oxide may be prepared by the pyrolysis of ammonium pertechnetate. It is similar to $ReO_2$, and, like the latter has the $MoO_2$ structure. It is readily oxidized by oxygen to $Tc_2O_7$. The element resembles manganese rather than rhenium in that $TcCl_4$ is the highest known chloride. Also, unlike rhenium, the tetravalent complex $K_2TcCl_6$ is not stable, and it is readily hydrolysed to $TcO_2$ in aqueous solution. Even in the presence of 3N hydrochloric acid, changes in the optical absorption spectrum occur within 24 hours.

There is no very convincing evidence for the existence of a simple trivalent ion of technetium in solution, although it may exist (37). There is no solid lattice which contains a trivalent technetium ion, such as that found in $Mn_2O_3$. Very stable bi- and trivalent technetium complexes can be made with the ditertiary arsine to which reference has been made above, and these complexes are similar to those formed by rhenium. The rhenium complexes were prepared first (88) and the analogous technetium compounds were shortly afterwards prepared on the 15-mg scale (89). The general formulae of these compounds are stated to be

$$[M(\text{ii})D_2X_2]$$
$$[M(\text{iii})D_2X_2]ClO_4$$

where $M(\text{ii})$ and $M(\text{iii})$ represent respectively bi- and trivalent rhenium or technetium and X represents chlorine, bromine or iodine.

It was not found possible to carry out a complete analysis of the technetium compounds, and they were characterized on the basis of their chemical reactions:

(i) The amount of less electronegative halogen which could enter the compound and the amount of more electronegative halogen which was thereby displaced were measured.

(ii) Exactly one equivalent of iodine was absorbed in the reaction which was formulated as

$$[Tc(\text{ii})D_2I_2] \longrightarrow [Tc(\text{iii})D_2I_2]I$$

In addition, the X-ray diffraction photographs of $[TcD_2I_2]$ and $[ReD_2I_2]$ were found to be very similar. Confirmatory evidence was also forthcoming from conductivity, molecular weight and magnetic measurements. This is a good example of the way in which the composition of a compound may be inferred from its chemical reactions and its physical properties. A 'classical chemist' may however reasonably feel that composition has not been rigidly established until an analysis by classical methods has been carried out. Too little attention has so far generally been paid to the extent to which deductive methods of the determination of the composition of compounds can take the place of older methods.

The evidence for the existence of the $Tc^-$ ion is even less convincing than is that for the $Rh^-$ ion; it is derived from a study of the polarographic reduction of potassium pertechnetate (90).

As would be expected from its position in the periodic table, technetium resembles manganese in some ways, and rhenium in others. Its greatest similarities to manganese are found in the lower valency states. Considerable further work must be done before a satisfactory explanation can be given of all the differences in chemical behaviour exhibited by these three elements.

The third group of $d$-type transition elements which will be discussed is that in which the incomplete sub-shell is nearly filled. The elements in this category are usually described as being grouped in 'triads'. They include the iron group of elements, and the noble elements which resemble platinum. The chemical properties of the elements in each triad are similar, but the differences between them are more marked than is often supposed. This will be illustrated by considering the properties of two elements of neighbouring atomic number, ruthenium and rhodium. Each of these metals occurs in the earth's crust to about the same extent as osmium or iridium.

Ruthenium is not oxidized in the air in the cold, but it combines with oxygen on heating more readily than any other of the platinum group of metals except osmium. The solid chemistry of ruthenium compounds is not known with certainty, but it is possible that a hydride, carbide and nitride are formed. It has been reported that a phosphide is formed by heating ruthenium to 1000° C under a pressure of one atmosphere of phosphorus vapour (91). It forms a tetroxide $RuO_4$ which is similar to osmium tetroxide, although it is less stable than the latter.

The perruthenates in which the element is heptavalent have been identified spectrophotometrically in aqueous solution (92). These in many ways resemble the permanganates, pertechnetates and perrhenates, but the eighth group element has one more electron than do the latter. Complexes in which ruthenium is hexavalent are known. The ammonium 'salt' is probably a neutral complex $[RuO_2(NH_3)_2(OH_2)]$. No simple salts of the $[RuO_2]^{2+}$ cation have been isolated, and when $RuO_4$ is reduced in sulphuric acid solution it is probable that the anionic complex $[RuO_2(SO_4)_2]^{2-}$ is formed.

$RuF_6$ has recently been prepared by heating ruthenium powder in fluorine at a pressure of 300 mm. of mercury (93). It is necessary to carry out the reaction in a vessel which has a cold finger close to the heated zone, on which the volatile product may be condensed. The vapour density corresponds to the formula $RuF_6$, but chemical analysis shows a deficiency of ruthenium; this may possibly be due to volatilization of $RuO_4$ during the analysis. Both the X-ray diffraction pattern and the infra-red spectrum are similar to those of the other hexafluorides. It attacks pyrex glass rapidly, but it is reasonably stable in quartz. It decomposes at 200° C:

$$2RuF_6 = 2RuF_5 + F_2$$

It is because of this decomposition at a relatively low temperature that it is necessary to condense the product on the cold finger immediately after its formation.

A better method of preparing $RuF_5$ is by first reacting the metal with $BrF_3$. This takes place violently (94). After removal of the excess $BrF_3$ *in vacuo*, creamy-white $RuBrF_8$ remains, which melts at 120° C to give $BrF_3$ and emerald-green droplets of $RuF_5$ which does not appear to attack dry glass. Ruff and Vidic (95) had claimed the preparation of $RuF_5$ in 1925 by the action of fluorine on ruthenium metal. In spite of the doubt which has been cast on much of the early work on binary fluorine compounds, it does seem possible that the claim of these workers was justified, particularly in view of the decomposition of $RuF_6$ at 200° C. $RuBrF_8$ is presumably $[BrF_2]^+[RuF_6]^-$. It reacts with $KBrF_4$ to give $KRuF_6$ and $BrF_3$. Thallous ruthenium hexafluoride can be made by mixing solutions of thallous fluoride and ruthenium pentafluoride in solution in selenium tetrafluoride. Other salts of the $[RuF_6]^-$ anion have been made, notably those of calcium, silver, strontium and barium, and they are all stable in dry air. Such salts do not appear to be formed with cations which have a radius less than 0·99 ÅU.

The very stable oxide $RuO_2$ is seldom stoicheiometric; it is formed when the metal is heated in oxygen. The slight blue colour which is sometimes observed may indicate the presence of some trivalent ruthenium. A hydrated dioxide of uncertain composition is also formed. No simple binary tetravalent halides are known, although the hydrated compounds $RuCl_4 . 5H_2O$ and $Ru(OH)Cl_3$ have been prepared. The direct action of halogens on $RuO_2$ leads to the formation of trivalent halides.

The trivalent state of ruthenium is the most stable, but again, simple salts are not known. $Ru(OH)_3$ can be precipitated by alkalis from trivalent ruthenium solutions, but it is easily oxidized to the hydrated dioxide. The solution chemistry of the trivalent state is notable for the very large number of stable complexes which are formed. The solid trivalent halides can be readily obtained; the trichloride, for example, is formed when the metal reacts with chlorine at 450° C.

The 6-covalent divalent complexes are extremely stable. They are generally formed with ligands such as $[CN]^-$ and $[NH_2]$ with which ruthenium can form Ru—N bonds. These complexes are diamagnetic. Solid RuO is not known. It has been suggested that the apparently tetravalent ruthenium chalcogenides $RuS_2$, $RuSe_2$ and $RuTe_2$ which have a pyrites structure, are compounds of divalent ruthenium with S—S, Se—Se and Te—Te bonds respectively. The existence of monovalent ruthenium compounds is not certain.

No attempt has been made in this brief outline to describe the complex solution chemistry of ruthenium. This has been extensively investigated because of its great technological importance. Radio-activity which is due to an isotope of ruthenium is a major constituent of the fission products formed in a nuclear reactor. Since the complexes can exist in a number of valency states, it is extremely difficult to separate the element from the desired plutonium in a solution chemical separation process. The 'ruthenium separation problem' was one of the major difficulties which had to be solved by the chemists working on the atomic energy programmes.

Rhodium metal is considerably more inert than ruthenium. Rhodium plating is increasingly used as a protection for ferrous metals in corrosive atmospheres. Rhodium absorbs some oxygen when it is heated, but it does not absorb hydrogen or nitrogen; carbon is slightly soluble in the molten metal, but graphite separates out when the melt is cooled. If the metal is strongly heated in air to 600–1000° C, the trivalent oxide $Rh_2O_3$ is formed, and the metal is soluble in this to a limited extent. The rhodium/sulphur system has been investigated in detail (96). Direct combination of the elements leads to the stable phases $Rh_2S_5$, $Rh_2S_3$, $Rh_3S_4$ and $Rh_9S_8$. The halides have been little investigated, but it is known that although platinum reacts rather rapidly with fluorine at 500° C rhodium is comparatively inert.

The sulphate $Rh_2(SO_4)_3$ may be obtained by fusing the metal with potassium bisulphate. A number of trivalent complexes are well known; $[Rh(CN)_6]^{3-}$ is particularly stable. Ammine and thiocyanate complexes have been studied, and complex halides of general formula $M_3[RhX_6]$ are well established.

The known chemistry of rhodium is considerably less complex than that of its congener ruthenium. This illustrates the very marked chemical differences between ostensibly similar members of the triads of transition elements in group VIII of the periodic table.

With the exception of technetium, all the elements which have been described so far have stable isotopes. A number of elements exist, of which all the known isotopes are radio-active, and of which it is virtually certain that there are no stable isotopes. The need for the protection of those working with such isotopes from the emitted radiation considerably complicates the experimental work. The nature of these precautions, the connexion of many of these elements with the utilization of atomic energy, and the secrecy which veils many of the established experimental facts, has overshadowed the great interest of their basic chemistry. This must be regretted, because the chemistry of these elements is an integral part of our understanding of chemical processes as a whole. In the following paragraphs, some of the more important points in their chemistry are reviewed; specifically radio-chemical reactions are not discussed except where these affect the 'normal' chemistry of the elements. It is important to remember that the information about the reactions of these elements and about the stability of their compounds does not differ in degree or kind from the similar information about more familiar elements with stable isotopes, and it must be fitted into, and used to throw more light upon, the general picture of chemical behaviour.

In spite of various claims to have isolated them, four elements with atomic numbers lower than that of uranium were still not definitely identified by the end of 1936. The isolation of the Group VII element, technetium has already been described. The 'Missing' rare earth, promethium, was isolated in weighable quantities in 1948 (97), and it was found to have all the chemical properties of a 'typical' rare earth. The remaining two elements, the heaviest halogen which we now know as astatine, and the heaviest alkali metal francium, had by that time been identified in the fission products from nuclear reactions, and had been produced in specific bombardment experiments in 1940 (98) and in 1939 (99) respectively.

Francium has hardly been studied except by Perey (100). It appears to have no properties which would not be expected from the next heaviest alkali metal above caesium with which it will co-precipitate as the perchlorate, chloroplatinate, silicotungstate or chlorostannate. Astatine, on the other hand, has been studied by a number of workers. About twenty isotopes are known, of which eighteen are well characterized. It has been identified in natural material in which it is formed in the beta-branching decay of $^{218}Po$, whereby for every two thousand atoms of polonium which decay, one atom of astatine is produced; the difficulty of detecting this is increased by the fact that it has only a 2-sec half-life (101). The total amount of astatine in the earth's crust has been estimated to be less than one ounce (102). As is to be expected, the chemistry of astatine closely resembles that of iodine. The element can exist in at least four oxidation states. In solution it can be reduced by strong agents such as sulphur dioxide or zinc and hydrochloric acid to what is probably the astatide ion; this will co-precipitate with silver chloride. In the elementary state, it is volatile, and it will extract into organic solvents. Strong oxidizing agents will oxidize it to an ion which is probably the astatate $(AtO_3)^-$. Weaker oxidising agents convert it to an intermediate state (103). No trace of the heptavalent state has been found. Later workers who tried to prepare this valency state found only the astatate ion and also an uncharacterized lower state (104). If astatine is oxidized with chlorine in 6M hydrochloric acid, a chloro-complex results. This is probably either $[AtCl_2]^-$ or $[AtCl_4]^-$. Whatever the species, it is found to extract into isopropyl ether, but not into benzene or carbon tetrachloride in which both $[ICl_2]^-$ and $[ICl_4]^-$ are also insoluble. Acidic solutions which presumably contain HAtO react with phenol to yield astatophenol which is analogous to iodophenol (105).

The absence of the heptavalent state may be more apparent than real. It is possible that in aqueous solution, such a state is at once reduced by the species which result from the decomposition of water under the influence of the intense radiation. $^{211}At$ is the astatine isotope with the longest half-life. This is only 7·5 h and although 40% of the nuclei decay to the long lived $^{207}Bi$, 60% decay by orbital electron capture to $^{211}Po$ which has a short half-life and a considerable decomposing effect on water.

The final transition series among the known elements is formally considered to start at actinium. This series is of considerable chemical interest because of the way in which the electrons are distributed among the unfilled shells, and of the effect which this has upon the chemical properties of the actinide elements. In passing from an element to its neighbour of higher atomic number, the energetically preferred level for the additional electron might be the 6d, on the analogy of the way in which electrons enter the 5d level in passing from hafnium to gold, or it might be the 5f on the analogy of the '4f transition series'—the rare earths from lanthanium to lutecium. As is so often the case in chemistry, when problems of this type arise, the answer to the question 'Which' seems to be 'Both!', at least in the lower members of the series. It has already been pointed out that the energy separations of the 5f and 6d levels are so small that changes in environment such as the difference in energy due to the crystal field in various compounds are sufficient for the electrons to occupy different levels in different states of the same element. There is no doubt that in compounds of elements of higher atomic number than actinium, the 5f level is sometimes occupied; there was at one time considerable disagreement as to the element at which the 5f level could be at least formally considered to be energetically available. It is now generally considered that actinium is the first member of the transition series, and that the actinide series may in some respects be regarded as an analogue of the lanthanide series.

| Number of 'f' electrons | ELEMENT | |
|:---:|:---:|:---:|
| | Lanthanides | Actinides |
| 0 | Lanthanum | Actinium |
| 1 | Cerium | Thorium |
| 2 | Praseodymium | Protactinium |
| 3 | Neodymium | Uranium |
| 4 | Promethium | Neptunium |
| 5 | Samarium | Plutonium |
| 6 | Europium | Americium |
| 7 | Gadolinium | Curium |
| 8 | Terbium | Berkelium |

The analogy must not be pursued too far. The elements in the actinide series from actinium to americium sometimes resemble a 'd' transition series more than they resemble the lanthanides, which exhibit few valency states other than the trivalent. It is not therefore surprising that the principal similarities occur when the trivalent ions of the two series are eluted from a cation exchange resin, e.g. Dowex 50 with, for example, ammonium α-hydroxy isobutyrate. In each case, the shape of the elution curves is similar, and it is most striking that there is a change in the elution behaviour at the point where the f shell is in each case presumed to be half-filled, that is to say between gadolinium and terbium, and between curium and berkelium. It should also be noted that the series of trivalent ions exhibits an 'actinide contraction' which is similar to the 'lanthanide contraction'.

Most of the evidence for the progressive filling of the $5f$ shell in the actinide series is derived from physical measurements. On the basis of the actinide theory, it can be calculated that the absorption spectra of the successive elements should show an increasing number of bands as the number of electrons in the $5f$ level increases from 1–5, and reach a maximum at $f^6$ and also at $f^8$, there being a slight decrease in the number at $f^7$. This has been found to be the case. The magnetic susceptibility data have been discussed in an earlier chapter, and the similarity between the susceptibility curves of $Sm^{3+}$ and $Pu^{3+}$ has been noted. Measurements of the paramagnetic resonance of certain compounds also confirms the distribution of $f$ electrons set out in the table above. From such measurements, the two Landé splitting factors have been calculated for hexavalent plutonium in $R_6[PuO_2(NO_3)_3]$. The values

$$
\begin{array}{ll}
g_{\parallel} & 5 \cdot 32 \\
g_{\perp} & 0
\end{array}
$$

were found. The calculated values for a $5f^2$ configuration are $\sim 6$ and $0$ respectively, while the presence of $d$ electrons would limit $g_{\parallel}$ to a value slightly greater than 3 (106). If $Am^{3+}$ has a $5f^6$ configuration, there should be no paramagnetic resonance lines. After a prolonged search, none were observed in the resonance spectrum from $Am_2Mg_3(NO_3)_{12}2H_2O$(107).

Apart from the rather qualitative evidence noted above concerning the observed number of lines in the absorption spectra of the individual actinides, there have been several detailed examinations of such spectra. From these measurements, information can be derived about the ground or other low-lying states of the gaseous elements and their ions. For instance, the following configurations have been derived for gaseous actinium in its first three oxidation states (108).

$$
\begin{array}{lll}
Ac^{\circ} & 6d7s^2 & (^2D) \\
Ac^+ & 7s^2 & (^1S) \\
Ac^{2+} & 7s & (^2S)
\end{array}
$$

Thorium is the lightest element in which a $5f$ state has been detected by this means. $Th^{\circ}$ was found to have the configuration $6d^27s^2(^3F_2)$ and the lowest states of $Th^+$ were distributed between $6d7s_7^2$, $6d^27s$ and $6d^3$ levels; however two prominent fairly low-lying states of this gaseous ion were found to be $5f7s^2$ and $5f6d7s$ (109). The energies of the possible electronic levels appear to be very similar. In $Th^{3+}$, the separation of the levels is particularly small, and as the degree of ionization increases, the $5f$ levels become the preferred ones. In passing up the actinide series, the $5f$ states predominate by the time americium is reached ($5f^7$). One of the most interesting aspects of the preparation of elements of higher atomic weight than those already known is the question of which electronic levels are occupied when the $5f$ level is full. This should occur at element 103, and the configuration of element 104 would be of great importance.

The 'parent' of the actinide series, actinium, is the element which is chemically most similar to its lanthanide analogue. The most stable isotope is $^{227}$Ac which has a half-life of twenty two years, and which can be obtained by the neutron bombardment of radium:

$$^{226}\text{Ra}(n,\gamma)\,^{227}\text{Ra} \xrightarrow{\;\beta-\;} {}^{227}\text{Ac}\begin{pmatrix} 98\cdot8\%\,\beta \\ 1\cdot2\%\,\alpha \end{pmatrix}$$

Milligram quantities of this isotope have been used to study the chemistry of the element, but this work has been difficult, not so much because of the comparatively short half-life of the element itself, but rather because of the strong gamma rays emitted by its daughters in the decay series. Enough is known of its chemistry to demonstrate its great similarity to lanthanum. Like lanthanum, the metal is very reactive, and in moist air it rapidly becomes covered with a protective coating of white oxide. The element is invariably trivalent in all its known compounds, and those which have been studied in the solid state have been found to have the same structure as the corresponding lanthanum compounds. The hydroxide, fluoride, oxalate, carbonate and phosphate are insoluble in water; this behaviour resembles that of the lanthanide element compounds. The fluoride and the chloride have been prepared from the hydroxide, by the action on it of hydrogen fluoride and of carbon tetrachloride respectively. The bromide has been prepared by the action of aluminium tribromide on the oxide $Ac_2O_3$, and the sulphide similarly by the action of hydrogen sulphide.

The second member of the actinide series, thorium, shows little resemblance to cerium. Thorium is almost invariably tetravalent, and in many respects it behaves like a Group IV typical element rather than as a member of a transition series. The metal is very reactive, and it can only be prepared from the oxide $ThO_2$ by very vigorous reduction such as by heating the oxide to a high temperature with a large excess of calcium in a flux of fused calcium chloride (110). The metal will combine with oxygen to form $ThO_2$ at 250° C (111). It reacts readily with nitrogen and with hydrogen. It is not easily attacked by mineral acids such as dilute hydrofluoric, nitric and sulphuric or concentrated phosphoric, and perchloric or concentrated nitric acid renders it passive.

The dioxide is extremely stable, and there is very little information available about non-stoicheiometric compounds with a lower oxygen to thorium ratio that 2 : 1. By way of contrast, the thorium–hydrogen system is extremely complex. Reactions with hydrogen causes the complete disintegration of the structure of the massive metal. Two phases, $ThH_2$ and

11

$Th_4H_{15}$ have been identified. The hydrides are useful starting points for the preparation of other thorium compounds. The boride which has been best characterized is $ThB_4$, but a phase of composition $ThB_6$ may exist. The highest carbide is $ThC_2$. Thorium metal forms a complete series of solid solutions with the lower carbide ThC. The tetravalent halides are white solids; apart from interstitial compounds, the element appears only to be capable of a valency of less than four in the iodide system. $ThI_3$ and $ThI_2$ have been reported, and their crystal structure has been determined by X-ray diffraction methods (112). In aqueous solution, the highly charged $Th^{4+}$ cation readily forms polynuclear complexes, but many thorium salts are insoluble.

There is thus little tendency for a single electron in thorium to occupy a stable non-bonding $f$-orbital. Nor does the next higher element, protactinium show much tendency towards variable valency; much less is, however, known of its chemistry than of that of its neighbours uranium and thorium. Protactinium is found in nature as a decay product of natural $^{235}U$ with which it occurs to the extent of 0·34 p.p.m., and from which its separation by chemical means is difficult. This isotope is a rather long-lived alpha-emitter with a half-life of $3·43 \times 10^4$ years which is about half as long again as that of $^{239}Pu$. Since protactinium does not have the technological importance of plutonium, and large quantities of the element are not readily available, little work has been carried out even with gramme quantities of the element, and most of the results have been obtained with samples of about 0·1 mg. It is not easy to carry out accurate chemical analyses on this scale, and most of its compounds have been characterized in other ways. The element has been obtained by the neutron irradiation of $^{230}Th$:

$$^{230}Th(n,\gamma)\,^{231}Th \xrightarrow[25·6h]{\beta^-} {}^{231}Pa$$

Protactinium metal has been obtained in 50-$\mu$g globules by reducing the tetrafluoride with barium. Zachariasen (113) states that the crystal structure of the metal in this form is a unique tetragonal system, and he interprets other observed reflections in the X-ray diffraction photographs as being due to the phases PaO and $PaO_2$. Since these phases may occur in the metal samples which have been studied, observations of their physical properties must be treated with reserve. It is, however, stated to be malleable and about as hard as uranium. In contrast to thorium, protactinium forms a trivalent hydride, $PaH_3$; this resembles uranium hydride $UH_3$ which is discussed below. In all its other known compounds, protactinium appears to exhibit only the valencies 4 and 5. The most stable oxide is $Pa_2O_5$, and at 1500° C this can be reduced by hydrogen to $PaO_2$. The higher oxide is white, and the lower black, and a range of stable oxides exists with intermediate compositions. The fluoride is not very volatile; it may be made by the action of gaseous hydrogen fluoride on $PaO_2$. Little is known about the pentavalent halides; a compound has been prepared which could be either $PaOF_3$ or $PaF_5$; $PaCl_5$ may also have been prepared.

As is the case with thorium, the solution chemistry is dominated by the strong polarizing effect of the simple cation $Pa^{5+}$ which cannot exist in appreciable quantity in solution without being highly complexed. The $[PaO_2]^+$ cation may exist in a highly hydrated state. Information about the solution chemistry of protactinium is chiefly derived from chromatographic experiments (114), and from deductions from the ultra-violet spectrum of protactinium solutions (115). In aqueous solutions of hydrofluoric acid, protactinium occurs in anionic complexes at any acidity. In aqueous solutions of mineral acids such as hydrochloric, it is in the form of hydrolysed cations at low acidities, and anionic complexes at high acidities. When the mineral acid is non-complexing, for example perchloric, the element is present in cationic complexes at any acidity. In solutions of complexing mineral acids of medium acidity, anionic complexes, neutral forms, and cationic complexes may be in equilibrium. In addition to the true complex ions, there is a tendency for colloid formation to take place at low acidities. A strong persistent band is found in the ultra-violet spectrum of such solutions in aqueous hydrochloric or sulphuric acid. Its wave-length is 2100–2150 ÅU, and it is considered that this originates in a $[PaO]^{3+}$ grouping which becomes hydrolysed in such a way that chains are formed.

$$\ldots\;-O-\underset{\overset{\displaystyle |}{\underset{\displaystyle \vdots}{O}\;\overset{\displaystyle \diagdown}{OH}}}{\overset{\overset{\displaystyle OH}{\diagup}}{Pa}}-O-\underset{\overset{\displaystyle |}{\underset{\displaystyle \vdots}{O}\;\overset{\displaystyle \diagdown}{OH}}}{\overset{\overset{\displaystyle OH}{\diagup}}{Pa}}-O-\underset{\overset{\displaystyle |}{\underset{\displaystyle \vdots}{O}\;\overset{\displaystyle \diagdown}{OH}}}{\overset{\overset{\displaystyle OH}{\diagup}}{Pa}}-O-\;\ldots$$

A non-complexing mineral acid may break some of these Pa—O bonds to form

$$\left[\begin{matrix}O\\ \parallel\\ Pa-O-Pa \diagup^{OH}_{\diagdown OH}\\ \parallel\\ O\end{matrix}\right]^{2+}$$

but a complexing acid such as hydrochloric may cause at least one hydroxyl group to be replaced:

$$\left[\begin{matrix}O\\ \parallel\\ Pa-O-Pa \diagup^{Cl}_{\diagdown OH}\\ \parallel\\ O\end{matrix}\right]^{2+}$$

Such a reaction is consonant with the observation that the intensity of the absorption band in such circumstances becomes weaker with time. At higher acidities the $[PaOCl]^{2+}$ cation may be formed. Further complexing may then take place with the formation of $[PaOCl_x]^{(x-3)-}$ and

$[PaCl_y]^{(y-5)-}$. Various observations confirm this possibility (116). The attainment of equilibrium between these various ionic species will probably be a slow process, and this may explain many of the contradictory statements which have been made about the solution chemistry of protactinium(v).

In protactinium(iv) solutions, no ultra-violet absorption band has been observed in the wave-length range between 2100 and 2150 ÅV. If the interpretation of the Pa(v) spectrum is correct, the absence of these bands in Pa(iv) solutions may indicate that in this state no Pa—O bonds are formed. The bands which have been observed correspond to the calculated energy change for the $5f$–$6d$ transition, and in solutions of Pa(iv) protactinium may be behaving as a true $f$-transition series element. Such solutions are stable in the absence of oxygen, and the absorption spectrum is similar to that of trivalent cerium solutions (117).

Transition behaviour is well established in the next three elements. There is little doubt that in many of their compounds one or more electrons occupy the $5f$ level, but the elements resemble those in a $d$-transition series rather than an $f$ one. Stable compounds of various valency states of each element can be prepared, and there is little evidence of a highly-preferred $f$ electronic state as is the case with their lanthanide analogues, neodymium, promethium and samarium. Much is known of the chemistry of all three of these actinides. Although neptunium (118) and plutonium (119) were recognized as recently as 1940 the technological needs of the nuclear energy programmes have caused a vast quantity of research into their physical and chemical properties to be carried out. A large number of isotopes of these elements have been identified. The most common naturally occurring isotopes of uranium are $^{235}U$ and $^{239}U$. The longest lived isotope of neptunium is $^{237}Np$ ($2 \cdot 2 \times 10^6$ years) and that of plutonium is $^{239}Pu$ ($2 \cdot 436 \times 10^4$ years). In the following paragraphs certain aspects of the chemistry of neptunium and plutonium are briefly reviewed, and their compounds are compared with those of uranium where points of particular interest arise.

All three elements are silvery-white metals which tarnish rapidly on exposure to air. Neptunium has two or three allotropic forms, and melts at 648° C. There are six known allotropes of plutonium. The $\delta$ and $\delta^-$ phases which are stable in the temperature range 319–477° C have negative coefficients of expansion; that is to say, they contract on heating and expand on cooling. This has led to considerable difficulties when it has been necessary to cast plutonium billets to close dimensional tolerances. The stable oxide of plutonium is $PuO_2$, and this is formed when many compounds of plutonium are heated in air; these include the hydroxide, oxalate and nitrate. If the ignition is carried out above 1200° C, the compound $PuO_2$ is stoicheiometric, but ignition at lower temperatures results in the formation of oxides of variable composition between $Pu_{2.00}$ and $Pu_{2.09}$. There are no higher oxides, but there is a lower phase which is stable within the composition range $Pu_2O_3$–$Pu_4O_7$. This is usually described as $Pu_2O_3$ but it does not resemble the $M_2O_3$ series of oxides formed by the lanthanides, and is semi-metallic. It normally occurs in a hexagonal form, but a body-centred cubic lattice has also been identified. A monoxide PuO may exist, but it is probably an interstitial compound or a solution of oxygen in the metal.

Uranium has a much wider range of true oxides. The system is very complex, although it has now been worked out in detail (120). There are three stoicheiometric oxides, $UO_2$, $U_3O_8$ and $UO_3$. UO has been reported, but the $U/UO_2$ portion of the phase diagram is probably heterogeneous. The stoicheiometric compounds may be regarded as the limiting compositions of phases in which the proportion of uranium to oxygen can vary within wide limits. $UO_2$ has a fluorite structure, and as oxygen atoms are added to the lattice, this structure persists up to a limiting composition $UO_{2.25}(U_4O_9)$. At higher temperatures, homogeneous phases in this region of composition disproportionate to two cubic structures $UO_2$ and $U_4O_9$. Above the composition $U_4O_9$, there is a gradual change to tetragonal symmetry which persists up to a composition $UO_{2.40}$. The lower limit of the $U_3O_8$ or $UO_{2.67}$ phase is $UO_{2.56}$ at high temperatures, and $UO_{2.64}$ at room temperature. Between $UO_{2.40}$ and these limiting compositions, the system is heterogeneous. From $U_3O_8$ to $UO_3$ it may be homogeneous.

The oxides of neptunium form a series intermediate between that formed by uranium and by plutonium. Both $NpO_2$ and $Np_3O_8$ are stable, but no $NpO_3$ is known. Intermediate phases may exist, but they have not been extensively investigated.

All three metals form hydrides. $UH_3$ has a variable composition over a small range of U : H ratios. Little is known about neptunium hydrides except that they appear to vary in composition from $NpH_{3.6}$ to $NpH_{3.8}$. The plutonium/hydrogen system differs from that of uranium and of neptunium. The metal reacts with hydrogen between 150 and 200° C to produce a grey substance of metallic appearance which has the composition $PuH_{2.7}$. This may be $PuH_2$ together with absorbed hydrogen. $PuH_3$ is not stable in air at normal temperatures and pressures, and a greater hydrogen/plutonium ratio than 2·7 : 1 can only be obtained under high partial pressures of hydrogen. $PuH_2$ appears to have a fluorite structure; this changes to the cubic form as more hydrogen is introduced into the lattice. At a composition of $PuH_{2.75}$, the structure begins to change to the hexagonal $PuH_3$. $PuH_{2.7}$ is stable in air, while $PuH_3$ is in equilibrium with a partial pressure of hydrogen equivalent to 350 mm of Hg at room temperature (121).

There are also differences between the carbides of the three elements.

Uranium forms three carbides. UC and $UC_2$ can be made by the following reactions:

$$U + CH_4 \xrightarrow{\phantom{xx}625-900°C\phantom{xx}} UC + 2H_2$$

$$U + 2C \xrightarrow{\phantom{xx}2400°C\phantom{xx}} UC_2$$

These two carbides form a complete range of solid solutions. The third carbide $U_2C_3$ cannot be made by simply heating together a mixture of the two elements; if this is done, an equimolecular mixture of the first two carbides is formed. However, the sesquicarbide is formed from this mixture if it is heated *in vacuo* to a temperature of 1250–1800° C (122). There is only one carbide of neptunium known, $NpC_2$. This is formed if the oxide $NpO_2$ is heated in a graphite crucible at 2660–2800° C. The plutonium carbides were originally reported solely on the basis of X-ray diffraction data, and they appeared to be PuC (123) and $Pu_2C_3$ (124). It is now known that they can be prepared by the following reactions:

$$Pu + C \xrightarrow{\phantom{xx}1800°C\phantom{xx}} PuC$$

$$PuO_2 + 3C \xrightarrow{\phantom{xx}1800°C\phantom{xx}} PuC + 2CO$$

$$2PuO_2 + 7C \xrightarrow{\phantom{xx}1850°C\phantom{xx}} Pu_2C_3 + 4CO$$

PuC melts at 1850° C, and is said to be reactive and easily hydrolysed; $Pu_2C_3$ melts at 1900° C.

When uranium is heated in an atmosphere of nitrogen, a mixture of nitrides is formed. The best defined phases in the resultant mixture are $U_2N_3$ and $UN_2$. If the mixture is heated to 1300°, UN is formed. All three uranium nitrides are stable, and do not react readily with hydrogen. NpN can be prepared by the action of ammonia on neptunium hydride at 800° C, and is also unattacked by water. The plutonium/nitrogen system differs from that of uranium and neptunium. When the metal is heated in an atmosphere of nitrogen, PuN is formed, but only a surface coating is formed on the massive metal at 800–1000°C. However, if the finely divided hydride is acted on by nitrogen at 230°C, it is all converted to the black mononitride. Unlike the uranium and neptunium nitrides, this is readily hydrolysed, and turns brown after a few days' exposure to the atmosphere. It dissolves in mineral acids, and the plutonium is converted to the insoluble hydrated oxide, while the nitrogen is converted quantitatively to the ammonium ion (125).

The difference in behaviour of these three elements in combination with hydrogen, carbon and nitrogen has not been adequately explained. The great differences between the systems is surprising, because in many ways the binary compounds of the elements resemble each other closely. The halides, for instance, are generally very similar. In each case, the elements exhibit their highest valency in combination with fluorine, and the number of halides formed decreases from uranium to plutonium. The latter resembles the lanthanide elements more than do uranium and neptunium, and the only chloride, bromide and iodide formed by plutonium are trivalent. The complete range of known halides of these elements is as follows.

| | | | | | | | |
|---|---|---|---|---|---|---|---|
| $UF_3$ | $UF_4$ | $UF_5$ | $UF_6$ | $UCl_3$ | $UCl_4$ | $UCl_5$ | $UCl_6$ |
| $NpF_3$ | $NpF_4$ | | $NpF_6$ | $NpCl_3$ | $NpCl_4$ | | |
| $PuF_3$ | $PuF_4$ | | $PuF_6$ | $PuCl_3$ | | | |

| | | | | |
|---|---|---|---|---|
| $UBr_3$ | $UBr_4$ | $UBr_5(?)$ (126) | $UI_3$ | $UI_4$ |
| $NpBr_3$ | $NpBr_4$ | | $NpI_3$ | |
| $PuBr_3$ | | | $PuI_3$ | |

The tri- and tetra-fluorides are insoluble in water, although they can be hydrolysed by steam. The remaining compounds are excessively hygroscopic, and they are extremely difficult to handle. The hexafluorides are volatile, and they are readily hydrolysed to the $(MO_2)F_2$ compounds with the production of hydrogen fluoride. $PuF_6$ is very volatile, but it is a comparatively stable compound and does not attack dry glass. If the slightest trace of moisture is present, hydrolysis of all the material rapidly takes place by a series of reactions, similar to that which occurs with all hexafluorides in similar circumstances.

$$PuF_6 + 2H_2O \longrightarrow PuO_2F_2 + 4HF$$
$$4HF + SiO_2 \longrightarrow SiF_4 + 2H_2O$$
$$2H_2O + PuF_6 \longrightarrow PuO_2F_2 + 4HF$$
$$\text{etc.}$$

The alpha-particles emitted by plutonium rupture the Pu—F bonds in $PuF_6$ and the compound slowly decomposes from this cause; the rate of decomposition is 1–2% per day, and fluorine and lower fluorides are produced.

As would be expected, plutonium is less stable in the 6 + oxidation state than are uranium and plutonium. For example $BrF_3$ will convert $UF_4$ to $UF_6$ but it is oxidized by $PuF_6$ to $BrF_5$ (127). Oxygen will oxidize $UF_4$ readily to $UF_6$ at 600–900° C

$$2UF_4 + O_2 \longrightarrow UO_2F_2 + UF_6$$

but it does not seem to be possible to prepare $PuF_6$ in this way (128). The hexafluorides are usually prepared by the action of fluorine on the oxides or on the lower fluorides at 500–700° C. The colour of hexafluorides deepens as the atomic number increases; $UF_6$ is white, $NpF_6$ is orange and $PuF_6$ chocolate-brown.

The trifluorides can be prepared by acting on the oxides with hydrogen fluoride in the presence of hydrogen; in the presence of oxygen the oxides or trifluorides are converted by hydrogen fluoride to the tetrafluorides. The fluorides are useful intermediaries in the preparation of the metals.

$$2Ba + NpF_4 \longrightarrow 2BaF_2 + Np$$
$$3Ca + 2PuF_3 \longrightarrow 3CaF_2 + 2Pu$$

These reductions take place around 1200° C. The trichlorides can be made by the action of carbon tetrachloride on the oxides, and the tribromides and tri-iodides by the action of hydrogen bromide and hydrogen iodide respectively at temperatures in the range 300–600° C.

In aqueous solution, the elements can exist in the 3, 4, 5 or 6 valency state. Since in many cases ions can co-exist in more than one valency state in the same solution, the solution chemistry is not straightforward. The most stable uranium ion is the uranyl ion $[UO_2]^{2+}$ while neptunium is most stable in the pentavalent state $[NpO_2]^+$, at least in molar solutions of hydrochloric or perchloric acid. At higher acidities it disproportionates (129).

$$2[NpO_2]^+ + 4H^+ = Np^{4+} + [NpO_2]^{2+} + 2H_2O$$

The behaviour of the plutonium ions in solution illustrates well why the study of these elements is important to the basic understanding of chemistry in general. In a recent text-book on the actinide elements, this is expressed as follows (130).

> In a real sense, by virtue of its complexity, plutonium exhibits nearly all the solution behaviour shown by any of the other elements, and the study of the solution chemistry of plutonium contributes not only to the general understanding of plutonium chemistry *per se* but also a general understanding of a most important class of phenomena.

$Pu^{3+}$, $Pu^{4+}$, $[PuO_2]^+$ and $[PuO_2]^{2+}$ can exist together in the same solution. The formal charge on each plutonium ion is three or more, and they are therefore electron acceptors. They are thus very susceptible to hydrolytic attack and to the formation of complexes with anions.

The $Pu^{4+}$ ion is initially hydrolysed to $[Pu(OH)]^{3+}$. The $U^{4+}$ ion exhibits similar behaviour, and in each case colloidal aggregates are formed. If a solution of tetravalent plutonium in 0·3M nitric acid is heated, a bright green solution is produced, containing a polymer which appears to be held together by oxide or hydroxide bridges. If the acidity is increased to 6M and the solution is heated to 90° C, depolymerization occurs very rapidly.

$Pu^{4+}$ tends to disproportionate to $Pu^{3+}$ and $[PuO_2]^{2+}$. If a solution of pure tetravalent plutonium ion in 0·5M perchloric acid is maintained at a temperature of 25° C, after a few days the solution will contain approximately 50% $Pu^{4+}$, 33% $Pu^{3+}$ and 17% $[PuO_2]^{2+}$. The $[PuO_2]^+$ ion will be present to the extent of less than 1% (131). The mechanism of this reaction has been extensively studied. It seems most probable that in hydrochloric acid solution, two bimolecular steps are involved, the first of which is a slow reaction

$$Pu^{4+} + Pu^{4+} \longrightarrow Pu^{3+} + [PuO_2]^+ + 4H^+$$

in which Pu—O bonds are formed, followed by a fast reaction

$$Pu^{4+} + [PuO_2]^+ \longrightarrow Pu^{3+} + [PuO_2]^{2+}$$

in which there is only an electron transfer (132). The experimental investigation of this reaction is complicated by the auto-reduction of the hexavalent plutonium by reducing species formed from the solvent by radio-active bombardment by alpha-particles emitted in the disintegrating plutonium atoms. After very long standing the final equilibrium state contains 90% $Pu^{3+}$ and 10% $Pu^{4+}$. These valency changes can be followed by the use of a spectrophotometer. The absorption spectrum of each of the ions contains a few sharp intensely-coloured bands which are attributed to transitions between the $5f$ electrons. Since the $5f$ level is so low-lying, the positions of the band peaks, and therefore the colours of the solutions are little affected by the chemical environment. $Pu^{3+}$ solutions are blue, and uncomplexed $Pu^{4+}$ solutions pink. Complexed solutions of the $Pu^{4+}$ ion appear green or greenish-brown, while $[PuO_2]^{2+}$ solutions are orange.

The next two elements, americium and curium, are more akin to the lanthanides, and show less resemblances to a $d$-transition series. Their most stable state is the trivalent, and there is only a small number of compounds known in which the elements exhibit higher valency $s$ states. Both these elements were first identified in 1944. They are formed in reactor fuel elements which contain plutonium after prolonged irradiation. $^{241}$Pu is first formed by the successive capture of two neutrons by $^{239}$Pu, and this undergoes beta decay to form $^{241}$Am. This can capture another neutron, and then subsequently decay with emission of a beta-particle to form $^{242}$Cm.

Americium compounds, but not those of curium have been prepared in the 3, 4, 5 and 6 valency states; the higher states are only produced by drastic oxidation processes. The lanthanide analogue, europium, can be prepared in a divalent state, but no $Am^{2+}$ ion is known. AmO and $AmH_2$ are interstitial and not ionic compounds; the stable oxide is $AmO_2$. Only one example is known of tetravalent americium in solution. A slurry of $Am(OH)_4$ has been prepared by heating $Am(OH)_3$ with a solution which is 0·2M in sodium hypochlorite and 0·2M in caustic soda (133). This slurry will dissolve completely in 15M ammonium fluoride to give a clear pink solution whose absorption spectrum differs from that of solutions of trivalent americium and is similar to that of solid $AmF_4$. The solution can be oxidized by ozone to $[AmO]_2^{2+}$, and this can be once more reduced to the presumed $Am^{4+}$ (134).

The radio-active bombardment of the solvent which takes place in americium solutions is even more intense than that which occurs in plutonium solutions, and reduction of the compound ions $[AmO_2]^+$ and $[AmO]^{2+}$ takes place even more readily than the reaction with the corresponding plutonium species. These compound ions of americium are prepared from the double carbonate $NaAm_2O_2CO_3$ which is precipitated when a solution of trivalent americium in excess carbonate is oxidized with hypochlorite or persulphate. This precipitate will dissolve in acid to give a brown solution of $[AmO_2]^+$. The pentavalent state disproportionates to form $[AmO_2]^{2+}$ and also presumably $Am^{4+}$ which is at once reduced to $Am^{3+}$. The $[AmO_2]^+$ ion can be oxidized to $[AmO_2]^{2+}$ by very strong oxidizing agents such as hot solutions of the persulphate ion, but it is itself such a strong oxidizing agent that it is at once reduced even by halide ions.

No penta- or hexavalent state of curium is known, and only a few compounds of the tetravalent state have been prepared. The stable oxide is $CmO_2$, and the typical lanthanide-like oxide $Cm_2O_3$ can be prepared from this by heating it to $600°$ C under a pressure of $10^{-4}$ mm of mercury. $CmF_4$ can be formed from $CmF_3$ by the action of fluorine at $300-400°$ C (135). The occurrence of these two tetravalent compounds suggests that the half-shell of 7$f$ electrons which is presumed to occur in curium is less stable than the corresponding half-shell in gadolinium. In curium, the effect on its environment of the bombardment by the particles emitted in its decay is even more severe than in the case of the longer-lived isotopes of the lower actinides. There is an almost insuperable difficulty in separating the inherent chemical behaviour of the curium ions from the reactions which they undergo with these reducing species. This difficulty extends even to the characterization of the solid curium compounds by X-ray diffraction methods. The radiation emitted by disintegrating $^{242}Cm$ has a strong gamma component which rapidly fogs X-ray photographic plates. It has however, been shown that $CmF_4$ has the same monoclinic structure as $UF_4$, $NpF_4$, $PuF_4$ and $AmF_4$ (136). The heat generated even by a milli-molar solution of curium is so great that it will soon evaporate the solution to dryness. The fact that no valency state other than the trivalent has been detected in solution may conceivably not be due to the inherent instability of the $Cm^{4+}$ ion, but rather to its instant reduction by the species which are formed in the intensely irradiated solvent.

The next two elements in the transition series are berkelium ($Z = 97$) and californium ($Z = 98$). The information about their properties has been summarized by Cunningham (137). The existence and nuclear properties of the elements are well established. 0·6 $\mu$g of berkelium and 1·2 $\mu$g of californium have been isolated and purified. Some of the isotopes are comparatively long lived—$^{247}Bk$ has a half-life of 7000 years, $^{249}Cf$ of 470 years and $^{251}Cf$, 660 years. In contrast to this most of the experimental work on curium has been carried out with $^{242}$Cm which has a half-life of only 162·7 days.

Both berkelium and californium form trivalent ions in solution. It is possible that a Bk$^{4+}$ ion also exists. No absorption bands were found in the visible spectra of either berkelium or californium solutions. It is unlikely that progress in our knowledge of these elements will take place rapidly because of the very small quantities of material which are available. Even the amounts which have already been isolated were only obtained after irradiating 10 g of $^{239}$Pu with a flux of $10^{14}$ neutrons/cm$^2$/sec for five years.

Nothing is really known of the chemistry of the elements beyond californium. The quantities obtained are so minute, and their life times so short that it can hardly be said that as yet there has been any possibility of investigating their properties by conventional chemical methods. In fact, as has been said in an earlier chapter, the existence of the elements of highest atomic number is to some extent inferred from their presumed elution behaviour, rather than that their chemical behaviour has been discovered after their existence had been certainly established. The predictions of present atomic theory do not hold out good prospects of the immediate discovery of long-lived isotopes of elements of very high atomic number, but few scientists would like to be eternally committed by the predictions of present theory. Chemists may yet find evidence about the behaviour of elements in which the $5f$ level is full.

# REFERENCES

(1)  CLIFFORD *Nature* **184** 2012 (1959)
(2)  SIMMONDS *Nature* **186** 154 (1960)
(3)  CLIFFORD *Nature* **186** 155 (1960)
(4)  DWIGHT *Nature* **187** 505 (1960)
(5)  CORBETT and MACMULLAN *J. Amer. Chem. Soc.* **77** 4217 (1955)
(6)  (*a*) WOODWARD and NORD *J. Chem. Soc.* 3721 (1956)
     (*b*) WOODWARD, GARTON and ROBERTS *J. Chem. Soc.* 3723 (1956)
(7)  GARTON and POWELL *J. Inorg. Nuclear Chem.* **4** 84 (1957)
(8)  CORBETT and MACMULLAN *J. Amer. Chem. Soc.* **78** 2906 (1956)
(9)  RUNDLE and CORBETT *J. Amer. Chem. Soc.* **79** 757 (1957)
(10) CARLSTON, GRISWOLD and KLEINBERG *J. Amer. Chem. Sci.* **80** 1532 (1958)
(11) ALI, BREWER, CADWICK and GARTON *J. Inorg. Nuclear Chem.* **9** 124 (1959)
(12) ROY, HILL and OSBORN *J. Amer. Chem. Soc.* **74** 719 (1952)
(13) LAUBENYAGER and ENGLE *J. Amer. Chem. Soc.* **61** 1210 (1959)
(14) MOELLER and KUNG *J. Phys. Colloid Chem.* **54** 999 (1950)
(15) WIBERG and JOHANNSEN *Angew. Chem.* **55** 38 (1942)
(16) (*a*) LONGUET-HIGGINS and BELL *J. Chem Soc.* 250 (1943)
     (*b*) LONGUET-HIGGINS *J. Chem. Soc.* 139 (1946)

(17) SCHLESINGER, BROWN and SCHAEFFER *J. Amer. Chem. Soc.* **65** 1838 (1943)

(18) (*a*) HEDBERG and SCHOMACHER *J. Amer. Chem. Soc.* **73** 1482 (1951)
(*b*) HEDBERG *J. Amer. Chem. Soc.* **74** 954 (1952)

(19) HAHN and JUGA *Z. anorg. Chem.* **244** 111 (1944)

(20) ROLLINS and EARLEY *J. Amer. Chem. Soc.* **81** 5571 (1959)

(21) JUGA and HAHN *Z. anorg. Chem.* **239** 285 (1938)

(22) (*a*) BRODE *Ann. Physik* **37** 344 (1940)
(*b*) STEVENSON and SCHOMAKER *J. Amer. Chem. Soc.* **64** 2514 (1942)

(23) CLARK, GRISWOLD and KLEINBERG *J. Amer. Chem. Soc.* **80** 4764 (1958)

(24) SCHUFLE, STUBBS and WHITMAN *J. Amer. Chem. Soc.* **73** 1013 (1951)

(25) HELPER, HUGUS and LATIMER *J. Amer. Chem. Soc.* **75** 5652 (1953)

(26) SIDGWICK *The Chemical Elements and their Compounds* p. 619 (Clarendon Press, 1950)

(27) BRAUER and RENNER *Z. anorg. Chem.* **278** 108 (1955)

(28) SCHWARTZ and BARONETZKY *Z. anorg. Chem.* **275** 1 (1954)

(29) SCHUMB and SMYTH *J. Amer. Chem. Soc.* **77** 2133 (1955)

(30) MOULTON and MILLER *J. Amer. Chem. Soc.* **78** 2702 (1956)

(31) SCHUMB and SMYTH *J. Amer. Chem. Soc.* **77** 3033 (1955)

(32) EVEREST and HAMSON *J. Chem. Soc.* 1439 1820 (1957)

(33) WADDINGTON and KLANBERG *Naturwiss.* **20** 578 (1958)

(34) MENZER *Angew. Chem.* **70** 656 (1958)

(35) GASTINGER *Z. anorg. Chem.* **285** 103 (1956)

(36) PIPER and WILSON *J. Inorg. Nuclear Chem.* **4** 22 (1957)

(37) (*a*) DENNIS, COREY and MOORE *J. Amer. Chem. Soc.* **69** 657 (1924)
(*b*) AMBERGER *Angew. Chem.* **71** 372 (1959)
(*c*) DRAKE and JOLLY *J. Chem. Soc.* 2807 (1962)

(38) BROWN and FOWLES *J. Chem. Soc.* 2811 (1958)

(39) KRAUS and BROWN *J. Amer. Chem. Soc.* **61** 3168 (1939)

(40) SCHWARZ and MEISSER *Ber.* **69** 579 (1936)

(41) MENGE and KLANG *Z. Naturforsch* **116** 115 (1956)

(42) GOODMAN *Nature* **179** 828 (1957)

(43) JUGA and UPHOF *Angew. Chem.* **69** 96 (1957)

(44) MOISSAN and LENGFELD *Bull. Soc. Chim. Paris* (**3**) **15** 1275(1896)

(45) DAVIS U.S. Patent 2, 411, 524

(46) McCULLOUGH and TRUEBLOOD *Acta Cryst.* **12** 507 (1959)

(47) D'EYE, BARDEN and HARPER *J. Inorg. Nuclear Chem.* **2** 192 (1956)

(48) MOORE and TYREE *J. Amer. Chem. Soc.* **76** 5253 (1954)

(49) BRADLEY, ABD-EL-HALIM, SADEK and WARDLAW *J. Chem. Soc.* 2032 (1952)

(50) LISTER and MCDONALD *J. Chem. Soc.* 4315 (1952)

(51) PATEL *J. Amer. Chem. Soc.* **73** 2958 (1951)

(52) (*a*) McTAGGART and WADSLEY *Austral. J. Chem.* **11** 445 (1958)
(*b*) BEAR and MCTAGGART *idem* 458
(*c*) McTAGGART *idem* 471
(*d*) McTAGGART and MOORE *idem* 481

(53) ANDERSON and MAGNELI *Acta Chem. Scand.* **11** 1065 (1957)
(54) EHRLICH *Z. Elektrochem.* **45** 362 (1939)
(55) SCHONBERG *Acta Chem. Scand.* **8** 221 (1954)
(56) AHRENS *J. Inorg. Nuclear Chem.* **4** 264 (1957)
(57) VORLANDER and DALICHAU *Ber.* **66** 1534 (1933)
(58) (*a*) MALM, SELIG and FRIED *J. Amer. Chem. Soc.* **82** 1510 (1960)
      (*b*) MALM and SELIG *J. Inorg. Nuclear Chem.* **20** 189 (1961)
(59) ENGELBRECHT and GROSSE *J. Amer. Chem. Soc.* **76** 2042 (1954)
(60) (*a*) AYNSLEY, PEACOCK and ROBINSON *J. Chem. Soc.* 1622 (1950)
      (*b*) CADY and HARGREAVES *J. Chem. Soc.* 1568 (1961)
(61) (*a*) NECHAMKIN, KURTZ and HICKEY *J. Amer. Chem. Soc.* **73** 2828
      (1951)
      (*b*) COLTON *Nature* **194** 374 (1962)
(62) HARGREAVES and PEACOCK *J. Chem. Soc.* 1099 (1960)
(63) KNOX, TYREE, SRIWASTAVA, NORMAN, BASSETT and HOLLOWAY
      *J. Amer. Chem. Soc.* **79** 3358 (1957)
(64) WILKINSON and BIRMINGHAM *J. Amer. Chem. Soc.* **77** 3421 (1955)
(65) DESCHANVRES *Ann. Chim. France* **4** 1217 (1959)
(66) HARGREAVES and PEACOCK *J. Chem. Soc.* 1099 (1960)
(67) PEACOCK, WELCH and WILSON *J. Chem. Soc.* 2901 (1958)
(68) BILTZ, WRIGGE, PRAUGE and LANGE *Z. anorg. Chem.* **234** 142
      (1937)
(69) MEIER and TREADWALL *Helv. Chim. Acta* **38** 1679 (1955)
(70) GRISVOLD, KLEINBERG and BRAVO *Science* **115** 375 (1952)
(71) VON GROSSE *Naturforoch* **86** 533 (1953)
(72) COLTON, DALZIEL, GRIFFITH and WILKINSON *Nature* **183** 1755
      (1959)
(73) (*a*) NODDACK, TACKE and BERG *Sitzber. Preuss. Akad.* 400 (1925)
      (*b*) TACKE *Z. angew. Chem.* **38** 1157 (1925)
(74) DANIELS *J. Phys. Chem.* **60** 707 (1956)
(75) (*a*) MERRILL *J. Roy. Astron. Soc. of Canada* **46** 335 (1952)
      (*b*) JORDAN *Naturwiss.* **40** 407 (1953)
(76) (*a*) PERRIER and SEGRE *Nature* **140** 193 (1937)
      (*b*) PERRIER and SEGRE *J. Chem. Phys.* **5** 712 (1937)
(77) BOYD *J. Chem. Educ.* **36** 3 (1959)
(78) COBBLE, NELSON, PARKER, SMITH and BOYD *J. Amer. Chem. Soc.* **74**
      1852 (1952)
(79) FRIED *J. Amer. Chem. Soc.* **70** 442 (1948)
(80) COBBLE *Doctoral dissertation Univ. of Tennessee* 98 (1952)
(81) CARTLEDGE *J. Amer. Chem. Soc.* **77** 2658 (1955)
(82) RULFS and MEINKE *J. Amer. Chem. Soc.* **74** 235 (1952)
(83) BUSEY and LARSON *ORNL—2584* (1958)
(84) SELIG, CHERNICK and MALM *J. Inorg. Nuclear Chem.* **19** 377 (1961)
(85) CROUTHAMEL *Analyt. Chem.* **29** 1756 (1957)
(86) FERGUSSON and NYHOLM *Chem. and Ind.* 347 (1960)
(87) THOMASON *ORNL—2453* (1958)
(88) CURTIS, FERGUSSON and NYHOLM *Chem. and Ind.* 625 1555 (1958)
(89) FERGUSSON and NYHOLM *Nature* **183** 1039 (1959)

(90) COTTON, DALZIEL, GRIFFITH and WILKINSON *Nature* **183** 1755 (1959)

(91) BILTZ, EHRHORN and MEISEL *Z. anorg. Chem.* **240** 117 (1939)

(92) CONNICK and HURLEY *J. Amer. Chem. Soc.* **74** 5012 (1952)

(93) CLAASEN, SELIG, MALM, CHERNICK and WEINSTOCK *J. Amer. Chem. Soc.* **83** 2390 (1961)

(94) HEPWORTH, PEACOCK and ROBINSON *J. Chem. Soc.* 1197 (1954)

(95) RUFF and VIDIC *Z. anorg. Chem.* **143** 171 (1925)

(96) BILTZ *Z. anorg. Chem.* **233** 282 (1937)

(97) PARKER and LANTZ *AECD*—2160 (1948)

(98) CORSTON, MACKENZIE and SEGRE *Phys. Rev.* **58** 672 (1940)

(99) PEREY *J. Phys. Radium* **10** 439 (1939)

(100) PEREY Thesis Univ. of Paris (1946)

(101) KARLICK and BEMERT *Naturwiss.* **31** 492 (1943)

(102) HYDE *J. Chem. Educ.* **36** 15 (1959)

(103) (a) JOHNSON, LEININGER and SEGRE, *J. Chem. Phys.* **17** 1 (1949)
(b) NEUMANN *J. Inorg. Nuclear Chem.* **21** 1185 (1953)

(104) APPELMAN *J. Amer. Chem. Soc.* **83** 805 (1961)

(105) NEUMANN *J. Inorg. Nuclear Chem.* **4** 349 (1957)

(106) (a) BLEANEY, LLEWELLYN, PRYCE and HALL *Phil. Mag.* **45** 991 (1954)
(b) EISENSTEIN and PRYCE *Proc. Roy. Soc.* **A229** 20 (1955) **A238** 31 (1956)

(107) BLEANEY, HAYES and LLEWELLYN quoted by KATZ and SEABORG *The Chemistry of the Actinide Elements* p. 456 (Methuen, London, 1957)

(108) MEGGERS, FRIED and TOMKINS *J. Res. Nat. Bur. Stand.* **58** 297 (1957)

(109) (a) McNALLY, HARRISON and PARK *J. Opt. Soc. America* **32** 334 (1942)
(b) BRUIN, SCHUURMANS and KLINKENBERG *Z. Physik.* **121** 667 (1943)

(110) MARDEN and RENTSCHLER *Ind. Eng. Chem.* **19** 97 (1927)

(111) LEVESQUE and CUBICCIOTTI *J. Amer. Chem. Soc.* **73** 2028 (1957)

(112) ANDERSON and D'EYE *J. Chem. Soc.* 244 (1949) (Suppl. 2)

(113) ZACHARIASEN *Acta Cryst.* **5** 19 (1952)

(114) JAKOVIC *J. Chromatog* **1** 289 (1958) **2** 411 (1959)

(115) GUILLAUMONT, MUXART, BOUISSIERES and HAISSINSKY *J. Chim. phys.* **57** 1019 (1960)

(116) CASEY and MADDOCK *J. Inorg. Nuclear Chem.* **10** 289 (1959)

(117) FRIED and HINDMAN *J. Amer. Chem. Soc.* **76** 4863 (1954)

(118) McMILLEN and ABELSON *Phys. Rev.* **57** 1185 (1940)

(119) SEABORG, MCMILLEN, KENNEDY and WAHL *Phys. Rev.* **69** 366 (1946)

(120) ALBERMAN and ANDERSON *J. Chem. Soc.* 303 (1949) (Suppl. 2)

(121) (a) BROWN, OCKENDEN and WELCH *J. Chem. Soc.* 3932 (1955)
(b) MULFORD and STURDY *J. Amer. Chem. Soc.* **78** 3897 (1956)

(122) MALLETT, GERDO and NELSON *J. Electrochem. Soc.* **99** 197 (1952)

(123) COFFINBERRY and ELLINGER, *Proc. Intern. Conf. At. En*, 1955 **9** 138 (1956)

(124) ZACHARIASEN *Acta Cryst.* **5** 17 (1952)

(125) BROWN, OCKENDEN and WELCH *J. Chem. Soc.* 4196 (1955)

(126) PRIGENT *Compt. rend.* **238** 102 (1954)

(127) (*a*) MANDLEBERG, RAE, HURST, LONG, DAVIES and FRANCIS *J. Inorg. Nuclear Chem.* **2** 358 (1956)
(*b*) FLORIN, TANNENBAUM and LEMONS *J. Inorg. Nuclear Chem.* **2** 368 (1956)
(*c*) WEINSTOCK and MALM *J. Inorg. Nuclear Chem.* **2** 380 (1956)

(128) (*a*) FRIED and DAVIDSON *AECD*—2081 (1945)
(*b*) MANDLEBERG and DAVIES *J. Inorg. Nuclear Chem.* **20** 58 (1961)

(129) SJOBLOM and HINDMAN *J. Amer. Chem. Soc.* **73** 1744 (1951)

(130) KATZ and SEABORG *The Chemistry of the Actinide Elements* p. 293 (Methuen, London, 1957)

(131) Ibid. p. 316

(132) CONNICK and MCVEY *J. Amer. Chem. Soc.* **75** 474 (1953)

(133) PENNEMANN, COLEMAN and KEENAN *J. Inorg. Nuclear Chem.* **17** 138 (1961)

(134) ASPREY and PENNEMANN *J. Amer. Chem. Soc.* **83** 2200 (1961)

(135) ASPREY, ELLINGER, FRIED and ZACHARIASEN *J. Amer. Chem. Soc.* **77** 1707 (1955)

(136) ASPREY, ELLINGER, FRIED and ZACHARIASEN *J. Amer. Chem. Soc.* **79** 5825 (1957)

(137) CUNNINGHAM *J. Chem. Educ.* **36** 32 (1959)

CHAPTER 7

# Some Compounds of the Non-metals

THE MAJORITY of the compounds described in this chapter are those formed between two or more of the elements which are usually described as non-metals. It should be noted in passing that there is no strict line of demarcation between the 'metals' and the 'non-metals': the terms are used for convenience and are not capable of strict scientific definition. In this chapter, we will regard as non-metals those elements which are able to form stable octets of electrons without co-ordination; to do this, the atom of the element must itself have at least four valency electrons. As Sidgwick has said, 'The property distinguishes Groups IV, V, VI and VII from the preceding groups, and involves a marked difference in chemical character' (1). He goes on to point out that the covalent octet is always very stable, and this is particularly true when the resulting electronic configuration is that of the next inert gas.

The compounds which are discussed below are of two principal types. The first type consists of fully covalent compounds, many of which are not only thermodynamically very stable, but chemically unreactive. $SF_6$ is an example of this, although here the sulphur atom has completed a dodecet of electrons and not an octet. The formal attainment by the sulphur atom of the electronic structure of the next inert gas implies that there is no point of attack for nucleophilic reagents. In the second type, the bonds formed by the non-metallic elements are covalent, but since the covalency maximum is not attained, there is a reactive centre in the molecule although the latter may be thermodynamically stable. Some of these compounds consist of complex cations or anions which are held together by electrovalencies. Where both cation and anion are complex, and the central atom of each ion is the same, the cation is susceptible to electrophilic attack because the atom cannot have here attained its covalency maximum; an example of this is 'phosphorus pentachloride' which must be formulated $[PCl_4]^+[PCl_6]^-$.

The non-metals which are discussed in this chapter and the next are therefore elements which are found on the right-hand side of the periodic table as it is usually written. They include boron, carbon, silicon, nitrogen, phosphorus, arsenic, antimony, oxygen, the chalcogenides and the halogens. The inert gases must also be included, because two types of compounds in which they take part have now been prepared. Some aspects

164

of carbon chemistry are dealt with in a separate chapter, but this is done purely as a matter of convenience. It is not intended to perpetuate the mystical connotations of the word 'organic', but rather to show how carbon chemistry must be integrated with that of all other elements.

Many of the compounds of the non-metals which are described in this chapter have been investigated in the last twenty years, and the structural formulae which are at present assigned to them are not yet well established; among such compounds are $O_2F_2$, $S_2F_2$, $P_2I_2$ and $[P(CF_3)]_4$. It must be emphasized that the formulae which are quoted below are those which seem most probable in the light of present knowledge, but it will not be surprising if in the future it becomes evident that other methods of representation are more appropriate.

Fluorine is an element whose chemistry has been considerably developed in recent years. It was first prepared by Moissan who electrolysed a solution of one part of potassium fluoride in twelve parts of hydrogen fluoride at $-30°C$. The experiments were costly, as Moissan used a platinum cell and platinum/iridium electrodes. Later, Ruff used copper cells but the experimental manipulation was inconvenient because he also used the low-temperature electrolyte. Modern fluorine cells are made of mild steel with carbon or nickel anodes, using a eutectic fluoride mixture with a high melting point. Laboratory cells still have an inconvenient tendency to explode, and it is often preferable to use cylinders of the compressed gas which is made in large cells, and marketed commercially.

Fluorine gas is very reactive, and under suitable conditions it will react with and inflame many inorganic materials which are usually considered to be inert. These include asbestos, mild steel and brick. It was for this reason that early workers used apparatus made of platinum (which is in fact volatile at $600°C$ in fluorine as the hexafluoride) (2) or of copper which rapidly attains a protective coating of fluoride. However, there are a number of materials in which fluorine can be safely handled provided that the apparatus is absolutely dry and free from dust, powder or chippings. Such materials include glass and polyethylene, as well as fully fluorinated polymers such as poly-tetrafluoroethylene.

The chemistry of fluorine is dominated by four considerations. These are the small size of the fluoride ion, the weakness of the F—F bond in the fluorine molecule, the very high energy which is required to promote an electron into the third quantum level, and the consequent invariant univalency of fluorine. The ionic radius of the fluoride ion is $1·36$ ÅU which is similar to that of the $O^{2-}$ ion. Isoelectronic oxides and fluorides such as MgO and NaF have the same crystal structure (3).

Three fluorides of oxygen are well known. The monofluoride $O_2F_2$ is a gas which is unstable above its boiling point of $-57°C$, rapidly decom-

12

posing into its elements. OF may be formed during the decomposition. The structure of the monofluoride is probably

$$O=O\diagdown_F^F$$

but more recent work has cast doubt on this (4a); study of the microwave spectrum and the dipole moment appears to indicate F—O—O—F.

The difluoride $OF_2$ is considerably more stable. It is only hydrolysed slowly by aqueous acids and alkalis, and it does not react with hydrogen or methane unless it is sparked. It is hydrolysed violently by steam. This rather stable compound is in marked contrast with ozone fluoride which is now considered to be well established (4b) and is said to be formed when ultra-violet radiation falls on a mixture of liquid oxygen and liquid fluorine. At $-183°$ it reacts vigorously with anhydrous ammonia, methane, sulphur, bromine or iodine. A fourth oxide, $O_4F_2$, which is even more unstable, is said to be a red-brown solid which decomposes between $-180$ and $-160°C$ into ozone fluoride (4c). It was prepared by passing an electrical discharge through a mixture of oxygen and fluorine at a temperature of approximately $-200°C$.

A number of compounds are formed between fluorine and the other halogens. ClF has been isolated and is fairly stable; it is formed as an intermediate during the preparation of $ClF_3$. BrF is too unstable to be isolated in the pure state, but $BrF_3$ and $BrF_5$ are well known. The lower iodine fluorides IF and $IF_3$ are unstable in comparison with $IF_5$ and $IF_7$. The stable halogen fluorides are all liquids which are powerful fluorinating agents. Since their fluorinating power varies from compound to compound, they have found extensive uses in organic chemistry (5). Chloryl fluoride $ClO_2F$ can be made by heating dichlorine hexaoxide in the presence of fluorine, since $Cl_2O_6$ decomposes on heating into $ClO_2$ and oxygen. It can also be made by reacting fluorine directly with chlorine dioxide (6). Perchloryl fluoride can be made by reacting a perchlorate with fluorosulphuric acid (7). It was originally prepared by the action of fluorine on potassium chlorate (8)

$$F_2 + KClO_3 \xrightarrow{-40°C} Cl_2 + ClF + ClO_2F + ClO_3F$$

$ClO_3F$ is a curious compound which, unlike chloryl fluoride and perchloryl oxyfluoride, is inert and stable to heat. At room temperature it is colourless, and neither toxic nor corrosive, although at higher temperatures it is a powerful oxidizing agent. It has the highest dielectric strength of any known gas (9). It undergoes a reaction of an unusual type with ammonia to form ammonium imidoperchlorate (10).

$$3NH_3 + ClO_3F \longrightarrow NH_4F + NH_4NHClO_3$$

When perchloryl fluoride decomposes, oxygen and chloryl fluoride are formed in a homogeneous unimolecular reaction (11). The form of the perchloryl fluoride molecule resembles a trigonal pyramid with the three oxygen atoms at the three corners of the base, above which is the chlorine atom, the fluorine atom being located at the fourth apex of the pyramid.

A number of oxyfluorides of the non-metals are known, and there are, for example, a variety of compounds containing fluorine, oxygen and sulphur. Fluorine fluorsulphonate can be made by the action of fluorine on sulphur trioxide in the presence of $AgF_2$. It melts at $-158.5°$ C, and boils at $-31.3°$ C, and is a strong oxidizing agent. It has the formula $SO_2F.OF$ (12). If thionyl fluoride is fluorinated in the presence of silver difluoride, the hypofluorite $FS_5.OF$ is formed. This is the oxyfluoride derivative of sulphur hexafluoride. The compound $F_4S=O$ is also formed in this reaction, both the products of which are gaseous at room temperature (13). In this curious compound, sulphur has the unusual co-ordination number of five. It may also be prepared by oxidizing sulphur tetrafluoride with dinitrogen tetroxide (14).

$$2SF_4 + N_2O_4 \longrightarrow 2SF_4O + 2NO$$

Fluorides have been prepared corresponding to each of the oxyacids of sulphur. Thionyl fluoride, for example, corresponds to sulphurous acid

$$O=S\begin{smallmatrix}OH\\OH\end{smallmatrix} \qquad\qquad O=S\begin{smallmatrix}F\\F\end{smallmatrix}$$

It can also be regarded as oxygen monofluoride in which one oxygen atom has been replaced by the next sixth group element, sulphur. Many other fluorine derivatives of the sulphur oxyacids have been isolated; however, although fluorosulphites have been prepared, fluorosulphurous acid is not known. Fluorosulphuric acid can be made by the action of hydrogen fluoride on sulphur trioxide. It is a colourless fuming liquid, which, in the absence of water, does not evolve hydrofluoric acid, and it can be handled in pyrex glass. Nitryl fluorosulphate was prepared in 1927 (15), but nitronium fluorosulphate $[NO_2][SO_3F]$ was not isolated until 1950 (16). If thallous or silver fluorosulphate is heated, pyrosulphuryl fluoride is formed (17). This has the formula $S_2O_5F_2$. If sulphur trioxide and fluorine are heated together to a high temperature, peroxydisulphuryl fluoride is formed:

$$F-\overset{\overset{\textstyle O}{\|}}{\underset{\underset{\textstyle O}{\|}}{S}}-O-O-\overset{\overset{\textstyle O}{\|}}{\underset{\underset{\textstyle O}{\|}}{S}}-F$$

This is a liquid freezing at $-55.4°$ C, and boiling at $67.1°$ C.

Sulphur forms a number of binary fluorides, and from some of these, other derivatives have been prepared. The monofluoride is not well characterized.

It was first reported in 1923 (18), but later workers have shown a singular lack of unanimity in describing its physical properties, although its formula is generally agreed to be F—S—S—F. It is said to be produced by the action of silver monofluoride on sulphur. It has also been claimed as a product of the decomposition of sulphur hexafluoride in an electric discharge, together with sulphur difluoride, $SF_2$, but the evidence quoted is not conclusive (19). The situation regarding both these two lower sulphur fluorides is so obscure that the author of a recent review concluded by saying (20) 'If the reader is now confused about $S_2F_2$ and $SF_2$, he is in the same position as the writer.'

The tetrafluoride has been investigated in considerable more detail. Three principal methods of preparation have been described:—

(1) by the action of fluorine on a thin film of sulphur at $-75°$ C (21),
(2) by the action of chlorine trifluoride on sulphur (22),
(3) by the action of iodine pentafluoride on sulphur (23).

The authors who describe the last method have also devised another curious procedure for its preparation, which involves fluorinating sulphur dichloride with sodium fluoride suspended in acetonitrile at 70–80° C. They write the reaction as

$$6SCl_2 + 4NaF \longrightarrow SF_4 + S_2Cl_2 + 4NaCl$$

The tetrafluoride is a colourless gas at room temperature; its boiling point is $-40°$ C. It is readily hydrolysed to thionyl fluoride

$$SF_4 + H_2O \longrightarrow SOF_2 + 2HF$$

It will react with organic carbonyl groups to give difluoro compounds (24)

$$CH_3—CO—CH_3 + SF_4 \xrightarrow{110°C} CH_3CF_2CH_3$$

This reaction is of great value since it is extremely specific. It is even said that it will react with carbonyl derivatives of unsaturated hydrocarbons without affecting any carbon–carbon double bonds. The tetrafluoride is a Lewis base, and can donate its unshared pair of electrons to such electrophilic compounds as boron trifluoride and arsenic and antimony pentafluorides. The resulting compounds were originally formulated as, for example, $BF_3.SF_4$ (25), but later work has shown that they are probably ionic complexes of the type $[BF_4]^-[SF_3]^+$ (26).

In contrast to the reactivity of the tetrafluoride, sulphur hexafluoride is extremely inert. In hexavalent sulphur compounds, the covalency maximum of 6 has been attained, and it is then equal to the co-ordination number. The bonds are hybrids of the $sp^3d^2$ type, and the overlap of the orbitals to form such a bond is at its maximum when fluorine is the ligand (27). Thus, not only is there no point of attack for hydrolysis, but the stability is decreased if any other atom or group is substituted for one of the fluorine atoms. The bonding is so rigid that little exchange is apparent between $SF_6$ and radio-active fluorine (28a). $SF_6$ is attacked neither by aqueous nor by fused alkali, nor does it react with oxygen or the alkali metals. It is however reductively degraded by $AlCl_3$ at 180–200°C. After 24 hours, about 15% of the latter is converted to $AlF_3$, and chlorine and chlorides of sulphur are also produced. If $SF_6$ is heated to 250°C in a sealed tube with $SO_3$, 20% is converted to $SO_2F_2$ in 24 hours; in this case the hexavalent state is retained.

Very different properties are shown by the extremely toxic higher homologue of sulphur hexafluoride, sulphur decafluoride. It was first detected as a by-product of the reaction of sulphur and fluorine (29), but it is now prepared by the photochemical reaction of $SF_5Cl$ with hydrogen (30). The decafluoride is stable to water and to aqueous alkali, but not to molten potassium hydroxide nor to molten sodium. At 200°C it rapidly decomposes to a mixture of $SF_6$ and $SF_4$ (31).

No other binary compounds of sulphur and fluorine are known. A number of fluorine-containing derivatives of sulphur di-, tetra-, and hexafluorides have been prepared. The majority of these are compounds in which one or more fluorine atoms have been replaced by an organic radical. The only known derivative of the hexafluoride in which another halogen atom has replaced one of the fluorine atoms is sulphur chloride pentafluoride, $SF_5Cl$. The best method of preparation of this compound is by the reaction of chlorine monofluoride with sulphur tetrafluoride at 350°C (32).

$$SF_4 + FCl = SF_5Cl$$

At room temperature, this compound is a colourless gas which is considerably less inert than sulphur hexafluoride. At 350–400°C it decomposes to form the hexafluoride, tetrafluoride and chlorine. It is rapidly hydrolysed by aqueous caustic soda, though not by aqueous acids. It is a strong oxidizing agent, and, for example, it will oxidize alcohols and aldehydes to carboxylic acids. It reacts with olefines by adding on across the double bond to form derivatives of $SF_6$. This behaviour of the compound indicates that in the intensely electronegative environment of the $[SF_5]^-$ group, the chlorine atom has some positive character. This is confirmed by the susceptibility of the compound to nucleophilic attack, in that the chlorine atom can be replaced by the hydroxyl ion. Typical addition reactions of $SF_5Cl$ are

$$CH_3—CH{=}CH_2 + SF_5Cl \longrightarrow CH_3—CHCl—CH_2—SF_5$$
$$CFCl{=}CF_2 + SF_5Cl \longrightarrow SF_5—CFCl—CF_2Cl$$

A number of perfluoro hydrocarbon derivatives of $[SF_5]^-$ have also been prepared. If $SF_5Cl$ is irradiated with ultra-violet light in the presence of oxygen, the compounds $(SF_5)$—O—$(SF_5)$ and $(SF_5)$—O—O—$(SF_5)$ are produced (33).

Sulphur forms an interesting series of compounds with nitrogen. The first of such compounds was described in 1835, but its formula $S_4N_4$ was not established until some sixty years later. Tetrasulphur tetranitride is an orange-yellow solid melting at 178° C. It can be prepared from sulphur tetrachloride and ammonia, and it appears to have the formula

$$
\begin{array}{ccc}
\text{N} & \!\!\!-\text{S}= & \!\!\!\text{N} \\
\| & & | \\
\text{S} & & \text{S} \\
| & & \| \\
\text{N} & \!\!\!=\text{S}- & \!\!\!\text{N}
\end{array}
$$

It can be reduced to the tetraimide

$$
\begin{array}{ccccc}
\text{H}-\text{N} & -\text{S} & -\text{N}-\text{H} \\
| & & | \\
\text{S} & & \text{S} \\
| & & | \\
\text{H}-\text{N} & -\text{S} & -\text{N}-\text{H}
\end{array}
$$

which forms colourless needles which melt at 152° C.

It seems certain that the compound $S_4N_4$ is a resonance hybrid of between 6 and 10 canonical forms. There has been considerable disagreement about the spatial arrangement of the 8 atoms. It is certain that the ring is a bent structure; according to one hypothesis, the nitrogen atoms lie in one plane, with the sulphur atoms between them at the apices of a somewhat distorted tetrahedron (34). However, other workers interpreted the diffraction patterns as indicating that it is the sulphur atoms which lie in a plane with the nitrogen atoms disposed alternately between them (35). The latest determination of the structure (36) seems to bear out the former hypothesis, but there appear to be pure $p$-bonds between the pairs of sulphur atoms at either side of the plane of the nitrogen atoms.

A compound $(SO_2)_4(NH)_4$ may be formally considered to be a derivative of $S_4N_4$ in which the sulphur has been oxidized to the hexavalent state. No such direct oxidation has been experimentally achieved, but the silver salt and an N-methyl derivative have been synthesized (37).

The puckered eight-membered ring of $S_4(NH)_4$ is reminiscent of the puckered ring formed by the $S_8$ molecule itself, with which it is isoelectronic, four sulphur atoms having been replaced by four NH groups. A similar compound in which only one of the atoms is replaced by an NH group is the mono-imide $S_7(NH)$ (38). This compound can be prepared by the action of ammonia on sulphur dichloride dissolved in dimethyl formamide at 0° C (39) and forms colourless crystals which melt at 113·5° C. Both the mono-imide and the tetra-imide form an addition compound with

formaldehyde; the former has the formula $S_7(NH.CH_2OH)$. The mono-imide forms the sulphonic acid $S_7(NSO_3H)$ with sulphur trioxide (40).
A diimide in which two of the sulphur atoms in $S_8$ may be considered to have been replaced by (NH) groups has been prepared in a similar way to the mono-imide. It was separated from the other products of the reaction by adsorption chromatography on alumina (41). It is insoluble in water, but soluble in some organic solvents and begins to decompose at its melting point of 140° C.

Disulphur dinitride can be prepared from $S_4N_4$ by rapidly cooling the vapour formed by heating it to 300° C at a low pressure. At room temperature $S_2N_2$ polymerizes to an extremely stable compound which is a semi-conductor.

When $S_4N_4$ is fluorinated with silver fluoride, the derivative

$$
\begin{array}{c}
\text{F} \\
| \\
\text{N}=\text{S}-\text{N} \\
| \qquad \| \\
\text{F}-\text{S} \qquad \text{S}-\text{F} \\
\| \qquad | \\
\text{N}-\text{S}=\text{N} \\
| \\
\text{F}
\end{array}
$$

is formed (42). The sulphur has been shown to be in the $+4$ oxidation state, and this formula is supported by measurements of the dipole moment (43). Tetrafluoro tetrasulphur tetranitride is a colourless solid. In the course of the fluorination, $SN_2F_2$ is also produced. On heating strongly, this decomposes to form $SF_4$, nitrogen, and a colourless gas SNF. If it is heated more gently, SNF and $SNF_3$ are produced (44). $SNF_3$ is extremely stable; here the sulphur is also tetravalent, and the formula is presumably $F_2S = NF$, and not $S = NF_3$ as is the case with the thio-phosphoryl fluoride $S = PF_3$ (45). If the gases $SN_2F_2$ and SNF are mixed, and left for some time at a low pressure, a compound $S_3N_2F_2$ which melts at 85° C is formed. It appears to be $F-S-N-S = N-S-F$, and to be stabilized by resonance. Alkali hydrolyses it quantitatively to ammonia (46). If chlorine reacts with a suspension of the tetranitride in carbon tetrachloride solution, the eight-membered ring is disrupted, and the chloride of a trimer is formed, containing a six-membered ring (47). In some ways this resembles an aromatic ring.

$$
\begin{array}{c}
\text{Cl}-\text{S}\overset{N}{\diagup}\overset{}{\diagdown}\text{S}-\text{Cl} \\
| \qquad \| \\
\text{N}\diagdown_{\text{S}}\diagup\text{N} \\
| \\
\text{Cl}
\end{array}
$$

In the tetrameric $S_4N_4$ the sulphur is trivalent, but in this cyclic compound it is tetravalent; treatment with hydrochloric acid results in the evolution of sulphur dioxide. A number of other reagents will combine with the constituent atoms without disrupting the ring, thus (48)

The ring is, however, destroyed by the action of ammonia.

Another series of stable compounds contains four sulphur and three nitrogen atoms, but little is known of the structure of this series. A cyclic nitride (I) with four sulphur and two nitrogen atoms can be prepared by heating tetrasulphur tetranitride with sulphur and is a dark red solid which melts at 23° C (49). Another series of compounds is derived from a similar ring system in which one of the sulphur atoms is replaced by an atom of oxygen (II).

This compound can be oxidized to the pentaoxide (III) (50).

The sulphur nitrides will act as ligands in complex anions. For example, the potassium nickel cyanide $K_4[Ni_2(CN)_6]$ which is known as Belucci's salt will dissolve in ethanol, and the addition of tetrasulphur tetranitride causes the solution to turn blood-red. A solid orange complex can be obtained from this, and appears to be (51)

The hydrogen atom must come from the solvent. The presence of a hydrogen atom in the $(SN)_x$ ligands has been demonstrated by a number of physical methods; it is obviously difficult to demonstrate the presence of one atom of hydrogen in such a compound by chemical analysis. There is, however, good chemical evidence for this, since the series of compounds with the transition metals, which were formerly believed to have the general formula $M[SN]_4$ cannot be prepared in aprotonic solvents such as carbon disulphide or benzene. The compound formed from nickel chloride and $(SN)_4$ is now considered to be $NiN_4S_4H_2$ (52) with the structure

$$
\begin{array}{c}
\text{H} \\
| \\
\text{N}{=}\text{S} \quad \text{N}{-}\text{S} \\
| \quad \text{Ni} \quad | \\
\text{S}{-}\text{N} \quad \text{S}{=}\text{N} \\
| \\
\text{H}
\end{array}
$$

An eight-membered heterocyclic ring with a puckered configuration is formed by hexasulphur di-imide (53)

$$
\begin{array}{c}
\text{H} \quad\quad \text{S}{=}\text{S}{-}\text{S} \quad\quad \text{H} \\
\text{N} \quad\quad\quad \text{N} \\
\text{H} \quad\quad \text{S}{-}\text{S}{=}\text{S} \quad\quad \text{H}
\end{array}
$$

There is an obvious possibility of resonance stabilization here, but the compound has not been extensively investigated.

A number of heterocyclic compounds of sulphur with phosphorus are known. $P_4S_3$ appears to have the symmetrical structure (54)

$$
\begin{array}{c}
\text{P} \\
\text{S} \quad\quad \text{S} \\
\text{S} \\
\text{P} \\
\text{P}{-}\text{P}
\end{array}
$$

but $P_4S_5$ has the curious asymmetrical structure (55)

Both these sulphides react with liquid ammonia at $-33°$ C when they become bound in complex anions; the formulae of two of the resultant salts are stated to be $[NH_4]_2[P_4S_3(NH_2)_2]$ and $[NH_4]_3[P_4S_3(NH_2)_3]$ (56).

Sulphur can form part of a heterocyclic ring system in which carbon is the principal constituent. The aromatic thiophen ring is well known; small rings are formed as in the dimer of thiocarbonyl chloride (I) which can be hydrolysed to the carbonyl compound (II) (57)

$$
\begin{array}{ccc}
\text{Cl} \quad \text{S} \quad \text{Cl} & & \text{Cl} \quad \text{S} \\
\text{C} \quad\quad \text{C} & & \text{C} \quad\quad \text{C}{=}\text{O} \\
\text{Cl} \quad \text{S} \quad \text{Cl} & & \text{Cl} \quad \text{S} \\
\text{(I)} & & \text{(II)}
\end{array}
$$

The polymers of carbonyl chloride, on the other hand, do not have a cyclic structure. Another heterocyclic ring containing sulphur is the so-called γ-form of sulphur dioxide which appears to have the structure

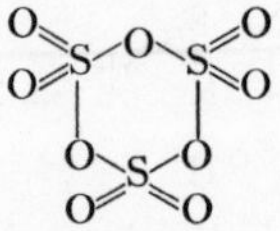

This has certain points of similarity with the sulphur nitride pentaoxide referred to above. Three molecules of sulphur trioxide will condense with two molecules of arsenic trifluoride. There is as yet no crystallographic information about the structure of the resultant compound, but nuclear magnetic resonance studies have been interpreted as indicating the ring structure (58):

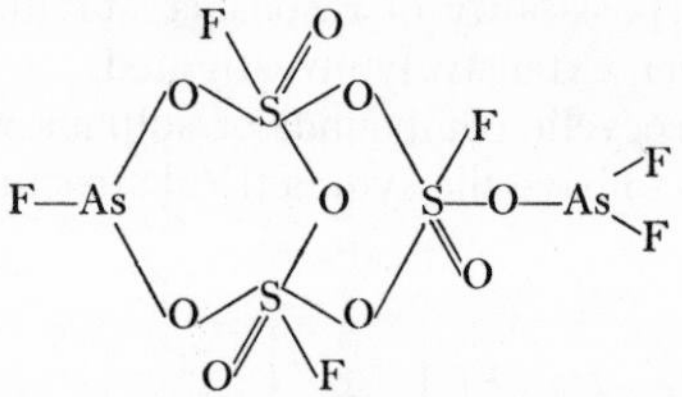

In the fifth group of the periodic table, phosphorus forms some homo-cyclic compounds. For example, if the compound $CF_3 . PI_2$ is treated with mercury at room temperature, a compound $(CF_3 . P)_4$ is formed (59). This probably has the structure:

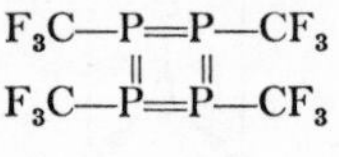

$$F_3C—P{=}P—CF_3$$
$$F_3C—P{=}P—CF_3$$

The pentamer $(CF_3 . P)_5$ is also formed, but is less stable than the tetramer to which it is converted on heating. The tetramer melts at 66° C, and the pentamer at $-33°$ C; this difference in melting point perhaps illustrates the greater ease of packing of structures with a four-fold axis of symmetry as compared with those in which the axis is five-fold. A similar compound, phosphorbenzene, has been known since 1877. It is a very stable yellow solid melting at 150° C, which can be prepared by reacting diphenyl phosphine with diphenylchlorophosphine

$$2C_6H_5 . PH_2 + 2C_6H_5 . PCl_2 \longrightarrow (C_6H_5)_4P_4 + 4HCl$$

Phosphorbenzene will react with sulphur to form $(C_6H_5 . PS)_4$ and $(C_6H_5 . PS_2)_4$. It is possible that the ring of four phosphorus atoms which is common to all these compounds has been stabilized by additional bonding in which the lone pair of electrons on each phosphorus atom combine to form an octet utilizing the available $3d$-orbitals.

Some of the most interesting compounds of the fifth group elements are those which they form with the halogens. Two series of simple halides are formed, in which the elements are tri- and penta-valent respectively. In the trivalent compounds, the fifth group atom is situated at the apex of a pyramid, and the three halogen atoms are equally disposed at the base. In some cases the pentahalides occur as molecular species in which the fifth group atom is at the centre of the five halide atoms, but more commonly the compound consists of $[AX_4]^+$ cations and $[AX_6]^-$ or $X^-$ anions.

Of the nitrogen trihalides, only the bromide has not been isolated in the pure state. The trifluoride is prepared by the electrolysis of ammonium hydrogen fluoride, and the trichloride by the reaction of chlorine on an ammonium compound such as the hydroxide or sulphate. The tri-iodide is usually made by the reaction of the mixed halide $KIBr_2$ with ammonia. A mixed halide $NF_2Cl$ has been reported (60).

A number of mixed halides of the other fifth group elements has been investigated. For instance, it has been shown that a mixture of $PF_3$ and $PCl_3$ which is allowed to come to equilibrium contains $PF_2Cl$ and $PFCl_2$ (61); both of these mixed halides have been isolated. Similar compounds have been detected in other equilibrium mixtures, but it has not yet been possible to prepare pure examples by direct synthesis.

Since some of the pentahalides of the fifth group elements exist as molecular compounds, in which five halogen atoms are distributed about the central atom, it is possible to formulate mixed halides in a variety of stereoisomeric forms. Structural isomers are also possible. A compound $[PCl_4]^+[PF_6]^-$ is formed when phosphorus trichloride reacts with fluorine in the vapour phase (62) and when phosphorus pentachloride $[PCl_4]^+[PCl_6]^-$ is fluorinated by $AsF_3$ in $AsCl_3$ solution. It sublimes at $135°$ C with some decomposition. The empirical formula of this compound is the same as that of the molecular compound $PF_3Cl_2$ which is a gas at room temperature (63). The molecular compound slowly undergoes a transition into the ionic form (64a). The molecular tetrabromofluoride, $PBr_4F$, can be prepared by the action of bromine on phosphorus dibromo-fluoride at $-75°$ C. The ionic form $[PBr_4]^+F^-$ is the stable form at room temperature, and the molecular compound $PBr_4F$ slowly changes to this (64b). One of the products of the decomposition of $[PCl_4]^+[PF_6]^-$ is $PCl_4F$, which exists as a molecular compound in the liquid phase, but as a crystalline solid it consists of $[PCl_4]^+$ cations and $F^-$ anions (64c).

The ion $[PCl_4]^+$ is well known from investigations into the crystal structure of phosphorus pentachloride. In the solid crystalline form, $PCl_5$ was found entirely to consist of $[PCl_4]^+$ cations and $[PCl_6]^-$ anions (65). On the other hand, $PBr_5$ consists of tetrahedral $[PBr_4]^+$ cations and $Br^-$ anions. The latter are situated twice as far from a phosphorus atom as are the bromine atoms in the 4-covalent cations. An ion $[PBr_6]^-$ would presumably be unstable owing to the large size of the bromine atoms (66).

When phosphorus trichloride reacts with bromine, the simple cation $[PCl_4]^+$ is formed together with a mixed anion $[PCl_5Br]^-$ (67). Other products are also present, but there is considerable disagreement about their formulation. The mixed ionic compound $[PBr_4]^+[PF_6]^-$ can be prepared by the fluorination of phosphorus pentabromide with arsenic trifluoride (68). It is also possible to synthesize compounds of the type $PX_5IY$ where X and Y are different halogens. This may be done either by fusing together the constituents $PX_5$ and IY, or by dissolving them in $CCl_4$. $PBr_5ICl$ has been made by the latter method. It forms cherry-red crystals which melts at $112\cdot8°C$ and probably has the composition $[PBr_4]^+[BrICl]^-$. $PCl_5IBr$ forms yellow crystals which melt with some decomposition at $140°C$ (69).

The mixed halide $PCl_6I$ results from the combination of phosphorus pentachloride and iodine monochloride in carbon disulphide solution, and is readily hydrolysed by traces of moisture. The structure of the solid seems to be based on tetrahedral $[PCl_4]^+$ cations, and linear $[Cl—I—Cl]^-$ anions (70). It dissociates in this way in a polar ionizing solvent such as acetonitrile, but in a non-polar solvent such as carbon tetrachloride it dissociates into its constituents $PCl_5$ and ICl. $PBr_6I$ similarly forms $[PBr_4]^+$ and $[IBr_2]^-$ in acetonitrile; however in carbon tetrachloride it dissociates into $PBr_3$, IBr and $Br_2$ (71).

Arsenic pentachloride has never been prepared, although the $[AsCl_4]^+$ cation is well known; nor has $[AsCl_4]^+F^-$, although the mixed ionic halide $[AsCl_4]^+[AsF_6]^-$ has been reported (72). However, the antimony compound $[SbCl_4]^+F^-$ has been made by fluorinating antimony pentachloride with arsenic trifluoride (73). The sulphate of this antimony chloride cation is produced when antimony pentachloride reacts with sulphur trioxide in solution in sulphuryl chloride (74).

Antimony and bismuth pentafluorides and antimony pentachloride are known. It seems probable that the failure to isolate arsenic pentachloride is due to the fact that the separations between the $s$, $p$ and $d$ electronic levels are greater in the fourth period than they are in the third and the fifth. In the case of arsenic, the bonds formed by hybridization will therefore be less stable than those formed by either antimony or phosphorus. Since a more electronegative ligand will tend to increase bond stability, the pentafluorides are inherently more stable than the pentachlorides.

A small number of fifth group halides have been prepared in which there are two central atoms joined by a common bond. $P_2I_2$ appears to have a non-planar structure in which the plane of the iodine atoms is at right angles to that of the phosphorus atoms:

$P_2Cl_2$ is also known, and possibly $P_2F_2$. The only other compounds of this type formed by fifth group elements are $As_2I_4$ and $Bi_4Cl_4$.

In addition to the homocyclic rings described above, phosphorus can be a member of a number of heterocyclic rings. Trimethylphosphoryl chloride (I) is formed by the action of phosphoryl chloride on phosphorus pentoxide at 200° C. This compound may be compared with the cyclic sulphur nitride derivative discussed above (II)

(I)

(II)

The ring skeletons are formally isoelectronic, but whereas in the sulphur nitride derivative it is the sixth group atom, sulphur, which has $3d$-orbitals available to accommodate an electronic dodecet, in the phosphoric oxide derivative, it is the fifth group element phosphorus which attains its covalency maximum in this way.

The most important series of heterocyclic phosphorus compounds are the phosphonitrilic rings. Their principal interest lies in the marked aromatic character possessed by them. They have been known for many years, and the best preparative method dates from 1924 (75). Phosphorus pentachloride is dissolved in s-tetrachlorethane, and the solution is refluxed with a small excess of finely divided ammonium chloride. When the reaction is complete, the excess ammonium chloride is filtered off, and the solution concentrated by evaporation. A mixture of phosphonitrilic polymers $(PNCl_2)_n$ can then be extracted into low-boiling petroleum ether. An insoluble portion remains behind; this probably consists of linear polymers of the formula $(PNCl_2)_n \cdot PCl_5$. The extractable portion consists of compounds which are almost certainly monocyclic; the trimeric compound

is said to contain an almost planar ring.

The relative quantities of the various polymers produced in this reaction are:

| | |
|---|---|
| $n = 3$, | 40–45% |
| $n = 4$, | 15–20% |
| $n = 5$, | 15–20% |
| $n = 6$, | 1– 3% |
| $n \geqslant 7$ | 25% |

A compound $P_6N_7Cl_9$ occurs in the hexameric fraction, and this may be a polycyclic compound (76). A symmetrical structure is probable because of its low dipole moment (77).

Phosphonitrilic bromides can also be made by a similar reaction to that in which the chlorides are prepared, but the yield is low on account of the thermal instability of ammonium bromide, and only polymers in which $n = 2$ or 3 are formed. The mixed halide $P_3N_3Cl_5Br$ can be prepared by using ammonium bromide in conjunction with phosphorus pentachloride, and the dibromo and tetrabromochlorides can be made if phosphorus chlorobromides are used as the starting material (78). The fluorides cannot be made in this type of reaction, ammonium hexafluorophosphate being formed instead (79), but the tetramer can be prepared by the following reaction (80):

$$(PNCl_2)_4 + 8KSO_2F \longrightarrow (PNF_2)_4 + 8KCl + 8SO_2$$

The mixed fluorochlorides result when the chloride tetramer is treated with lead fluoride. These polymerize at 300°C under high pressure, but at atmospheric pressure, pyrolysis of the tetramer leads to a mixture of trimeric fluorochlorides. No iodides are known, possibly because of the large size of the iodine atom.

Of all these compounds, it is the chlorides which have been most extensively investigated. They are chemically inert and are prepared as thermally stable crystalline solids; the trimer is said to have a faint camphor-like smell. They do not appear to be toxic, but they have a delayed irritant effect upon the eyes and nose. They all polymerize further at 250–300°C to a substance which has an average molecular weight of at least 20,000 and which swells in benzene and in organic solvents.

The two chlorine atoms which are attached to each phosphorus atom in the monocyclic polymers have been shown to be at right angles to the plane of the ring (81). The trimeric ring has been shown to be planar by a number of methods, for example from examination of its infra-red (82) and its Raman (83) spectrum, and this structure has been further confirmed by X-ray diffraction measurements (84). The tetramer has a puckered structure in which the bond lengths are equal; the nitrogen and phosphorus atoms alternate. The phosphorus bonds are disposed approximately tetrahedrally, and the P–N distance is 1·67 ÅU (85). This distance is intermediate between that of 1·78–1·81 found for single bonds (for example, in sodium phosphoramidate) and the double bond distance of 1·61 ÅU. This strongly suggests that the ring system is stabilized by resonance, and may have some aromatic character. Such aromaticity differs from that exhibited by the compounds of carbon which are discussed in the next chapter, because one electron on each phosphorus atom occupies a $d$-orbital (86). It may, however, be noted in passing that cyclo-octatetraene (which might as logically be called the 'tetramer of acetylene') has no aromatic properties, and this is apparently due to the necessity in conjugated carbon rings for there to be $(4n+2)$ available electrons if they are to occupy $\pi$-orbitals. (See Chapter VIII.) In the case of the phosphonitrilic derivatives in which any 'aromatic resonance' will be concerned with $d$-orbitals, the method of Molecular Orbitals has been used to show that any even number of electrons can form a closed shell of the required type (87). In addition, 'aromatic' resonance can occur even if the ring is not perfectly planar, since the $d$-orbitals have some lateral extension. The phosphonitrilic rings containing ten or more atoms appear to be considerably folded, and this results in a reduction in 'aromatic' properties since the departure from planarity is too great to be accommodated by the $d$-orbitals.

The six-membered ring of the trimer can be preserved through a wide variety of reactions. Hydrolysis of the chloride is slow, although the fluoride is hydrolysed rather more rapidly. The compound $(P_3N_3)Cl_4(OH)_2$ has been isolated (88). The tetramers are less resistant to hydrolysis than the trimers. The chloride trimer can readily be esterified to form, for example, $(PN)_3(OCH_3)_6$ (89), by reacting it with the alcohol or with the alkoxide. Peramines can be prepared, but they tend to lose ammonia to give phospham $(PN=NH)_n$ above the temperature of liquid ammonia. The fully aminated derivaties of aromatic amines are very much more stable; the hexa-anilide, and hexa-piperidide are among the amino compounds of the trimer which have been prepared, but the only known corresponding compound of the tetramer is the octa-anilide. It has been claimed that the hexaphexyl derivative of the trimeric chloride can be prepared by the Grignard reaction, using phenyl magnesium bromide (90) but doubt was cast on this by later workers (91). The claim has, however, recently been repeated (92). The hexaphenyl derivative has been prepared by another reaction in which sodium azide is reacted with diphenyl chlorophosphine at 160–170° C (93). The methyl derivative may be made by reacting $(CH_3)_2PCl_3$ with ammonium chloride (94a). These latter compounds are remarkable in that they will dissolve in water without decomposition. When heated, they decompose at 350–400 C. The Friedel–Crafts type of reaction does not yield the fully phenylated compounds, and the action of aluminium chloride and benzene upon the trimeric chloride produces a diphenyl derivative in which both phenyl groups are attached to the same phosphorus atom.

The eight-membered ring in octamethyl cyclotetra phosphonitrile has been shown to be non-planar. The bond length of 1·596 ÅU is similar to that in $(PNCl_2)_3$ -1·60; this is much smaller than the sum of the covalent radii (1·76 ÅU) and indicates some double bond character (94b).

With hydrazine in ethereal solution, the trimeric chloride forms

$(PN)_3(N_2H_3)_6$ and it reacts in acetone solution with potassium thio-cyanate to give $(PN)_3(NCS)_6$ (95). An azido derivative with the remark-able empirical formula $PN_7$ is formed by reacting the trimeric chloride with sodium azide. This compound is $(PN)_3(N_3)_6$. It is a colourless oil which is soluble in the common organic solvents. If it is heated slowly, it will evaporate without decomposition at $250°$ C. It is readily hydrolysed by acids, but is moderately stable to alkalis. It is very sensitive to shock.

The diamido derivatives are formed when a solution of the trimeric chloride in ether is slowly added to an excess of liquid ammonia, and the solution stirred for some hours. These compounds are soluble in water by which they are slowly decomposed (97).

It is well known that the property of forming molecules containing rings or chains of atoms which is exhibited by so many non-metals is exhibited to a greater degree by carbon than by any other element. This cannot be explained solely on the grounds of the stability of wholly covalent octet formation because atoms of other elements take part in compounds in which this occurs, but these elements do not form such a wide variety of com-pounds as is formed by carbon. It is of particular interest to see why there is not as wide a variety of silicon compounds as there are carbon compounds.

In the first place, the covalency maximum of carbon is the same as its co-ordination number. The four valency electrons of carbon can each take part in the formation of one covalent bond, and a stable octet of electrons is then formed. In the ground state of the carbon atom, two of these electrons inhabit $s$-orbitals, and two, $p$-orbitals. The energy relationships of the electronic levels is such that hybridization of the orbitals takes place easily, and all the eight electrons occupy a hybridized $sp^3$-orbital. In a binary compound such as $CH_4$, each of the bonds is of the same strength as the other three, and the bonds are symmetrically directed in space; there is therefore no preferred point of attack for any reagent. The energy difference between levels with a principal quantum number of 2, and those with one of 3 is so great that no bonding orbitals other than these $sp^3$ hybrids are possible. Many reactions of covalently bonded molecules take place through the transient formation of metastable co-ordination complexes, but in saturated carbon compounds no donation or acceptance of electron pairs by the carbon atoms is possible.

Hydrolysis is a typical example of a reaction in which an intermediate co-ordination complex is formed. In alkaline hydrolysis, the $[OH]^-$ group is a potential electron donor, or nucleophilic group. Silicon hydride, $SiH_4$, is formally very similar to methane $CH_4$, but since the silicon atom has not attained its co-ordination maximum, and since $3d$-orbitals are energetically available for at least temporary acceptance of electrons, it is susceptible to hydroxylic attack. In addition, anionic attack of a saturated hydrocarbon is not easy, because in the C—H bond, the carbon atom has a fractional negative charge with respect to the hydrogen atom whereas in a Si—H bond, the silicon atom has a fractional positive charge, and therefore potentially attracts anionic reagents.

These factors demonstrate how the compounds of these elements differ in their susceptibility to anionic attack, but not why the bonds formed by carbon are so often directed to another carbon atom, while silicon chains are less stable than chains containing alternate silicon and oxygen atoms. The key to this situation is found in the relative bond strengths. The covalent bonds formed by carbon are not only intrinsically strong so that a considerable input of energy is required to break them, but also the bond strength of carbon–carbon links differs little from that of bonds formed between carbon and a variety of other elements. This is not the case with silicon, as is shown in the following table adapted from Sidgwick (98):

| Bond | Energy (kcal) |
|-------|-------|
| C—C | 81·6 |
| C—O | 81·5 |
| | $\Delta E +$  0·1 |
| Si—Si | 42·5 |
| Si—O | 89·3 |
| | $\Delta E -$ 48·6 |

A silicon–oxygen bond is thus considerably more stable than a silicon–silicon bond, whereas carbon–carbon bonds have virtually the same energy as carbon–oxygen bonds. Even more important is the relative strengths of the bonds formed by the elements with hydrogen. The C—H bond is one of the strongest formed by the element (98·8 kcal) while the Si—H bond is much weaker (75·1 kcal). The C—H bond is thus much stronger than the C—O bond, while the Si—H bond is appreciably weaker than the Si—O bond. Provided that the energy barrier present is not too high, and that sufficient activation energy can be provided, a system will be driven to assume a state of lower potential energy. Since the energy states of many of the bonds formed by carbon with other elements are so nearly equal, the energetic gain in forming a bond with the atom of one element rather than another is often either small or non-existent, whereas with silicon, the strength of the Si—O bond dominates all the chemistry of the element, and hydrolytic attack on any silicon compound eventually tends to result in the formation of the exceptionally stable $SiO_2$ structure.

None of these factors in reality operates independently. All bonds have some electrostatic nature (except perhaps in diatomic states of a single element such as $O_2$ or $N_2$), but covalent bond formation depends primarily on electronic interaction, and the disposition of the electrons controls the formal electric charges which contribute to the electrostatic component of the bond energy. Co-ordination depends upon steric considerations (or, more crudely, upon the size of the central atom and the ligands) and upon the availability of orbitals for electron acceptance. Unfortunately, theory can as yet predict bond strengths only in the simplest cases, and the chemist has to rely on experiment and observation to determine the relative stability of most of the compounds of the elements. It is for precisely this reason that the investigation of all possible chemical systems is of such importance, and fresh theoretical advances can often be made when the unexpected properties of a particular system have been demonstrated.

The difference in properties between compounds of carbon and apparently analogous compounds of silicon is very well illustrated by a consideration of the chemistry of the saturated paraffins $C_xH_{2x+2}$ and the silanes $Si_xH_{2x+2}$ and of their derivatives. The silanes have been known for over a century (99), but owing to the practical difficulties involved in their manipulation, they were little investigated before the work of Stock and his collaborators in the nineteen twenties. The silanes are extremely reactive; they are spontaneously inflammable in air and may even be explosive, although they are not affected by water in the absence of alkali. In its presence they are at once hydrolysed to silicates which contain the strong $Si—O$ bond. The first six members of the series ($SiH_4 - Si_6H_{14}$) have been characterized, and their investigation has been possible largely owing to the vacuum transfer technique devised by Stock.

The preparation and properties of their simple derivatives differ considerably from those of the corresponding carbon compounds. The tetrafluoride, which is a colourless gas, can be prepared by the action of hydrofluoric acid on silicon, and the tetrachloride is best prepared either from the elements, or by heating carbon, silicon and chlorine to a temperature of $1500°-2000°$ C. Both the tetrachloride and the tetrabromide are hydrolysed violently by water; hydrolysis of the tetrafluoride takes place less vigorously with the formation of the strong acid, fluorosilicic acid, $H_2SiF_6$. This behaviour is in marked contrast with that of the carbon tetrahalides. $CF_4$ and $CCl_4$ are even unaffected by hot aqueous solutions of alkali. $CBr_4$ and $CI_4$ are also stable to hydrolysis, although they decompose below their melting points. This is probably due to an inherent instability which arises when the mutually repellent large bromine and iodine atoms are packed in a tetrahedral arrangement around the small carbon atom. This is borne out by the fact that the thermal stability of silicon tetrabromide and tetra-iodide is greater than that of the carbon compounds; the separation of the large halogen atoms is greater when they are combined with silicon because of the larger covalent radius of the latter.

A number of silyl halides have been prepared in which all the hydrogen atoms are not replaced by halogen, and mixed halides such as $SiFCl_2Br$ are known (100). All these compounds are either volatile liquids or gases at room temperature. Disilanyl chloride and bromide are known, as well as polyhalogen substitution products of $Si_2H_6$. No pure samples of trisilane halides have been separated from the mixture of isomers which results when trisilane reacts with chloroform in the presence of aluminium chloride (101). The longest silicon chain halide which has been prepared is the perchloro compound $Si_6Cl_{14}$; this is formed when hexachlorodisilane disproportionates in the presence of trimethylamine, silicon tetrachloride also being formed. It is a fairly stable solid which sublimes at $125°\%$ at a pressure of $10^{-5}$ mm of mercury (102).

The aliphatic alcohols and amines differ considerably from the corresponding compounds derived from the lower silanes. Silanol, $SiH_3OH$ has never been prepared, because in reactions in which its formation would be expected, there is an immediate condensation to form Si—O—Si bonds. Disilyl ether is produced in this way, and its similarity to dimethyl ether is very marked, since they each contain strong bonds between the oxygen atom and the carbon and silicon atoms respectively. Disilyl ether will burn in air if it is ignited, but it is not spontaneously inflammable, and it may be heated to $300°C$ without decomposition. It can also be prepared by hydrolysing the less stable disilyl sulphide or selenide with water, but it is itself hydrolysed by aqueous alkali. The only known higher silicon ether is $(Si_2H_5)_2O$ which was prepared by Stock (103).

Few silyl amines are known. The primary and secondary monosilylamines spontaneously condense to form the tertiary amine $N(SiH_3)_3$. This compound does not resemble trimethylamine, and is spontaneously inflammable in air. It is vigorously hydrolysed by water to form silica, with the evolution of ammonia and hydrogen. Quaternary ammonium compounds with more than one silyl group are unstable and readily decompose.

Compounds between silane derivatives and organic compounds of carbon containing carbon–silicon bonds are in general reasonably stable. The strength of the C—Si bond (69·1 kcal) (104) is higher than that of the Si—Si bond, though not as high as that of the Si—O bond, and such mixed compounds are only slowly hydrolysed by water or aqueous alkali. They can be prepared for example, by reacting silyl chloride with a zinc dialkyl. Owing to the weakness of the Si—H bond, if a compound such as $CH_3.SiH_3$ is treated with hydrogen chloride in the presence of aluminium chloride, a hydrogen atom attached to silicon can be replaced, and $CH_3—SiH_2Cl$ is formed. The presence of one halide atom makes further replacement more difficult. This behaviour is clearly in accord with the bond energies (98).

| | |
|---|---|
| Si—Cl | 85·8 kcal |
| C—H | 98·8 |
| C—Cl | 78·0 |

the silicon–chlorine bond being only a little weaker than the silicon–oxygen bond.

The hydrolysis of the alkyl silyl trichloride derivatives leads to the formation of a number of extremely interesting ring systems. The nature of these cyclic polymers depends upon the nature, and particularly upon the size, of the alkyl group (105). When this is the ethyl group, an infinite sheet polymer is formed.

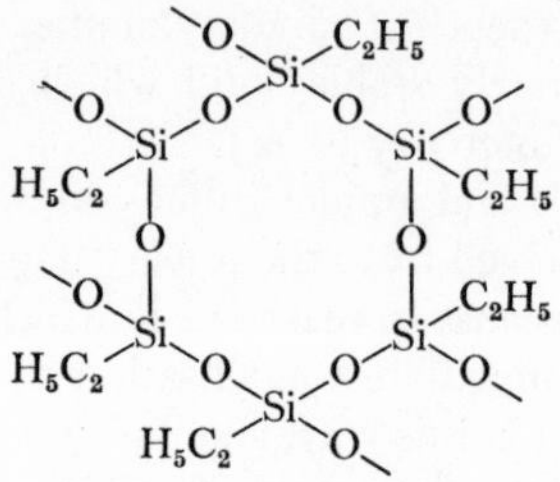

This is similar to the polymer of formula $(H_2Si_2O_3)$ formed when trichlorsilane itself is hydrolysed under controlled conditions. The butyl group is apparently too large to fit into such a structure, and the hydrolysis of butyl silyl trichloride leads to the formation of the finite tetramer:

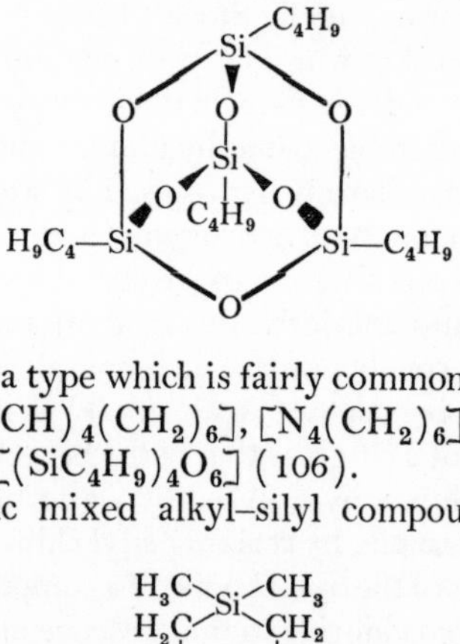

This ring system is of a type which is fairly common among compounds of the non metals, and $[(CH)_4(CH_2)_6]$, $[N_4(CH_2)_6]$ and $[(CH)_4S_6]$ have a similar structure to $[(SiC_4H_9)_4O_6]$ (106).

A number of cyclic mixed alkyl–silyl compounds are known. For example,

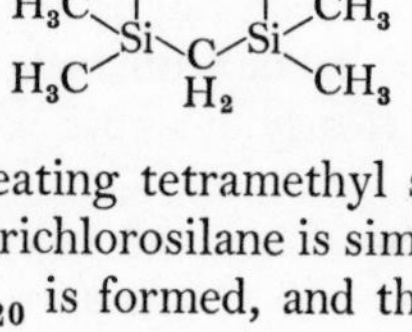

can be made by rapidly heating tetramethyl silicon to 720°C at a low pressure (107). If methyl trichlorosilane is similarly pyrolysed, a crystalline compound $Si_4C_9Cl_4H_{20}$ is formed, and this is believed to have the structure (108)

$$\begin{array}{c}
\text{H}_3\text{C} \quad \text{Cl} \\
\diagdown \text{Si} \diagup \\
\text{CH}_2 \quad \text{CH}_2 \\
\text{ClH}_2\text{C}-\text{Si}-\!\!-\!\!-\text{CH}_2-\!\!-\!\!-\text{Si}-\text{CH}_2\text{Cl} \\
\text{CH}_2 \quad \text{CH}_2 \\
\diagdown \text{Si} \diagup \\
\text{Cl} \quad \text{CH}_3
\end{array}$$

A heterocyclic compound in which the ring consists of atoms of silicon and of nitrogen has been prepared by eliminating silicon tetrachloride from tri-trichlorosilylamine, $(SiCl_3)_3N$, which is formed when silicon tetrachloride is passed with nitrogen through a glow discharge (109).

$$\begin{array}{c}
\text{Cl} \quad \text{Cl} \\
\text{Cl}_3\text{Si} \diagdown \quad \diagdown \diagup \quad \diagup \text{SiCl}_3 \\
\text{N}-\text{Si}-\text{N} \\
\text{Cl} \quad | \qquad \qquad | \quad \text{Cl} \\
\diagdown \text{Si} \qquad \qquad \text{Si} \diagup \\
\text{Cl} \diagup \quad | \qquad \qquad | \quad \diagdown \text{Cl} \\
\text{N}-\text{Si}-\text{N} \\
\text{Cl}_3\text{Si} \diagup \quad \diagup \quad \diagdown \quad \diagdown \text{SiCl}_3 \\
\text{Cl} \quad \text{Cl}
\end{array}$$

A series of oily linear polymers are also produced, of which $Si_5N_2Cl_{14}$ is the lowest member.

$$\begin{array}{c}
\text{Cl} \\
\text{Cl}_3\text{Si} \diagdown \qquad | \qquad \diagup \text{SiCl}_3 \\
\text{N}-\text{Si}-\text{N} \\
\text{Cl}_3\text{Si} \diagup \quad | \quad \diagdown \text{SiCl}_3 \\
\text{Cl}
\end{array}$$

This brief outline of the chemistry of some of the compounds of silicon demonstrates that there are no major outstanding problems in silicon chemistry which bring the known data into conflict with 'classical' electronic valency theory. This theory was not however adequate to describe the properties of the hydrides of boron and their derivatives. The simplest of these compounds which contains more than one atom of boron is diborane, $B_2H_6$. If an ethane-like structural formula is written for this compound, it can be seen that this representation contains seven bonds, and only twelve electrons are available for bonding orbitals. It is therefore impossible for each bond to be derived from a 'classical' pair of electrons. The expected molecular formula for a hydride containing two boron atoms would be $B_2H_4$. The corresponding chloride $B_2Cl_4$ can in fact be prepared by passing an electric discharge through the vapour of the trichloride $BCl_3$. The bromide is not known, perhaps because of steric interference between the large bromide atoms, but the fluoride $B_2F_4$ can be made by fluorinating $B_2Cl_4$ with antimony trifluoride (110). The $B_2X_4$ structure does not appear to be a particularly stable one, and above 0° C, $B_2Cl_4$ decomposes to form principally $B_4Cl_4$. In this compound, a tetrahedron of four boron atoms have each an associated chlorine atom (111). A higher condensation product

$B_8Cl_8$ has also been reported as a result of this decomposition (112). Here the boron atoms appear to form a dodecahedron with triangular faces. One chlorine projects outwards from each boron atom (113).

The boron compounds in the series of which $B_2H_6$ is the simplest member, are described as 'electron deficient' compounds. Reference has already been made to similar compounds of gallium (Chapter VI). One of the reasons for the importance of these compounds is that they indicated that the valency theory which had been developed by Sidgwick and by Pauling was inadequate to describe all types of chemical bonding. Pauling (114) had attempted to suggest a series of plausible resonance structures for the boranes which would be consistent with an ethane-like model, but this model was itself inconsistent with the experimental facts. There were two main chemical reasons for rejecting the ethane-like structure. In the first place, only four of the six hydrogens could be replaced by methyl groups. $B(CH_3)_3$ is well known, but it does not form a dimer $(CH_3)_3B.B(CH_3)_3$. This suggested that two of the hydrogen atoms played a different role to the remaining four. In the second place, neither the infra-red nor the Raman spectrum could be interpreted on the basis that six equivalent hydrogen atoms were present in the molecule.

As long ago as 1921, when electronic valency theory was in its infancy, Dilthey (115) had suggested that two of the hydrogen atoms had a bonding or bridging role between the two boron atoms. Twenty years later, this idea was developed by Longuet-Higgins and Bell in the wave-mechanical terms of molecular orbital theory (116). A number of subsequent measurements have confirmed the general correctness of this approach, and have indicated that in $B_2H_6$ two of the hydrogen atoms can be distinguished from the remaining four. The rotational lines in the infra-red spectrum of diborane have been shown to resemble those derived from the ethylene molecule much more closely than they do those from ethane (117). The nuclear magnetic resonance spectrum of diborane can be interpreted quantitatively in terms of the splitting due to the effect of the spins of two boron nuclei upon two bridge protons. In addition, these measurements indicate that two protons, presumably those that form the bridge, are more electronegative than the other four (118). Such an excess electronegativity of the bridging protons was subsequently shown to be in accord with molecular orbital theory (119).

According to molecular orbital theory, the bridging or bonding effect of the hydrogen atoms is not best interpreted as a resultant of a number of resonance structures. Longuet-Higgins and Bell considered the inter-relationship of the 1s-orbitals of the two hydrogen atoms. They showed that bonding orbitals of a hitherto unknown type could be formed, and they referred to these as 'three centre bonds'. Two electrons, one contributed by one of the boron atoms, and one contributed by a hydrogen atom, can form a bond on a line joining the centres of the boron atoms, with the proton, as it were, 'embedded' in the bond. A second bond involving the other hydrogen atom and the electron from the second boron atom is formed on another line joining the two centres. The embedded proton is an essential feature of this type of bond. It is not acidic as would be the case if a positively charged hydrogen atom (proton) were in some way outside the bond, and attached to the molecule by electrostatic forces as was suggested by Pitzer (120).

In the boron/hydrogen system, the electronegativities of the two atoms forming the bond are very similar, but this is not an essential feature of this type of bond as is shown by the existence of three centre bonds in compounds of aluminium and gallium. In all these compounds, a bond is basically formed by the interactions of two electrons, but the bond involves three atomic centres and not two as in the 'classical' covalent bonds. Compounds containing such bonds are invariably Lewis acids, and will react with Lewis bases with the consequent formation of 'two centre' bonds in place of the bridge type.

Lipscomb (121) accepted the idea of three-centre bond formation, and worked out the formulae of the possible boron hydrides on the basis of the topological configurations which could be constructed using this concept. For a number of years, no boron hydrides other than those predicted by Lipscomb were known; the higher members of this series are $B_4H_{10}$, $B_5H_9$, $B_5H_{11}$, $B_6H_{10}$, $B_9H_{15}$, and $B_{10}H_{14}$. This provided strong confirmatory evidence for the validity of the concept developed by Longuet-Higgins and Bell.

However, in 1962, a new type of boron hydride was identified in which there were boron atoms unattached to hydrogen. The first member of this series was $B_{10}H_{16}$ which was prepared by passing hydrogen over $B_5H_9$ at $-78°C$, and then submitting the product to an electric discharge at a potential of 2800 volts A.C. The $B_{10}H_{16}$ which was produced was found to be stable in air at room temperature; when it was heated with iodine in a sealed tube to 150°C, the following reaction took place if the proportions of the reactants were stoicheiometric:

$$B_{10}H_{16} + I_2 = B_{10}H_{14} + 2HI$$

An excess of iodine led to the production of $B_{10}H_{12}I_2$. At room temperature HI slowly cleaves $B_{10}H_{16}$ to $B_5H_9$ and $B_5H_8I$ (122a, b). The existence of this compound led to the possibility that many more boron hydrides could be prepared than had hitherto been supposed on the basis of Lipscomb's topological theory.

At the same time that $B_{10}H_{16}$ was being identified, a number of borane anions were also being investigated—in particular the polyhedral $B_{10}H_{10}^-$ and $B_{12}H_{12}^{2-}$. These ionic species were found to be very stable to strong bases, strong acids, and oxidizing agents, and to be inert to hot aqueous solutions of sodium hydroxide ($122c$). The theoretical treatment of these very stable ions is not yet fully worked out, but it seems probable that the former has a closed polyhedral $D_{4d}$ configuration, and that the latter has closed icosohedral symmetry ($122d$).

The two ions can be converted to acids $(H_3O)_2B_{10}H_{10}.xH_2O$ and $(H_3O)_2B_{12}H_{12}.xH_2O$ which are slightly stronger than sulphuric acid. Stable, apparently covalent, silver salts are formed. The anions react with some reagents, particularly electrophilic species, to form stable derivatives in which hydrogen atoms are replaced by the attacking group. The halogens, for example, react smoothly with aqueous or alcoholic solutions of the anions to give products in which some or all of the hydrogen atoms have been replaced by the halogen: for example $B_{10}Cl_{10}^{2-}$, and $B_{10}H_3Br_7^{2-}$. The halogenated salts are chemically and thermally very stable; $Cs_2B_{10}Cl_{10}$ can be heated to 400°C in air without decomposition. $B_{12}H_{12}^{2-}$ can be nitrated to form $B_{12}H_{11}(NO_2)^{2-}$. Other groups which have been substituted for a hydrogen atom include benzoyl, —OCHO, —N$(CH_3)_2$H, —$(OCH_2CH_2OCH_3)$ and —$(SCH_2)$. These authors of the paper in which this work is described go so far as to say that these reactions signify 'a derivative chemistry of such scope and diversity as to presage a new major area of inorganic chemistry'.

A further reaction of $B_{10}H_{10}^{2-}$ was found to be that if the salt

$$B_{10}H_{10}[HN(C_2H_5)_3]_2$$

was oxidized by reacting a dilute aqueous solution with ferric chloride, the $B_{20}H_{18}^{2-}$ ion was formed ($122e$). This ion could be hydrolysed to form a '$B_{18}$' borane, the infra-red spectrum of which indicated a complex skeletal structure. Further work identified this compound as $B_{18}H_{22}$ and it apparently contained 'three-centre bonds' of the Longuet-Higgins type, and also three-boron atom bonds in which the centre atom had no hydrogen atom attached. The structure of the compound was established by X-ray diffraction analysis ($122f$); the skeleton was found to be a centro-symmetrical three-dimensional structure. There is one terminal hydrogen atom (omitted in the formula below) on each of the 16 3-bonded boron atoms.

The only known reaction of this compound is the loss of a proton to form the anion $B_{18}H_{21}^-$.

The great technological interest in these compounds, makes it possible that all the facts discovered about boron hydrides are not generally available because of defence or industrial security requirements. The most valuable method of preparing diborane which so far has appeared in the published literature is based on the interaction of a Lewis base with a Lewis acid. The base $LiAlH_4$ has been reacted with boron trichloride

$$3LiAlH_4 + BCl_3 = 2B_2H_6 + 3LiCl + 3AlCl_3$$

and similarly $LiBH_4$ has been used in conjunction with boron trifluoride. The yield of diborane is reported to be 99% of that calculated on the basis of the above equation (123a). Many of the higher boranes are conveniently prepared by the pyrolysis of diborane, the product being condensed either on a cold finger or upon the chilled wall of the reaction vessel. Thus, if diborane is heated to 120° C, a mixture of tetraborane-10 and penta-borane-11 is formed. (In boron hydride chemistry, the Greek prefix refers to the number of boron atoms in the molecule, and the Arabic numeral suffix to the number of hydrogen atoms.) Pyrolysis of tetraborane-10 leads to the condensation of pentaborane-11 at −30° C. Decaborane-14 is the most stable boron hydride. It is formed if any of the lower hydrides are heated for long periods to temperatures approaching 160° C, and it may then be condensed in a cold trap. Above 200° C, it forms a solid polymer of unknown composition (123b). Little is known about the compound $B_9H_{15}$, but its existence is now well substantiated; both the melting point and the crystal structure have been established (124). These pyrolytic prepara-tions give very much better yields of the higher hydrides than do the old established Wurtz-type syntheses.

A large number of compounds are known which contain boron–nitrogen bonds. The reaction of diborane with ammonia takes a number of different courses depending on the experimental conditions. At −120° C, a 'diammoniate' $B_2H_6 . 2NH_3$ is formed; this has been known for some years, but its structure has only recently been determined. It is now thought to be a boronate (or borohydride) $[H_2B(NH_3)_2]^+[BH_4]^-$. It is soluble in liquid ammonia, and when the solution is treated with lithium, sodium or potassium, the alkali boronate is formed. With ammonium chloride, salts of the $[H_2B(NH_3)_2]^+$ cation are precipitated. These salts have been analysed by conventional methods, and their structure has been determined by X-ray diffraction analysis (125). In diethyl ether solution, lithium boronate reacts with ammonium chloride to form the adduct $H_3B . NH_3$ in 45% yield (126a). It is soluble in ether, and on long standing the boronate described above separates out. A similar compound of tetraborane-10 $[H_2B(NH_3)_2][B_3H_8]$ has also been identified (126b).

When diborane is heated with a large excess of ammonia, first the imide and then the nitride of boron are formed. If one part of diborane is heated with two parts of ammonia (or alternatively if the diammoniate is heated) borazole is formed. This is a colourless mobile liquid at room temperature, and it contains a heterocyclic ring. It is isoelectronic with benzene, but it is

$$
\begin{array}{c}
\text{H} \\
| \\
\text{H—B}\overset{\text{N}}{\underset{}{\diagdown}}\text{B—H} \\
\| \qquad | \\
\text{H—N}\underset{\text{B}}{\diagdown}\overset{}{\diagup}\text{N—H} \\
| \\
\text{H}
\end{array}
$$

not a fully aromatic compound (127a). A pair of electrons is localized on each nitrogen atom, and the tendency for a stable aromatic $\pi$-orbital to be formed is thereby reduced. This localization is manifested chemically by the fact that an additive rather than a substitutive reaction takes place when, for example, hydrogen chloride reacts with borazole. In this case, the nucleophilic halogen adds on to the boron atoms, and the electrophilic protons add on to the nitrogen atoms to form:

$$
\begin{array}{c}
\text{H} \qquad \text{H} \\
\text{Cl} \diagdown \quad \text{N} \quad \diagup \text{H} \\
\quad \text{B} \qquad \text{B} \\
\text{H} \diagup \quad | \qquad | \quad \diagdown \text{Cl} \\
\text{H} \diagdown \quad \text{N} \qquad \text{N} \quad \diagup \text{H} \\
\text{H} \diagup \quad \text{B} \quad \diagdown \text{H} \\
\text{Cl} \qquad \text{H}
\end{array}
$$

If this compound is reduced with sodium borohydride, the non-volatile solid $B_3N_3H_{12}$ is formed. This is stable to atmospheric oxygen, and soluble only in organic solvents which are more polar than benzene. Hydroxylic reagents such as water or methanol form similar adducts with borazole. If these are heated gently, they decompose to give boron substituted trihydroxy and trimethoxy derivatives of borazole respectively. The aromatic character is increased by an inductive effect if methyl groups are substituted for hydrogen atoms on the nitrogen atoms of the ring, and chlorine atoms are similarly substituted on the boron atoms. These tend to reduce the degree to which electrons are localized on the nitrogen atoms, and the formation of an aromatic $\pi$-orbital is encouraged because the electronic density is equalized by this inductive effect over the whole of the borazole ring.

A number of substitution reactions do however take place, but since many such reactions involve nucleophilic reagents, substitution usually takes place at the boron rather than at the nitrogen atoms where the electron density is higher. Trimethyl borine, for example, will react with borazole to give a mixture of mono-, di- and tri-substituted B-methyl borazoles. Grignard reagents and organic derivatives of lithium will react with N-methyl borazoles, but the incoming substituent replaces one of the hydrogen atoms which are attached to boron. Different methods of synthesis must be used in order to prepare N-substituted and B-substituted borazoles. For example, the B-trichloro derivative can be prepared from boron trichloride and ammonium chloride at temperatures between 100 and 200° C. If an amine hydrochloride is used in this reaction in place of ammonium chloride, the reaction product is an N-substituted B-trichloro-borazole derivative (128). The chlorine atoms can be replaced by hydrogen by the use of lithium aluminium hydride (129), and N-substituted bora-zoles are therefore available. B-alkoxy borazoles can be prepared by acting on the B-trichloro derivative with sodium alkoxide. The chlorine atoms may also be replaced by the common ions by treating the B-trichloro-borazole with the appropriate silver salts; treatment with amines yields a nearly quantitative amount of B-trisalkylamino borazole.

Since substituents such as the methyl group may be attached either to the nitrogen or to the boron atoms of the borazole ring, a number of stereo-isomers are possible—there are two such isomers even of a mono-substitution product. Some of these have been identified unambiguously by appropriate synthetic methods, but considerable work remains to be done on this subject. Even so, a formidable list of known borazole derivatives has been published. Shildon and Smith (130a) have collated the physical properties of eighteen borazoles which are substituted on the boron atoms alone, sixteen N-substituted borazoles, and fifty-six which are substituted on both boron and nitrogen atoms.

The borazoles are trimeric borazynes. Tetrameric borazynes have also been reported, and it has been tentatively suggested that they contain an eight-membered ring (130b), and may be called borazocines. Measure-ments of the dielectric polarization and of the nuclear magnetic resonance spectrum were considered to rule out various other sterically possible polycyclic structures. The borazocine principally studied was the tetra-N(tertiary butyl)tetra-B chloro derivative which is a white solid melting in vacuo at 248° C. It is readily soluble in non-polar, but less soluble in polar organic solvents. It is stable to hydrolysis and considerably less reactive than the trichloro-derivatives of the borazoles.

Polymers somewhat similar to borazole are formed with other fifth group elements in place of nitrogen in the ring and both tetramers and trimers have been identified. For example, if the adduct $(CH_3)_2PH \cdot BH_3$

is heated, a compound $(BH_2)_3[P(CH_3)_2]_3$ is formed; X-ray diffraction analysis indicates that its structure is probably (131)

$$
\begin{array}{c}
P(CH_3)_2 \\
H_2B \diagup \quad \diagdown BH_2 \\
| \qquad\qquad | \\
(CH_3)_2P \diagdown B \diagup P(CH_3)_2 \\
H_2
\end{array}
$$

This compound is unusually stable. It may be heated *in vacuo* to 400° C without decomposition taking place, and it is only slowly hydrolysed even by concentrated nitric acid at 300° C. The phosphorus atoms in the ring have *d*-orbitals available for occupation. This is not the case with the nitrogen atoms in borazole, and it may be that in the phosphorus compound there is some resonance stabilization involving electron 'feed-back' from the boron–hydrogen bonds.

Tetraborane forms a compound $(CH_2)_2B_4H_8$ on being heated to 60–70° C with ethylene, and it has been suggested that this is a bicyclic compound containing both a heterocyclic ring and also three-centre bonds (132).

$$
\begin{array}{c}
H \\
| \\
B \\
H \diagup \quad \diagdown H \\
H-B \diagup \qquad \diagdown B-H \\
\diagdown H \diagdown \quad \diagup H \diagup \\
B \\
| \\
H \\
\\
CH_2 \underline{\qquad\qquad} CH_2
\end{array}
$$

If this remarkable formula is correct, it is the first bicyclic compound of this type to be prepared, although very many heterocylic compounds containing boron–carbon bonds are known.

Among the many other compounds of boron which exhibit points of particular interest may be mentioned:

(*a*) A solid product is obtained by the action of hydrogen sulphide on elementary boron. If this solid is heated in a mass spectrograph to 300–500° C, a large number of cations can be identified ranging from $[B_2S_3]^+$ to $[B_{10}S_{17}]^+$; it has been suggested that these are derived from the fragmentation of a larger molecule (132*b*).

(*b*) Free radicals which contain boron and chlorine only have been identified as a result of the decomposition of diboron tetrachloride. One of these has not yet been fully characterized, but the other appears to be $B_{12}Cl_{11}$ (dodecaboron undecachloride). This is a deep red solid which sublimes *in vacuo* at 100° C and melts with little decomposition in air at 115° C. The infra-red spectrum has been interpreted as indicating a cage structure which may involve a large number of possible resonance forms which contribute to the stability of the species ( 132c).

( c ) The trifluoroboroxine $B_3O_3F_3$ is said to be readily generated by the action of gaseous boron trifluoride on boric oxide ( 132d).

The final group of elements which are certainly non-metals and to the compounds of which we will refer in this chapter are the inert gases. The inert gases are potential Lewis bases, with an octet of electrons which are in principle all available for donation to electrophilic atoms. This possibility has been investigated on a number of occasions, and the preparation of inert gas hydrates, which were stable only at low temperatures, has been claimed. A phase-rule study of the inert gas argon and the Lewis acid boron trifluoride appeared to indicate that there were a number of phases of the general formula $A \cdot xBF_3$. However, it was apparent that $x = 1, 2, 3,$ 6, 8, or 16, and it was difficult to reconcile this with the number of electrons which it would be expected that the inert gas could donate ( 133a).

The question of the formation of inert gas compounds was reopened in 1962 by the preparation of dioxygen hexafluoroplatinate in which the platinum was pentavalent ( 133b). The formula $PtO_2F_6$ was established by conventional methods of chemical analysis, and the pentavalency of the platinum was similarly demonstrated. It was shown by X-ray diffraction analysis that the structure was similar to that of $NO^+[OsF_6]^-$, and more detailed investigation indicated that discrete $O_2$ and $PtF_6$ species existed in the lattice. Shortly after the publication of this work, a further communication from the same laboratory claimed the preparation of $Xe^+[PtF_6]^-$ ( 133c). This was an orange-yellow solid, insoluble in carbon tetrachloride, and having a neglible vapour pressure at room temperature. It sublimed *in vacuo*; the sublimate was hydrolyzed by water vapour in accordance with the equation

$$2XePtF_6 + 6H_2O = 2Xe + O_2 + 2PtO_2 + 12HF$$

It was pointed out that if the existence of the charge-transfer oxygenyl platinifluoride was considered to be established, the stability of the xenon compound was not surprising since the first ionization potential of molecular xenon is $12 \cdot 13$ eV compared with $12 \cdot 20$ for molecular oxygen.

Shortly after the publication of this paper, it was claimed that a binary fluoride of xenon could be prepared by the direct combination of the elements by heating them to $400°C$ for an hour followed by rapid cooling to room temperature ( 133d). The scrupulously careful chemical analysis was described in great detail, and it appears highly probable that the compound $XeF_4$ was in fact prepared. It is described as a colourless solid with a negligible vapour pressure at $-78°C$ and a pressure of 3 mmHg at room temperature. It was stable in nickel or glass at room temperature for at least a week. The melting point was above $100°C$. The infra-red spectrum indicated a highly symmetrical structure. It could be reduced by hydrogen:

$$XeF_4 + 2H_2 = Xe + 4HF$$

More recently still, a similar fluoride of radon has been reported (133e).

The final class of compounds which will be discussed in this chapter are those described as 'clathrate' compounds. They provide a further example of the difficulty of rigidly defining some of the terms used in chemistry. As will be seen in the succeeding paragraphs, it is not easy to force the clathrate compounds into any useful definition of the words 'compound' and 'molecule'. These compounds were first recognized by Powell in 1948 (134a), although he refers to their preparation sixty years earlier by Mylius (134b) who did not appreciate their nature. In a recent review by Mandelcorn (135), a clathrate compound is defined as a single-phase solid consisting of two distinct components, the host and the guest; the guest is retained in cavities or cages provided by the crystalline structure of the host. The molecules of the guest are firmly retained in these cavities, but there is no chemical bond between the guest and the host, although non-directional short range Van der Waals forces must come into play. The guest molecules can only be released by a breakdown of the host lattice. This may come about by change of state, that is to say by either sublimation, melting or dissolution, or to a lesser extent by mechanical disruption such as grinding. The notation 'host' and 'guest' is so useful that it will be adhered to in the following paragraphs.

The first host substance which was studied by Powell was quinol. The lattice of $\beta$-quinol forms a three-dimensional cage-work in which for every three quinol molecules, there is a hole which can accommodate such varied molecules as $SO_2$, $H_2S$, HCN, HBr, HCOOH, $CH_3OH$ or $CH_3CN$. Quinol does not form a clathrate with acetone, but a molecular lattice occurs in which infinite chains of alternate quinol and acetone molecules are joined by hydrogen bonds (136). The clathrate compounds which are formed by $\beta$-quinol have the limiting composition $3[C_6H_4(OH)_2].M$. The $\alpha$-quinol lattice has only half as many holes as are present in the $\beta$-quinol lattice, so that here the limiting composition of the clathrate is $6[C_6H_4(OH)_2].M$.

The compounds are prepared by crystallizing the quinol under a high pressure of the guest gas. In this way, Powell succeeded in incorporating successively argon, krypton and xenon in $\beta$-quinol clathrate systems. The 'compounds' were perfectly stable at atmospheric pressure, although in one such case the internal pressure of argon within the lattice was calculated to be 73 atm. Compounds of the rare gases which contained 80% of the limiting quantity expressed by the formula $3[C_6H_4(OH_2].M$ were obtained (137).

Other types of clathrates are known. In some of these an inorganic host contains an organic guest. For example, monoammine nickel(II) cyanide

$[Ni(NH_3)](CN)_2$ crystallizes in sheets in which the nickel atoms and the cyanogen groups resemble a single layer of the Prussian Blue structure, with the ammonia groups projecting above and below these sheets. One of the features of this structure is that alternate nickel atoms have planar and octahedral co-ordination respectively. It contains a large amount of free space, and unless this is occupied by trapped solvent molecules, the structure is apparently unstable. Crystallization will in fact not take place unless solvent molecules of a suitable size such as benzene or thiophen are present (138).

Some organic compounds crystallize in such a manner that there are long channels running through the crystal. Tri-o-thymotide is an example of this:

The central annulus can be occupied by long chain paraffins (139). A similar type of structure is adopted by the cyclohexa-amylose/iodine system. Each iodine molecule is coaxial with, and enclosed within a cylindrical carbohydrate molecule (140).

Finally, what are the conditions which must obtain in order for clathrate formation to take place, and what is the status of the system which is formed? The host molecules must have some special features which prevent them from becoming packed into a compact lattice. Either they must be large molecules with an irregular shape, or else they must be strong molecular dipoles so that the electrostatic attraction and repulsion opposes the adoption of the sterically preferred arrangement. The guest molecules must be of an appropriate size to be accommodated within the host, and the two partners must not react chemically with each other. However, if there are any attractive forces between them, such as dipole interactions, or Van der Waals forces, the stability of the lattice will be increased. Whether the systems should be regarded as chemical compounds depends upon how the word compound is defined, but strong arguments can be put forward for regarding them as compounds and not as molecular mixtures. The systems have positive heats of formation. All translational energy must be given up by a guest molecule when it becomes trapped in the lattice, and a proportion of its vibrational and rotational energy must usually be given up as well. Since X-ray diffraction measurements sometimes attribute a high degree of symmetry to the guest molecule, some degrees of rotational freedom must however remain. In such a case, there should be a rotational fine structure in the spectrum of the compound, although this will be diminished by collisions with the walls of the cavity. Traces of such a fine structure have been found in the spectrum of the quinol–carbon dioxide clathrate at a wave-length of 2350 cm$^{-1}$ (141). This cannot occur in the inert gas–quinol systems, but it seems reasonable to consider them also as being true compounds.

REFERENCES

(1)  SIDGWICK *The Chemical Elements and Their Compounds* p. 488 (Clarendon Press, 1950)

(2)  (*a*) WEINSTOCK, CLAASEN and MALM *J. Amer. Chem. Soc.* **79** 5832 (1957)
     (*b*) WEINSTOCK and MALM *J. Amer. Chem. Soc.* **80** 4466 (1958)
     (*c*) WEINSTOCK, MALM and WEAVER *J. Amer. Chem. Soc.* **83** 4310 (1961)

(3)  WELLS *Quart. Rev.* **8** 380 (1954)

(4)  (*a*) JACKSON *J. Chem. Soc.* 4585 (1962)
     (*b*) KIRSCHENBAUM and VON GROSSE *J. Amer. Chem. Soc.* **81** 1277 (1959)
     (*c*) VON GROSSE, STRENG and KIRSCHENBAUM *J. Amer. Chem. Soc.* **83** 1004 (1961)

(5)  MUSGRAVE *Adv. in Fluorine Chem.* **1** 1 (1960)

(6)  ARVIA, BASUALDO and SCHUMACHER *Z. anorg. Chem.* **286** 58 (1956)

(7)  BARTH-WEHRENALP, *J. Inorg. Nuclear Chem.* **2** 266 (1956)

(8)  (*a*) ENGELBRECHT and ATZWANGER *Monatsh.* **83** 1087 (1952)
     (*b*) ENGELBRECHT *Angew. Chem.* **66** 442 (1954)

(9)  (*a*) JARRY *J. Phys. Chem.* **61** 498 (1957)
     (*b*) SIMKIN and JARRY *J. Phys. Chem.* **61** 503 (1957)
     (*c*) MARGOTT and KRYDER *J. Chem. Phys.* **27** 1121 (1957)

(10)  ENGELBRECHT and ATZWANGER *J. Inorg. Nuclear Chem.* **2** 266 (1956)

(11)  (*a*) HERAS, AYMONINO and SCHUMACHER *Z. phys. Chem.* (*Frankfurt*) **22** 161 (1959)
      (*b*) GATTI, SICRE and SCHUMACHER *Z. phys. Chem.* (*Frankfurt*) **23** 164 (1960)

(12)  DUDLEY, CADY and EGGERS *J. Amer. Chem. Soc.* **78** 290 (1956)

(13)  (*a*) DUDLEY, CADY and EGGERS *J. Amer. Chem. Soc.* **78** 1953 (1956)
      (*b*) DUDLEY, SHOOLEY and CADY *J. Amer. Chem. Soc.* **78** 568 (1956)

(14)  SEEL and DETMER *Z. anorg. Chem.* **301** 113 (1959)

(15)  LANGE *Ber.* **60** 967 (1927)

(16)  GODDARD, HUGHES and INGOLD *J. Chem. Soc.* 2559 (1950)

(17)  HAYEK, CZALOUM and KRISMER *Monatsh.* **87** 741 (1956)

(18) CENTNERSZWER and STRENCK *Ber.* **56** 2249 (1923)
(19) SCHUMB, TRUMP and PRIEST *Ind. Eng. Chem.* **41** 1348 (1949)
(20) CADY *Adv. Inorg. Chem. Radiochem.* **2** 105 (1960)
(21) BROWN and ROBINSON *J. Chem. Soc.* 3147 (1955)
(22) British Pat. Appn. 16404 (1959)
(23) TULLOCK, FAWCETT, SMITH and COFFMAN *J. Amer. Chem. Soc.* **82** 539 (1960)
(24) HASEK, SMITH and ENGELHARDT *J. Amer. Chem. Soc.* **82** 543 (196)
(25) (*a*) BARTLETT and ROBINSON *Chem. and Ind.* 1351 (1956)
      (*b*) BARTLETT and ROBINSON *Proc. Chem. Soc.* 230 (1957)
(26) (*a*) COTTON and GEORGE *J. Inorg. Nuclear Chem.* **7** 397 (1958)
      (*b*) SEEL and DETMER *Z. anorg. Chem.* **301** 113 (1959)
(27) CRAIG and MAGNUSSON *J. Chem. Soc.* 4895 (1956)
(28) (*a*) CASE and NYMAN *Nature* **193** 473 (1962)
      (*b*) ROGERS and KATZ *J. Amer. Chem. Soc.* **74** 1375 (1952)
(29) DENBIGH and WHYTLAW-GRAY *J. Chem. Soc.* 1346 (1934)
(30) ROBERTS *J. Chem. Soc.* 3183 (1962)
(31) TROST and MCINTOSH *Canad. J. Chem.* **29** 508 (1951)
(32) NYMAN and ROBERTS *J. Chem. Soc.* 3180 (1962)
(33) ROBERTS *J. Chem. Soc.* 665 2774 (1960)
(34) CLARK *J. Chem. Soc.* 1615 (1952)
(35) HESSEL and VIERVOLL *Tidsskr. Kjemi Bergvesen Met.* **3** 7 (1943)
(36) LINDQVIST *J. Inorg. Nuclear Chem.* **6** 159 (1958)
(37) APPEL and GOEHRING *Z. anorg. Chem.* **271** 171 (1953)
(38) ARNOLD Brit. Pat. 544,577 (1942)
(39) BECKE−GOEHRING, JENNE and FLUCK *Ber.* **91** 1947 (1958)
(40) GOEHRING and HOHENSCHUTZ *Naturwiss.* **40** 291 (1953)
(41) WEISS *Angew. Chem.* **71** 246 (1959)
(42) GLEMSER, SCHRODER and HAESELER *Z. anorg. Chem.* **278** 53 (1955)
(43) LUND and SVENDSEN *Acto Chim. Scand.* **11** 940 (1957)
(44) GLEMSER and HAESELER *Z. anorg. Chem.* **287** 54 (1956)
(45) GLEMSER and SCHRODER *Z. anorg. Chem.* **284** 97 (1956)
(46) GLEMSER and WYSZOMIRSKI *Angew. Chem.* **69** 534 (1957)
(47) SCHRODER and GLEMSER *Z. anorg. Chem.* **298** 78 (1959)
(48) GOEHRING and MALY *Z. Naturforsch* **96** 567 (1954)
(49) MUTHMAN and CLEVER *Z. anorg. Chem.* **13** 200 (1897)
      (*b*) USHER *J. Chem. Soc.* **127** 730 (1925)
      (*c*) NEUWSEN *Z. anorg. Chem.* **266** **266** 250 (1951)
(50) GOEHRING, HOHENSCHUTZ and EBERT *Z. anorg. Chem.* **276** 47 (1954)
(51) WEISS *Z. Naturforsch* **126** 481 (1957)
(52) PIPER *Chem. and Ind.* 1101 (1957)
(53) WEISS *Z. anorg. Chem.* **303** 28 (1960)
(54) GERDING, MAARSEN and NOBEL *Acta Cryst.* **10** 156 (1957)
(55) VAN HOUTEN and WIEBANGA *Acta. Cryst.* **10** 156 (1957)
(56) BEHRENS and HUBER *Ber.* **93** 921 (1960)
(57) IDRIS JONES, KYNASTON and HALES *J. Chem. Soc.* 614 (1957)
(58) GILLESPIE and OUBRIDGE *Proc. Chem. Soc.* 308 (1960)

(59) MAHLER and BURG *J. Amer. Chem. Soc.* **79** 251 (1957)
(60) PETRY *J. Amer. Chem. Soc.* **82** 2400 (1960)
(61) BOOTH and BOZARTH *J. Amer. Chem. Soc.* **55** 3890 (1933)
(62) PAYNE *Quart. Rev.* **15** 183 (1961)
(63) KOLDITZ *Z. anorg. Chem.* **284** 144 (1956)
(64) (a) KENNEDY and PAYNE *J. Chem. Soc.* 1228 (1959)
      (b) KOLDITZ and BAUER *Z. anorg. Chem.* **302** 241 (1959)
      (c) KOLDITZ *Z. anorg. Chem.* **286** 307 (1956)
(65) (a) POWELL and CLARK *J. Chem. Soc.* 971 (1942)
      (b) CLARK, POWELL and WELLS *J. Chem. Soc.* **642** (1942)
(66) (a) POWELL and CLARK *J. Chem. Soc.* 971 (1942)
      (b) VAN DRIEL and MACGILLAVRY *Rec. Trav. chim.* **62** 167 (1943)
(67) KOLDITZ and FELTZ *Z. anorg. Chem.* **293** 286 (1957)
(68) KOLDITZ and FELTZ *Z. anorg. Chem.* **293** 147 (1957)
(69) MUZYKA and FIALKOV *Doklady Akad. Nauk S.S.S.R.* **83** 415 (1952)
(70) ZELEZNY and BAENZIGER *J. Amer. Chem. Soc.* **74** 6151 (1952)
(71) POPOV and SCHMORR *J. Amer. Chem. Soc.* **74** 4672 (1952)
(72) KOLDITZ *Z. anorg. Chem.* **280** 313 (1955)
(73) KOLDITZ *Z. anorg. Chem.* **289** 128 (1957)
(74) APPEL *Z. anorg. Chem.* **285** 114 (1956)
(75) SCHENK and ROMER *Ber.* **57 B** 1343 (1924)
(76) STOKES *Amer. Chem. J.* **20** 740 (1898)
(77) KRAUZE *Z. Elektrochem.* **59** 1004 (1955)
(78) RICE, DAASCH, HOLDEN and KOHN *J. Inorg. Nuclear Chem.* **5** 190 (1958)
(79) LANGE and VON KRUEGER *Ber.* **65** 1253 (1932)
(80) SEEL and LANGER *Angew. Chem.* **68** 461 (1956)
(81) BROCKWAY and BRIGHT *J. Amer. Chem. Soc.* **65** 1551 (1943)
(82) DAASCH *J. Amer. Chem. Soc.* **76** 3403 (1954)
(83) DE FIXQUELMONT, MAYAT and ACHS, *Compt. rend.* **208** 1900 (1939)
(84) (a) WILSON and CARROLL *Chem. and Ind.* 1558 (1958)
      (b) WILSON and CARROLL *J. Chem. Soc.* 2548 (1960)
(85) KETELAAR and DE VRIES *Rec. Trav. chim.* **58** 1081 (1939)
(86) CRAIG *Chem. and Ind.* 3 (1958)
(87) CRAIG and PADDOCK *Nature* **181** 1052 (1958)
(88) STOKES *Ber.* **28** 437 (1895)
(89) DISHON *J. Amer. Chem. Soc.* 2251 (1949)
(90) ROSSET *Compt. rend.* **180** 750 (1925)
(91) BODE and BACH *Ber.* **75 B** 215 (1942)
(92) EMELEUS *Proc. Chem. Soc.* 202 (1959)
(92) EMELEUS *Proc. Chem. Soc.* 202 (1959)
(93) (a) HERRING *Chem. and Ind.* 717 (1960)
      (b) BECKE–GOEHRING and JOHN *Z. anorg. Chem.* **304** 126 (1960)
(94) (a) SEARLE *Proc. Chem. Soc.* 7 (1959)
      (b) DOUGILL *J. Chem. Soc.* 5471 (1961)
(95) OTTO and AUDRIETH *J. Amer. Chem. Soc.* **80** 3575, 5894 (1958)
(96) GRUNDMANN and RATZ *Naturforsch* **101** 116 (1955)

(97) AUDRIETH and SOWERBY *Chem. and Ind.* 748 (1959)
(98) SIDGWICK *The Chemical Elements and Their Compounds* p. 490 (Clarendon Press, 1950)
(99) WOHLER and BUFF *Annalen.* **103** 218 (1857)
(100) SCHUMB and ANDERSON *J. Amer. Chem. Soc.* **59** 651 (1937)
(101) STOCK and STIEBLER *Ber.* **56** 1087 (1923)
(102) KACZMERCZYK and URRY *J. Amer. Chem. Soc.* **82** 751 (1960)
(103) STOCK and SOMIESKI *Ber.* **53** 759 (1920)
(104) SIDGWICK *The Chemical Elements and Their Compounds* p. 556 (Clarendon Press, 1950)
(105) WIBERG and SIMMLER *Z. anorg. Chem.* **283** 401 (1956)
(106) (*a*) SCHWAB, GRABMAIER and SIMMLER *Z. phys. Chem.* (*Frankfurt*) **6** 376 (1956)
   (*b*) ANDERSON and LINDGVIST *Arkiv Kemi* **9** 169 (1956)
(107) FRITZ and RAABE *Z. Naturforsch* **11 b** 57 (1956)
(108) FRITZ *Z. Naturforsch* **12b** 123 (1957)
(109) PFLUGMACHER and DAHMEN *Z. anorg. Chem.* **290** 184 (1957)
(110) FINCH and SCHLESINGER *J. Amer. Chem. Soc.* **80** 3573 (1958)
(111) UREY, WARTIK, MOORE and SCHLESINGER *J. Amer. Chem. Soc.* **76** 5293 (1954)
(112) LIPSCOMB *Adv. Inorg. Chem. Radiochem.* **1** 118 (1958)
(113) JACOBSON and LIPSCOMB *J. Chem. Phys.* **31** 605 (1959)
(114) PAULING *The Nature of the Chemical Bond* (Cornell U.P. 1940)
(115) DILTHEY *Z. anorg. Chem.* **34** 596 (1921)
(116) (*a*) LONQUET–HIGGINS and BELL *J. Chem. Soc.* **250** (1943)
   (*b*) BELL and LONQUET–HIGGINS *Proc. Roy. Soc.* **183** 357 (1945)
   (*c*) BELL and LONQUET–HIGGINS *Nature* **155** 328 (1945)
   (*d*) LONQUET–HIGGINS *J. Chem. Soc.* 139 (1946)
   (*e*) LONQUET–HIGGINS *Quart. Rev.* **11** 121 (1957)
(117) (*a*) PRICE *J. Chem. Phys.* **15** 614 (1947)
   (*b*) PRICE *J. Chem. Phys.* **16** 894 (1948)
(118) OGG *J. Chem. Phys.* **22** 1933 (1954)
(119) (*a*) HAMILTON *Proc. Roy. Soc.* **A235** 395 (1956)
   (*b*) WATLEY and PEASE *J. Amer. Chem. Soc.* **76** 835 (1954)
(120) PITZER *J. Amer. Chem. Soc.* **67** 1126 (1945)
(121) (*a*) DALMAGE and LIPSCOMB *J. Amer. Chem. Soc.* **73** 3539 (1951)
   (*b*) NORDMAN and LIPSCOMB *J. Amer. Chem. Soc.* **75** 4116 (1953)
   (*c*) LAVINE and LIPSCOMB *J. Chem. Phys.* **22** 614 (1954)
   (*d*) EBERHARDT, CRAWFORD and LIPSCOMB *J. Chem. Phys.* **22** 989 (1954)
   (*e*) LIPSCOMB *Proc. Nat. Acad. Sci. U.S.A.* **47** 1791 (1961)
(122) (*a*) GRIMES, WANG, LEWIN and LIPSCOMB *Proc. Nat. Acad. Sci. U.S.A.* **47** 996 (1961)
   (*b*) GRIMES and LIPSCOMB *Proc. Nat. Acad. Sci. U.S.A.* **48** 496 (1962)
   (*c*) KUOTH, MILLER, ENGLAND, PARSHALL and MUETTERTIES *J. Amer. Chem. Soc.* **84** 1056 (1962)
   (*d*) HOFFMANN and LIPSCOMB *J. Chem. Phys.* **37** 520 (1962)

(*e*) KACZMARCZYK, DOBROTT and LIPSCOMB *Proc. Nat. Acad. Sci. U.S.A.* **48** 729 (1962)

(*f*) SIMPSON and LIPSCOMB *Proc. Acad. Nat. Sci. U.S.A.* **48** 1490 (1962)

(123) (*a*) FINHOLT, BOND and SCHLESINGER *J. Amer. Chem. Soc.* **69** 1199 (1947)

(*b*) SIEGEL and MACK *J. Phys. Chem.* **62** 373 (1958)

(124) (*a*)DICKESON, WHEATLEY, HOWELL, LIPSCOMB and SCHAEFFER *J. Chem. Phys.* **25** 606 (1956) **27** 200 (1957)

(*b*) KOTLENSKY and SCHAEFFER *J. Amer. Chem. Soc.* **80** 4517 (1958)

(125) NORDMAN and PETERS *J. Amer. Chem. Soc.* **81** 3551 (1959)

(126) (*a*) SHORE and PARRY *J. Amer. Chem. Soc.* **77** 6084 (1955)

(*b*) KODAMA and PARRY *J. Amer. Chem. Soc.* **82** 6250 (1960)

(127) (*a*) WIBERG and BOLY *Ber.* **73** 209 (1940)

(*b*) DAHL and SCHAEFFER *J. Amer. Chem. Soc.* **83** 3032 (1960)

(128) RYSCHKEWITSCH, HARRIS and SISLER *J. Amer. Chem. Soc.* **80** 4515 (1958)

(129) SMALLEY and STAFIEJ *J. Amer. Chem. Soc.* **81** 582 (1959)

(130) (*a*) SHILDON and SMITH *Quart. Rev.* **14** 200 (1960)

(*b*) TURNER and WARNE *Proc. Chem. Soc.* **69** (1962)

(131) HAMILTON *Acta. Cryst.* **8** 199 (1955)

(132) (*a*) PETERS and NORDMAN *J. Amer. Chem. Soc.* **82** 5758 (1960)

(*b*) GREENE and GILLES *J. Amer. Chem .Soc.* **84** 3598 (1962)

(*c*) URRY, SCHRAM, and WEISSMAN *J. Amer. Chem. Soc.* **84** 2654 (1962)

(*d*) PORTER and SHOLETTE *J. Chem. Phys.* **37** 198 (1962)

(133) (*a*) BOOTH and WILLSON *J. Amer. Chem. Soc.* **57** 2273 (1935)

(*b*) BARTLETT and LOHMANN *Proc. Chem. Soc.* 115 (1962)

(*c*) BARTLETT *Proc. Chem. Soc.* 218 (1962)

(*d*) CLAASEN, SELIG and MALM *J. Amer. Chem. Soc.* **84** 3593 (1962)

(*e*) STEIN and ZIRIN *J. Amer. Chem. Soc.* **84** 4164 (1962)

(134) (*a*) POWELL *J. Chem. Soc.* **61** (1948)

(*b*) MYLIUS *Ber.* **19** 999 (1896)

(135) MANDELCORN *Chem. Rev.* **59** 827 (1959)

(136) LEE and WALLEVORK *Acta. Cryst.* **12** 210 (1959)

(137) POWELL *J. Chem. Soc.* 298 300 468 (1950)

(138) POWELL and RAYNER *Nature* **163** 566 (1949)

(139) (*a*) BAKER, GILBERT and ALLIS *J. Chem. Soc.* 1443 (1952)

(*b*) LAWTON and POWELL *J. Chem. Soc.* 2339 (1958)

(140) JAMES, FRENCH and RUNDLE *Acta. Cryst.* **12** 385 (1959)

(141) HEXTER and GOLDFARB *J. Inorg. Nuclear Chem.* **4** 171 (1957)

# CHAPTER 8

# Some Compounds of Carbon

A VERY large number of carbon compounds were synthesized and studied by organic chemists in the latter half of the nineteenth century and in the early years of the twentieth. From their observations, these chemists built up a system of organic structure which has needed little modification as a result of the more refined physical techniques which are available today. One of their achievements was the formulation of empirical rules to describe the way in which the organic compounds which they studied behaved when they combined with a variety of reagents. This was of particular interest because it was necessary to account for the pronounced differences in behaviour of molecules which had the same basic carbon skeleton with various different substituent groups. These rules were generalizations based on observations of chemical reactions which in the absence of a satisfactory valency theory, seemed to some extent divorced from those in which inorganic chemical compounds took part. Fifty years ago, inorganic chemistry was more predominantly the chemistry of electrolytes in aqueous solution than it is today, and the difference between such reactions and those of what we now know as covalent carbon compounds was very marked. It is this difference between the behaviour of covalent and electrovalent compounds which has to some extent perpetuated the idea that carbon chemistry is 'different' from that of the remaining elements, although it is more than 130 years since Wohler synthesized organic urea from inorganic ammonium cyanate. In recent years there have been extensive developments in the chemistry of covalent inorganic compounds, as we have seen in the last chapter, and there is no doubt that, for example, further investigation of aromatic systems which contain no carbon atoms will add to our knowledge of the behaviour of bond systems in general, particularly in terms of molecular orbital theory.

Before discussing the modern views of the principles underlying organic substitution reactions, we will briefly repeat the properties of carbon which enable it to form such a vast number of stable compounds. Carbon–carbon bonds are not only strong, but they are similar in strength to the bonds formed between carbon and many other elements. The covalency maximum and the co-ordination number of carbon are both numerically equal to four. Symmetrically disposed bonds can readily be formed by $sp^3$ hybridization. In addition carbon occupies a central position in the table of electro negativity and it can readily tolerate an environment either of fractional electronic deficiency or fractional electronic excess.

It is this latter property which is of great importance in determining the varying ways in which carbon compounds react. Substituents are in general electron-attracting or electron-repelling, and it is only in unbranched saturated hydrocarbons that the formal electronic charge is equal on all the carbon atoms. If an electronegative atom or group is substituted for a hydrogen atom at one end of such a compound, the carbon atom to which it is attached acquires a fractional positive charge. This has an attractive effect on the electron cloud associated with the neighbouring carbon atom. A fractional charge transfer then occurs; this diminishes the positive charge on the first atom, with the consequence that the second atom also acquires a fractional positive charge. In this way the effect of the electronegative group is transmitted along the chain of carbon atoms by a process of electrostatic induction. This effect is gradually damped out in passing through successive carbon atoms and it is usually inappreciable after the process has involved three carbon atoms. An opposite charge shift takes place if the substituent group has a fractional positive charge. The group is said to be electron-repelling if the electron density in the carbon chain is higher when the group is present than when it is absent, and this is known as a positive induction effect; the reverse situation is known as a negative induction effect. Groups which have a positive induction effect ( +I ) include —O, —S and CO.O; those with a negative induction effect include —NR$_3$, —SR$_2$, —NO$_2$, —SO$_2$R as well as —NH$_2$, —OH and the halogens. The induction effect of fluorine is greater than that of any of the other halogens, while that of iodine is the weakest.

One of the most straightforward examples of the way in which this induction effect operates and how it affects chemical properties can be found in the series of monochloro- aliphatic carboxylic acids. This series has often been used to illustrate the induction effect, and the data upon which it is based were originally recorded by Ostwald. He observed that in the series of acids X.CH$_2$.COOH, the degree of dissociation of the acid was increased by the substitution for the group X of a more electronegative group. For example, the dissociation of acetic acid, H.CH$_2$.COOH, $1 \cdot 82 \times 10^5$ is less than that of monochloracetic acid, $155 \times 10^5$. The chlorine atom is thus electron-attractive, the carbon atom to which it is attached being associated with a fractional positive charge. An electron-deficiency is then induced in the carbon atom of the carboxylic group, and, through it, to the oxygen atoms. Their small positive charge then tends to repel the proton H$^+$, and its ionization is thereby made easier.

The distance along a chain of carbon atoms through which the effect can be transmitted can be appreciated from a consideration of the series of monochloro- aliphatic carboxylic acids in which the chlorine atom is attached to the terminal carbon atom of the chain. The dissociation constants of the first members of this series are:

| | |
|---|---|
| Monochloracetic acid | $155 \cdot 0 \times 10^5$ |
| $\beta$-Chloropropionic acid | $8 \cdot 5 \times 10^5$ |
| $\gamma$-Chlorobutyric acid | $3 \cdot 0 \times 10^5$ |
| $\delta$-Chlorovaleric acid | $2 \cdot 0 \times 10^5$ |
| (Acetic acid) | $1 \cdot 82 \times 10^5$ |

It can be seen that the effect is inappreciable when the halogen is separated from the carboxylic group by more than three carbon atoms. The dissociation constant of the chlorovaleric acid is not very different from that of acetic acid itself.

A further process of electronic transfer takes place in any compound which contains a conjugated system of double bonds. In the early days of electronic valency theory, Lowry (2) ascribed the reactivity of compounds containing such a system of double bonds to a process of polarization in which two electrons of the bond became directly associated with one or other of the carbon atoms between which the bond had been formed. Ingold (3) described this process as one in which 'electrons whilst remaining in one octet, enter or leave another', and he called it an 'electromeric displacement'. If such a displacement should take place along a carbon chain which consists of alternate single and double bonds, the following change will occur:

$$C{=}C{-}C{=}C{-}C{=}C \longrightarrow \overset{+}{C}{-}C{=}C{-}C{=}C{-}\overset{-}{C}$$

Both these electronic arrangements are canonical forms in the wave-mechanical sense. The relative positions of the atomic nuclei are unchanged, and it is only the electron density which differs. There is not a large energy difference between these forms, and resonance is therefore possible between them. This situation is referred to as mesomerism.

If an amino group is present at one end of the chain, there is an effect which can be visualized as the lone pair of electrons on the nitrogen atom becoming conjugated with the bond system in the carbon chain. This tends to stabilize the electromeric displacement:

$$R_2N{-}C{=}C{-} \longrightarrow R_2\overset{}{N}{-}C{=}C{-}$$

The electron density is thus increased at particular points in the carbon chain. This is described as a positive mesomeric effect, and it is denoted by $+M$. The transfer of the lone pair of electrons is associated with considerable overlap of the $\pi$-orbitals, and this underlies the tendency of the inert pair to become shared. Mesomerism is therefore essentially a wave-mechanical effect, and it may or may not operate in the same direction as the electrostatic inductive effect. An anionic oxygen atom, such as occurs in an

ionized phenol, repels electrons because the atom is associated with a
negative electric charge, and this repulsion leads to an increase in electron
density in the remainder of the molecule through the process of electrostatic
induction. In addition, the tendency of a lone pair on the oxygen atom to
become conjugated with the aromatic system leads to a mesomeric displacement in the same direction as the inductive effect. However, when the
oxygen atom which is attached to the ring forms part of an alkoxy group,
the two effects act in opposing directions. The mesomeric effect is in the
same direction whether the oxygen atom is in a phenolic or in an alkoxy
group, but in the latter case the atom is electron-attracting, and the
inductive effect is opposed to the mesomeric effect.

One result of such behaviour can be seen if the different properties of
aliphatic and aromatic amines are compared. In the inductive sense a
nitrogen atom is electron-attracting when it is part of a substituent attached
to a carbon chain. In an aliphatic amine such as methylamine this electron
attraction causes the compound to behave as a strong molecular dipole:

$$\overset{\underset{|}{\longrightarrow}}{CH_3-NH_2}$$

The amino group is therefore readily accessible to electrophilic attack and
is a base in both the Lewis and the Brønsted sense. In particular it will
readily combine with a proton, and it is thus a strong base in protonic
solvents. Aniline is a much weaker base than methylamine. In this compound, a strong mesomeric effect opposes the dipolar electronic displacement because of the very strong tendency of the lone pair of electrons on
the nitrogen atom to become associated with the aromatic orbital, and
thereby conjugated with the aromatic system. This effect is so pronounced
that the sign of the dipole is actually reversed, and the nitrogen atom is at
the positive pole relative to the ring. The electron density in the neighbourhood of the nitrogen atom is so low that it does not readily combine with a
proton. Moreover in the anilinium cation, mesomeric delocalization is no
longer possible, and the additional resonance stabilization which is present
in the neutral molecule will no longer occur. The aniline molecule will
therefore be stabilized relative to its cation, and the equilibrium in the
equation

$$C_6H_5-NH_2 + H^+ \rightleftharpoons C_6H_5-\overset{+}{N}H_3$$

is displaced towards the left. Such considerations lead to a reasonable
qualitative explanation of the low basicity of aniline. There is, however,
still some disagreement about the quantitative interpretation of these
effects.

Although the energy difference between the principal canonical
structures of a conjugated system is not great, the energy associated with

the polar state is appreciably higher than that of the fully covalent state. Since states with a higher energy make a lesser contribution to the resonance hybrid than do those of a lower energy, the state of a linear chain will be predominantly covalent. However, if the system of conjugated double bonds is cyclic, the mesomeric effect cannot result in the production of polar terminal carbon atoms, and all the canonical forms will be entirely covalent. They will also be precisely equivalent, and each will therefore possess the same energy as the others. Under such conditions, the stability of any resonance hybrid will be a maximum, since the energy difference between the states is zero, and the solution of the appropriate wave-mechanical equations indicates that the smaller the energy differences between canonical forms, the greater will be the stabilization effected by resonance. The great stability of the aromatic ring systems is a consequence of this.

The application of the ideas of electronic valency theory and of wave mechanics has connected up the mechanism of the reactions of organic molecules with the general pattern of behaviour of chemical compounds. These fundamental approaches have benefited very greatly from the series of careful observations which were made by the classical organic chemists. The empirical rules which they had formulated to classify reaction types, and to systematize the effect on reactivity of various substituents, lead generally to the same results as those which can be derived from the more recent theories.

In some ways it is surprising how little the work of a practical organic chemist has been affected by the supersession of the ideas of Thiele and Kekulé and the substitution of ideas of aromatic stability based upon mesomeric resonance. The mode of reaction of organic compounds is remarkably well described by the theory of alternating affinity which was put forward in the early years of this century by Flurscheim (4). Vorlander was the earliest exponent of a theory of alternating polarity which was developed by Robinson, Lapworth and Fry before they adopted the electronic model which in the hands of these three men, together with Ingold, has proved to be of such value in resolving isolated empirical rules into a unified scheme of reaction behaviour. A basic approach which was peculiar to organic reactions would have been of far less value, however useful were its predictions.

One of the most striking ways in which the electronic theory of organic chemistry placed a variety of isolated rules on to a common basis was by demonstrating the principles which underlay the manner in which groups become attached to aromatic rings in substitution reactions. The majority of the common substituents are electrophilic, and we will restrict this discussion to such reagents although considerable advances have recently been made in the theory of nucleophilic substitution (5). The simple theory of inductomeric and mesomeric localization of electrons can readily be shown to describe in a qualitative way the manner in which a ring becomes activated by movements of electronic charge. It is well known that if one substituent is already attached to an aromatic ring, a second incoming substituent will usually occupy certain definite positions relative to the first one. In the particular case of the benzene ring, substituents have been described for a long time as *ortho/para* directing or as *meta* directing. Various empirical rules were deduced about this. In 1874, Korner connected the way in which substitution took place with the acidity of the original substituent. Crum Brown formulated the well-known rule that bears his name by considering the relation between the substituent and its oxidation products in connexion with its directional effect. Hollemann (6) investigated the matter in detail, and he determined with great accuracy the relative proportions of the *o-*, *m-* and *p-* isomers over a wide range of different substitution reactions. He showed that it was only in a few cases that the first substituent was either exclusively *meta* or exclusively *ortho/para* directing, but that in the majority of cases one or other of the two possible courses predominated.

An elementary demonstration of how this behaviour accords with electronic theory can be made as follows. If a substituent with an unshared pair of electrons is attached to a benzene ring, there will be a tendency for these electrons to undergo electromeric displacement in the direction of the ring. One way of looking at the effect of this is in terms of the possible unperturbed or canonical forms of the resultant resonance hybrid. Thus, if the substituent is an alkoxy group, these may be written:

The resultant of these will involve an excess of electrons at the *ortho* and *para* positions only, since it is impossible to formulate a *meta*-quinonoid form because this would involve a carbon atom with which more than eight electrons were associated.

A better representation of this behaviour is to use arrows to denote the mesomeric transfer:—

In this form it is easier to see that *o/p* activation takes place, and that the *meta* position cannot have an electronic excess directed to it. The benzene ring is readily polarized, that is to say the electronic structure is easily distorted by an approaching charged reactant. Thus when an electrophilic substituent approaches the ring, one of the quinonoid forms may become stabilized, at least temporarily, instead of being a hypothetical canonical form which is embodied in a resonance hybrid. Substitution can then readily take place at the *ortho* or *para* position. It is important to note that this electromeric transfer activates the ring as a whole. The effect is not only to localize the original electronic density at certain carbon atoms of the ring, but to increase the electronic density over the whole ring. The type of substituents which lead to this effect are therefore known as 'activating'.

On the other hand, substituents which attract electrons deactivate the whole ring, by withdrawing electrons from it. By a process which is the reverse of that described above, electrons are withdrawn from the *ortho* and *para* positions, and the highest electron density then remains at the *meta* positions. Since the ring as a whole is deactivated, and the *meta* carbon atoms are only the centres of a relative excess of electrons, their attraction for the incoming electrophilic reagent is more sluggish than is the case in the corresponding *ortho/para* substitution reactions.

In the above brief treatment, the benzene ring has been used as an example of a typical aromatic system. However, it has been shown experimentally that whereas some ring systems containing conjugated double bonds are aromatic, others are not. Benzene and naphthalene, for example, are aromatic but octatetraene is not. Aromatic systems cannot easily be reduced to fully saturated compounds; on partial reduction they lose their aromatic properties which include such typical reactions as sulphonation, and diazotization of their amine derivatives followed by subsequent diazo coupling with other compounds. However, the electronic configuration in aromatic compounds can be expressed in terms of molecular orbital theory. It will be remembered that in this treatment of electronic energy levels, groups of electrons are considered together to have entered one or more common orbitals. When benzene is considered in this way, it is apparent that of the 30 available valency electrons, 24 are required to form normal electron-pair bonds, leaving 6 electrons which can be supposed to enter molecular orbitals common to all six carbon atoms in the ring. These molecular orbitals are usually described as '$\pi$-orbitals'.

The detailed electronic explanation of the occurrence of 'aromaticity' was first undertaken by Hückel (7*a*, *b*) and it has been developed by Platt (7*c*) particularly from the standpoint of the spectra of aromatic compounds. Hückel described the behaviour of the $\pi$-electrons by means of complex wave-functions whose 'shape' was similar to that of the molecular perimeter. The $\pi$-orbitals may be visualized as exactly fitting into the perimeter length available; this molecular perimeter is approximately circular. The orbitals are combinations of sine and cosine functions of the general type $\cos m\phi - \sin m\phi$ where $\phi$ is an angular co-ordinate and $m$ is defined by Platt as the 'orbital ring quantum number'. If the composite function is to fit exactly into the circular path with perfect superposition of the peaks and nodes, $m$ can only have integral values: 0, $\pm 1$, $\pm 2$, $\pm 3$, .... The positive and negative values of each integer are degenerate in the spectroscopic sense. In accordance with normal exclusion principle considerations, two electrons can enter each level; Hückel premised that aromatic stability would be conferred when all the degenerate levels equal to, or lower than the orbital ring quantum number were filled, i.e. when there is a total of 2 electrons ($m = 0$), $2 + 4$ electrons ($m = 1$), $2 + 4 + 4$ electrons ($m = 2$) or in general when the number of electrons is equal to ($4n + 2$) where $n$ is an integer.

In order to see how these ideas can be applied, and to investigate the validity of the '($4n + 2$) theory', we will first consider a number of compounds which contain benzenoid rings. In the case of benzene itself, $n = 1$. Naphthalene and anthracene accord with the theory with $n = 2$ and $n = 3$ respectively. A less familiar condensed ring system is naphthacene in which $n = 4$. This compound can be nitrated (another typically aromatic reaction) in the same manner as anthracene. Naphthacene is of considerable interest as it is the parent of a series of antiobiotics known as the tetracyclines. These occur naturally as substituted quinonoid glycosides in various strains of *streptomyces* (8) and the complete synthesis of one such naturally occurring product has been claimed (9).

Some highly condensed cyclic systems which conform with Hückel's rule are exceedingly stable. For instance, hexabenzocoronene (10)

which contains 42 $\pi$-electrons ($n = 10$) has been synthesized by a number of different reactions. It melts above 700° C, the melting point of the glass tube in which the determination was attempted. It has, however, been suggested that the electrons from the whole molecule do not take part in the formation of a single molecular orbital, but that the system consists of 7 independent benzene rings (1 central and 6 peripheral) which are essentially joined by single or quasi-single bonds (11).

The (4n+2) rule is not satisfied by all compounds which are composed of a series of condensed benzene rings. When similar compounds can be made in which the number of π-orbitals in one satisfies the Hückel rule, while that in the other does not, the one in which the rule is satisfied is often the more stable of the pair. Clar (12) has illustrated this by reference to the two compounds 5,6-8,9-14,15-17,18,-tetrabenzoheptacene (I) and 5,6-14,15-dibenzoheptacene (II):

(I)

(II)

The former has 42 electrons (n = 10) and is a stable compound, orange in colour, which is soluble in sulphuric acid. The dibenzo compound has 36 π-electrons, and n can therefore not be an integer. Although this compound will form salts with acids, it does not exhibit truly aromatic properties, being oxidized on exposure to air. In Clar's view, some of these highly-condensed systems have 'blank' rings which prevent the whole structure entering into a single resonance system, and he would describe compound (I) as containing one benzenoid and two polycylic systems, each of which individually fulfils Hückel's conditions for aromaticity.

These conditions may also be tested by applying them to the various monocyclic polyenes which have been prepared in which there are an even number of carbon atoms. This latter condition is, of course, essential in order that an un-ionized fully conjugated system may be formed. One method of synthesizing such compounds with large rings is by the oxidative coupling of 1,5-hexadiyne, which undergoes a phototropic rearrangement which is followed by a selective reduction (13). The 18-carbon atom compound, cyclo-octadecanonaene, synthesized in this way has 18

$\pi$-electrons ($n = 4$) and is stable. However, although it undergoes addition reactions with, for example, bromine, it has not so far been possible to carry out electrophilic substitution reactions with this compound and it cannot yet be described as 'aromatic'.

The 24-carbon atom compound, cyclo-tetracosadodecaene was found to be decomposed by air or on exposure to sunlight; it is not a '$4n+2$' compound. However, the 30-carbon atom compound, cyclo-triaconta-pentadecaene, in which $n = 7$, is also not stable; it may be impossible for all the carbon atoms in so large a ring to be co-planar. It has been pointed out that in the 18-carbon atom compound, 6 of the hydrogen atoms must be attached by bonds which are directed to the centre of the ring:

Under these conditions, a planar configuration may be sterically impossible (14$a$). Similar considerations may apply to the non-planar and non-aromatic compound with 14-carbon atoms ($n = 3$).

It may be that Hückel's rule is not adequate by itself to describe all cases of aromatic resonance, but the behaviour of octatetraene appears to be in accord with its predictions. Octatetraene itself is non-planar, and possesses no aromatic properties. However, it will form a doubly-charged anion in compounds with the alkali metals. In this form, the ring system contains 10 electrons ($n = 2$). Electromagnetic resonance measurements indicate that in this anion, the ring is planar (14$b$,c). Unfortunately, there is as yet no chemical evidence about the aromaticity of the octatetraene ion.

A number of smaller ring systems have been studied in which $n = 0$ or 1. Without exception, these provide evidence in confirmation of the ($4n+2$) rule. This evidence is derived from the preparation of cationic rings with two $\pi$-electrons, the failure to prepare cyclo-butadiene by any one of a large number of different synthetic reactions, the stability of cyclopentadiene anions and of cycloheptatriene cations, and the behaviour of the doubly-charged cyclo-octatetraene anion noted above, as well as the typical behaviour of benzene.

The first ring system to be synthesized containing two $\pi$-electrons was the triphenylcyclopropenyl cation (15)

There is chemical proof of the aromaticity of this system, in that it will couple with diazonium salts (16). The phenyl groups are not essential to the stability of the system, for the dipropyl derivative which was reported four years later, was found to be just as stable (17).

Similar compounds in which the $\overset{+}{C}$—H group is replaced by a hetero atom with an available orbit should also show aromatic properties; *p–p–p* or *p–p–d* conjugation can then result. The germanium compound (I)

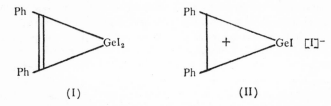

(I)                    (II)

has been prepared by reacting germanium diiodide with diphenyl acetylene above 200° C. It does not readily oxidize on heating nor does it add bromine across the formal double bond (18). It is therefore reasonable to suppose that this compound can be formulated in a similar manner to the cyclopropenyl cation (II). The silicon dimethyl analogue has also been reported to be very stable.

A very large number of attempts have been made to prepare cyclobutadiene, but no success has ever been reported. However, it was predicted on the basis of molecular orbital theory that metal complexes of the form ( $(C_4H_4)M(\text{II})X_2$ ) would be stable (19*a*) and the preparation of the nickel complex of a substituted cyclo-butadiene (19*b, c*) was quickly followed by the preparation of the silver nitrate complex of cyclo-butadiene itself (20).

Aromatic derivatives of the cyclopentadiene anion have been extensively studied. This anion can be stabilized in compounds which contain a compensating cation such as the triphenyl phosphonium ion (21):

The cyclopentadienyl anion is stable in non-aqueous solvents but not in water. However, the substituted anion dimethyl cyclopentadiene di-carboxylate is very stable; the sodium salt is soluble in water, and the lead and barium salts can be precipitated from this solution by double decomposition (22).

Metal derivatives of cyclopentadiene were first prepared in 1901 by Thiele (23) by the action of potassium upon a solution of freshly prepared cyclopentadiene in benzene. Various similar ionic derivatives have been prepared, such as those with the alkali metals, magnesium, zinc, the rare earths, thallium, and also manganese. In these compounds the cyclo-pentadiene is acidic, it reacts vigorously with air, and it forms carboxylic acids with carbon dioxide. The most stable compounds of this type to atmospheric oxidation are those with the rare earths.

In 1951 a different type of compound between cyclopentadiene and transition metals was discovered. The compound with iron was the first of these to be isolated and it was called ferrocene; this is often used as a generic name for all the compounds of this type (24). These compounds are covalent, and the metal is involved in $\pi$-electron bonding with the cyclo-pentadiene rings. The metal atom is sandwiched between two rings; the ferrous compound has the formula $[Fe(II)(C_5H_5)_2]$ (25).

An early preparation of ferrocene itself was carried out by treating the mercury cyclopentadienide with powdered iron (26). It is now more usual to prepare this type of compound by reacting the sodium salt with an anhydrous metal chloride in solution in tetrahydrofuran (27). Ferrocene itself crystallizes in orange needles which melt at 173–174° C. It is insoluble in water, but it dissolves in non-polar organic solvents. It is thermally stable to 470° C. The compound is diamagnetic, but it is possible to oxidize it to the $(Fe(C_5H_5)_2)^+$ cation and this has a magnetic moment which can be interpreted as resulting from a single unpaired electron (28). In general, the ferrocenes are volatile and are stable to air oxidation if the oxidation state of the metal is that in which it usually occurs in complexes. The neutral compounds involve the +2 state; this is more stable in the transition elements of the first long period than in those of the second and third periods, with the exception of ruthenium and osmium. With some elements such as rhenium, molybdenum and tungsten, cyclopentadienyl hydrides are formed in which the proton appears to be embedded in the bonding orbitals. When the +3 state of the transition element is the one which is usually found in complexes, cations such as $[Co(C_5H_5)_2]^+$ are formed. These can form salts with large anions such as bromide, picrate and tetraphenyl borate.

Ferrocene is certainly aromatic. It will undergo the Friedel–Crafts reaction, and will take part in diazo coupling. It is difficult to reduce, and decomposition is only achieved by the action of hydrogen under a pressure of 280 atm. at 300° C. The aldehyde undergoes the Canizzaro reaction, and although the hydroxylic compound is very unstable, it appears to be phenolic. The situation appears to be that the valency electrons of the transition metals go to complete the $\pi$-orbitals of the two rings. If it is assumed that, for example, the ferrous cation interacts with each of the six pairs of electrons, the iron atom maintains its normal co-ordination number of 6. It is unlikely that the reverse process happens; it does not appear that the $\pi$-electrons enter the metal orbitals to make up the configuration of the next inert gas.

The production of the ferrocenes was soon followed by similar derivatives of the zero oxidation state of transition metals with benzene. The preparation of dibenzene chromium $Cr(C_6H_6)_2$ was achieved by Fischer in 1955 (29) after he had theoretically demonstrated its possible existence. The monovalent cation was first prepared as its aluminochloride by heating in an autoclave a mixture of aluminium, aluminium chloride, chromic chloride and benzene. This was then reduced by sodium dithionate. Similar volatile, highly-coloured compounds of vanadium, molybdenum and tungsten have now also been prepared. Finally the preparation of the interesting mixed compound $C_5H_5CrC_6H_6$ has been reported (30).

Just as there are 6 electrons available for $\pi$-orbital formation in the cyclo-pentadienyl anion, so can cyclo-heptatriene achieve an aromatic structure by becoming a cation. It is probable that the bromide of this cation was first prepared by Merling in 1891, but he did not attempt to put forward a formula for the colourless water-soluble residue which he obtained by distilling dibromo-cycloheptatriene (31). The compound was rediscovered by Dewar (32) who found that certain derivatives of the natural products colchicine and stipatatic acid had aromatic properties which could best be accounted for by the presence of a tropolone ring. He formulated stipatatic acid as:

The tropylium (cyclo-heptatrienyl) ion appears to be symmetrical with all the carbon–carbon bonds equivalent. This has been indirectly shown to be correct by preparing the bromide with one atom of [14]C in the tropylium ring. This salt can then be converted to phenyl-cycloheptatriene and the seven-membered ring broken by oxidation to benzoic acid. The benzoic acid was found to have exactly one-seventh of the radio-activity of the original tropylium bromide. This indicates that when phenylation took place, all the seven ring positions were equally preferred and therefore that they were all electronically equivalent (33).

15

When tropylium bromide is treated with zinc dust, the red compound fulvalene results:

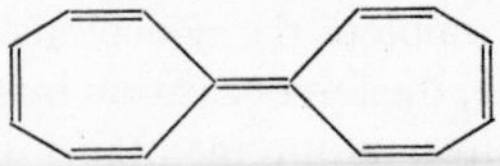

This compound is sensitive to acids, but otherwise it is reasonably stable (34).

Tropylium salts may be prepared in a number of different ways. If tropylidene is dissolved in acetonitrile and the solution is treated with triphenyl methyl perchlorate, the perchlorate of the cation is formed. Appropriately substituted tropylidenes can in this way be used to prepare similarly substituted tropylium ions (35). When cyclo-octatetraene is treated with potassium permanganate, ring closure takes place with the formation of a tropylium salt (36). The tropylium ion appears to be formed much more readily than was formerly supposed, and the $(C_7H_7)^+$ ion which occurs in the mass spectrum of toluene, benzyl alcohol and benzyl chloride has now been shown to be the tropylium ion and not the benzyl ion (37).

The tropolones, of which stipatatic acid is one, are quinone-like derivatives of the tropylium ion. They have been extensively investigated, particularly by Japanese workers. Tropolone itself has the formula:

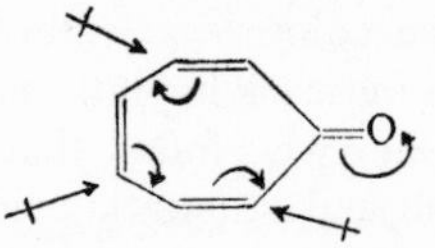

and it undergoes typical aromatic substitution reactions. The oxygen atom deactivates the whole ring, but causes a relatively high electron density to occur at three positions which are vulnerable to attack by electrophilic reagents. Tropone has a quinonoid structure with no hydroxyl group, and it can be prepared by oxidative bromination of cycloheptanone followed by catalytic removal of the three bromine atoms with hydrogen (38).

Condensed systems containing both five- and seven-numbered rings have been described. The simplest such system is azulene:

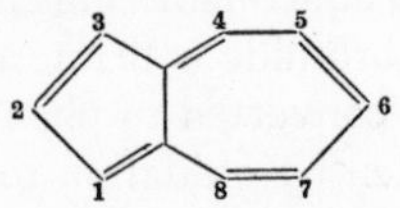

and it is a stable aromatic system containing ten electrons ($n = 2$). It can be benzylated to the 1-benzyl derivative with benzyl chloride and stannic chloride (39). It will undergo both nitration and the Friedel–Crafts reaction (40). Electrophilic attack takes place most readily at the 1 and 4 positions. Azulene has been identified as a by-product in the course of the commercial production of acetylene (41).

Unsubstituted condensed products of two five-membered rings have not been prepared. The tricyclic derivative

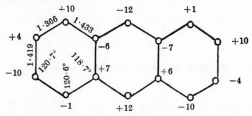

has been reported (42) as well as similar compounds substituted on the cyclopentadiene rings.

Some condensed systems containing a six-membered ring with five- and seven-membered rings have been described, and their stabilities have been compared with those predicted on the basis of the $(4n+2)$ rule. The experimental evidence does not always agree with the predictions, and much further investigation is necessary.

Before leaving the subject of aromatic systems, it is interesting to note the very refined X-ray diffraction measurements which have been made on solid crystalline anthracene. It is usual to state that aromatic systems whose properties depend upon the stabilization of $\pi$-orbitals must have a planar structure if resonance is to take place. However, some measurable distortion can take place in the solid phase, and the anthracene molecule is not planar, nor are all the bond angles between the carbon atoms exactly 120°. A very accurate series of measurements of electron density was carried out in 1950 by J. M. Robertson (43) and some of the most refined calculations yet attempted were based upon these measurements. Bond angles so calculated were estimated to be correct within $\pm 0·2°$, and the displacement of carbon atoms from the mean molecular plan was considered to be accurate to $\pm 0·004$ ÅU (44). The bond angles, bond lengths, and the heights of the atoms above or below this plane (in units of 0·001 Å) are shown in the following diagram:

The distortions are presumably caused by repulsions due to atoms in neighbouring molecules in the lattice.

In aromatic compounds, it is the bond problems which have the greatest interest. There are few such bond problems in the chemistry of polymers, and here it is the mechanism of formation, and the correlation of molecular structure with bulk properties which offer the widest scope for investigation. The simplest type of polymer consists of chains of identical repeating groups, and the least complex of these is polyethylene $(-CH_2-)_n$. In practice, such a polymer is almost invariably branched, and the length of the side chains and the extent of the branching is considerably affected by the method of preparation. A branched polymer may be cross-linked, that is to say the branches of one chain may form bonds with the branches of another chain. If the branching is extensive, large portions of the bulk polymer may be individually giant molecules. The units which make up the chains and the branches may be either aliphatic or aromatic. The latter type is found, for example, in the bakelite type of phenol–formaldehyde resins where the cross-linking is very highly developed. This structure produces a hard stable polymer.

Where the repeating chain is of the vinyl type, with substituent groups attached to the linear chain, it is possible for polymers with different steric arrangements to be formed. Natta (45) recognized three types of these. If the substituent groups were all on the same side of the chain, he named the polymer 'isotactic'.

If the substituents were arranged alternately, he called the polymer 'syndotactic'.

If the substituents were arranged in a random fashion, he described the structure as 'atactic'. Natta showed that if in addition to the polymerization initiators such as $TiCl_3$, stereo-specific catalysts were used, it was possible to produce polymers with particular orientations (46). These catalysts were typically chlorides of the highly electropositive metals in which the cation had a small radius—such salts as LiCl, $BeCl_2$, $MgCl_2$, $ZnCl_2$ and $AlCl_3$. He attributes their action in vinyl type polymerizations to the polarization of the double bond, that is to say to a mesomeric transfer of electrons to the carbon atoms where co-ordination will take place with the strongly electrophilic metal ions.

Mark had earlier pointed out the effect of specific structure upon the properties of the bulk polymer (47). He showed that when a polyester was formed from *trans*-butenediol and fumaric acid, the product was a crystalline substance with a high melting point. However, if the polymer was formed from *cis*-butenediol and fumaric acid or from *trans*-butenediol and maleic acid, the resulting products were rubbery substances which had low melting points, and which did not show any tendency to crystallize. It has similarly been shown that natural rubber is an isotactic polymer. A product which has not only the same molecular weight distribution as natural *hevea* rubber, but also the same isotactic structure, only results when isoprene is polymerized with stereospecific catalysts (48).

Stereochemical factors are also of great importance in determining the fibre-forming properties of polymers. Fibrous polymers must have some tendency to crystallize, although complete crystallization of this type of polymer rarely, if ever, takes place. In a typical fibre, the individual long-chain molecules pass through a number of crystalline regions, which have between them regions which are considerably less ordered. A structure containing long linear molecules with no crystalline axes will be weak. Crystallization will usually take place if the chain has no large side groups attached to it (49). In particular, any such side groups must not be of such a type that they take part in the formation of extensive cross-links. The glyptals, for example, which form extensive cross-links do not form fibres (50). Molecules of fibre-forming polymers usually have a molecular weight of not less than 10,000 units, and a chain length of not less than 1000 ÅU.

This partly-crystalline, partly disordered structure accords well with the observed fact of the unsharp melting point of such compounds. A complex situation develops both at crystallization and at melting, when there is some reaction between the ordered and disordered regions which are penetrated by the same long-chain molecules (51). It is, however, now generally agreed that the melting points of these polymers mark the onset of true first order transitions.

Mark extended the idea of stereo-specificity, and suggested that polymers with long-chain periodicities would be of great interest. An example of this is a polystyrene chain with a maleic acid link between each fifty styrene monomers. He pointed out that an arrangement of this type was present in certain proteins such as keratin and myosin which have periodicities of several hundred Ångstrom units. He went on to propose two new types of polymer with a stereospecific arrangement. He suggested that it would be possible to form polymeric macro-molecules containing more than one kind of structural unit, and in which the different constituents were arranged in a non-random manner. He distinguished two types of such structures. 'Graft' co-polymers would consist of chains of one structural type to which branches of a different kind of unit were attached:

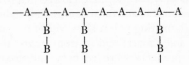

On the other hand 'block' co-polymers would consist of chains comprised of more than one kind of structural unit arranged in blocks, and not interspersed at random:

$$-A-A-A-B-B-B-B-B-A-A-A-A-A-A-B-B-B-A-$$

A number of block and graft co-polymers of the types suggested by Mark have now been prepared, and a number of general preparative methods have been developed. One simple method of synthesizing graft co-polymers is to polymerize a monomer in the presence of a pre-formed chain polymer. The pre-formed chain polymer may become a 'giant free radical' by a process of proton transfer and the consequent production of active centres, which are then accessible to the incipient chains being formed by the monomer molecules. The consequent co-polymer will be disordered and far from homogeneous (52).

Alternatively, active centres may be produced by, for instance, irradiation with ultra-violet light or with gamma radiation. If the irradiated polymer is a poly-ketone, this procedure gives rise to active centres on the main chain (53). The production of active centres may also be achieved by ionic attack. If polyvinyl chloride is treated with aluminium chloride, a positively charged giant free radical will be formed together with $[AlCl_4]^+$. Styrene residues can then be condensed on to the polyvinyl chain (54).

All these three methods lead to products in which the distribution and lengths of the grafted side-chains are random. In order that a polymer with an ordered arrangement may be made, the reactants must be fractionated so that the initial material is itself homogeneous. If such fractionated products have complementary reactive groupings, controlled grafting will occur. In this way it is possible to attach polyethylene oxide groups onto the aromatic nucleus in terylene (55).

It is considerably more difficult to produce satisfactory block co-polymers than it is to produce graft co-polymers. Active sites must be present at the chain ends, but they must not be active in such a way that the reaction of one polymer molecule will take place with another chain of the same kind. Active sites of the required type may be established by photolysis. They may also be formed by using certain catalysts to produce the original polymer chain from the monomer. If the polymerization is initiated by a diperoxide, there will be some peroxide links in the resultant chain. It is sometimes possible to break these peroxide bonds by heating the polymer, and if this is done in solution of the monomer with which it is desired to effect co-polymerization, a block co-polymer will result. In this way it is possible to co-polymerize methyl methacrylate with polystyrene containing peroxy groups derived from a phthalyl peroxide initiator (56).

Russian workers have suggested a mechanical method of providing free radicals necessary to effect co-polymerization. Chains can be broken either by high-speed milling or by ultrasonic vibration in the presence of a monomer. A mixture of phenol–formaldehyde (bakelite) and nitrile rubber was co-polymerized in this way (57).

An ingenious method has been used to prepare block co-polymers of polystyrene (55). The polymerization of the styrene monomer is initiated by means of a sodium–naphthalene complex. This results in the production of a growing chain with an anionic active centre at each end. No chain termination occurs, and if another monomer is added, its polymerization is also initiated, and such a polymer will grow on the end of the polystyrene chains. A variety of different monomers may be added to the mixture in succession.

The structure of polymers has largely been investigated by X-ray methods. Diffraction analysis has confirmed the ordered/disordered structure of fibre-forming polymers which has been referred to above, and the photographs have been interpreted as indicating the presence of a large number of small crystallites. The principal axis of the crystallites will be oriented parallel to the fibre axis in a well-crystallized fibre polymer system. The other axes of the crystallites will be arranged at random around the fibre axis, and a single X-ray diffraction photograph of the system will correspond to a rotation photograph of a single crystal. That is to say, the photograph will include all the three-dimensional reflections on a two-dimensional plate. From such a photograph it is possible to deduce the size of the crystallographic repeat unit in the direction of the fibre axis, but other dimensions are more difficult to calculate. The interpretation of these photographs is complicated by the large amount of incoherent background scattering from the disordered regions in the fibre. It is virtually impossible to deduce the crystal structure without a fairly exact knowledge of the chemical composition of the fibre. If this is not known with certainty, it is usual to postulate various possible models, and to calculate their consequent diffraction properties. These are compared with that which is actually observed. It is usually found that the symmetry of long fibre-like molecules involves a screw axis—that is to say, the chains appear to be helical. There may be more than one chain in the helix, like strands in a rope.

X-ray diffraction methods have been extensively used to assist in the determination of the structure of other long-chain molecules. The polypeptide chains, for example, have been studied in this way (59). The known facts about the chemistry of the system made it probable that the six atoms of the peptide group ( —C—CO—NH—C— ) should lie in a plane. Only if this was the case could the apparent resonance-stabilization of the short —CO—NH— bond be achieved. Rotation is possible about the alpha carbon atom, and it could be said that the bond angles and bond lengths of the hydrogen bonds must fall between certain limits. This chemical data made the interpretation of the X-ray diffraction evidence considerably easier. The physical conformation of these long-chain molecules can however be extremely complex. Not only must the symmetry of the individual repeating units be considered in terms of screw axes, but the rotation of the 'rope' formed by a number of fibre-like molecules must also be taken into account. One of the most complex substances so far studied in this way is deoxy-ribonucleic acid (DNA).

Both the chemistry and the crystallography of the proteins and the nucleic acids is extremely complicated. In the crystalline proteins, solvent may be held within the unit cell to such an extent that as much as one-half of the crystal may consist of water or of an aqueous salt solution. The water appears to be an integral part of the structure—dyes can usually be diffused within the cell without altering the crystal structure, although this is not always the case. The structure of ribonuclease is altered when indophenol is added to it (60). Some of the aqueous solution may be bound in such a way that the dye cannot diffuse into it. In horse haemoglobin, the bound water comprises 30% of the structure (61).

The work of Perutz (62) on the structure of horse haemoglobin illustrates the way in which chemical, physical and crystallographic evidence must be combined in order to discover the structure of such complex compounds. Haemoglobin was known to contain free sulphydryl groups and in order to obtain information about their location, Perutz reacted it with P-chloromercuribenzoate (PCMB). Mercury atoms entered the haemoglobin molecule, and it was assumed that these occupied positions which were adjacent to those occupied by the hydrogen atoms in the original sulphydryl groups. The crystal dimensions of the molecule were, however, unchanged by this substitution. The presence of the mercury atoms had a dominant influence upon the diffraction pattern; this is a variant of the 'heavy atom' method of structure determination which has been previously described (Chapter 4). The diffraction photographs indicated that the mercury atoms were arranged within the haemoglobin molecule in pairs which were related by a dyad symmetry axis. There were four possible molecular arrangements by which this condition could be satisfied, and Perutz selected for study one of these which he intuitively considered to be the most probable. By the use of this model in combination with the X-ray diffraction data which he already possessed, he was able to construct an approximate map of the electron density over the unit cell. From this, he deduced the approximate shape of the molecule, and he was able to indicate the probable relative positions of a number of the constituent atoms which were separated by distances greater than 6 ÅU.

Further information about the disposition of the constituent groups was obtained by chemical means (63). The sulphydryl groups were titrated amperometrically with $HgCl_2$, PCMB and silver nitrate. It was found that while four molecules of silver nitrate were needed to react with the sulphydryl groups in one molecule of haemoglobin, only two molecules of mercuric chloride were required. This indicated that two of the groups were sufficiently close together for one molecule of the titrant to react with two groups. However, although it requires one molecule of PCMB to saturate a sulphydryl group, only two molecules of PCMB would react with one molecule of haemoglobin. It was considered that this confirmed the hypothesis that in each pair of sulphydryl groups, the groups themselves were close together, for in this case it would be sterically impossible for a molecule of PCMB to react with each —SH group of each pair.

A number of further X-ray diffraction measurements were then made by Perutz, using various heavy ions as substituents in the haemoglobin molecule. He studied the phase differences of 1200 X-ray reflections (64). From this data, and from that derived from further chemical work which was carried out in the U.S.A. (65), he was able to establish that in the molecule, four polypeptide chains were arranged in identical pairs. Haem units are attached to the polypeptide chains, and electron spin resonance measurements were used to assist in determining the location and orientation of these units (66). The four chains are packed together to form a structure of high symmetry, with the four haem units arranged at the apices of a slightly distorted tetrahedron. The sequence of the amino-acid residues in the polypeptide chains has now been worked out, and a full understanding of the structure has almost been achieved.

The investigation of the structure of the ribonucleic acids is proceeding in a similar fashion to that in which the structure of haemoglobin was worked out. These acids are, however, considerably more complex. The elucidation of their structure is only a first stage in their study, but without it, it will not be possible to obtain a detailed knowledge of their bio-chemistry, and its fundamental biological and evolutionary implications. The most complex molecule whose structure is now substantially known in detail is Vitamin $B_{12}$, whose atomic formula is $C_{63}H_{88}O_{14}N_{14}PCo$. When its structure was established by the teams which were led by Mrs. Crowfoot-Hodgkin (67) she pointed out that the molecule was spherical in form, with all the more chemically reactive groups on the surface of the sphere. It was, as she put it, 'beautifully composed'.

## REFERENCES

(1) OSTWALD *Z. Phys. Chem.* **3** 418 (1889)
(2) LOWRY *J. Chem. Soc.* **123** 822 (1923)
(3) INGOLD *Rec. Trav. Chem.* **48** 798 (1929)
(4) Reviewed anonymously in *Chem. and Ind.* **44** 246 (1925)
(5) BUNNETT *Quart. Rev.* XII 1 (1958)
(6) HOLLEMANN *Die direkte Einfuhrung von Substitutuenten in den Benzolkern* (Leipzig, 1910)
(7) (*a*) HÜCKEL *Z. Phys.* **70** 204 (1931)
　　(*b*) HÜCKEL *Z. Elektrochem.* **43** 752 857 (1937)
　　(*c*) PLATT *J. Chem. Phys.* **17** 470 484 (1949)
(8) PRELOG *et al. Chem. Ber.* **92** 1867 (1959)
(9) MUXFELDT, ROGALSKI and STRIEGLER *Angew. Chem.* **72** 170 (1960)
(10) (*a*) CLAR and IRONSIDE *Proc. Chem. Soc.* 150 (1958)
　　(*b*) HALLEUX, MARTIN and KING *Helv. Chim. Acta* **41** 1177 (1958)
　　(*c*) CLAR, IRONSIDE and ZANDER *J. Chem. Soc.* 142 (1959)
(11) CLAR and ZANDER *J. Chem. Soc.* 1861 (1959)
(12) CLAR, FELL and RICHMOND *Tetrahedron* **2** 96 (1960)
(13) SONDHEIMER, AMIEL and WOLOVSKY *J. Amer. Chem. Soc.* **79** 4247 (1957)
　　(*b*) SONDHEIMER and WOLOVSKY *J. Amer. Chem. Soc.* **81** 1771 (1959)
　　(*c*) SONDHEIMER and WOLOVSKY *Tetrahedron Letters* **3** 3 (1959)
　　(*d*) SONDHEIMER and WOLOVSKY *J. Amer. Chem. Soc.* **81** 4755 (1959)
　　(*e*) SONDHEIMER and GAONI *J. Amer. Chem. Soc.* **82** 755 (1960)
　　(*f*) SONDHEIMER, WOLOVSKY and GAONI *J. Amer. Chem. Soc.* **82** 5765 (1960)
(14) (*a*) KATZ and STRAUSS *J. Chem. Phys.* **32** 1873 (1960)
　　(*b*) KATZ *J. Amer. Chem. Soc.* **82** 3784 (1960)
(15) BRESLOW *J. Amer. Chem. Soc.* **79** 5318 (1957)
(16) RAMIREZ and LEVY *J. Org. Chem.* **21** 1333 (1956)
(17) FARRIUM and BARR *J. Amer. Chem. Soc.* **82** 2651 (1960)
(18) VOL'PIN, KORESHKOV, DULOVA and KURSANOV *Tetrahedron* **18** 107 (1962)
(19) (*a*) LONGUET-HIGGINS and ORGEL *J. Chem. Soc.* 1969 (1956)
　　(*b*) CRIEGEE and MOSCHEL *Chem. Ber.* **92** 1088 (1959)
　　(*c*) CRIEGEE and SCHRODER *Angew. Chem.* **71** 70 (1959)

(20) AVRAM, MARICA and NENITYESOU *Chem. Ber.* **92** 1088 (1959)
(21) RAMIREZ and LEVY *J. Org. Chem.* **21** 488 (1956)
(22) PETERS *J. Chem. Soc.* 1757 (1959)
(23) THIELE *Ber.* **34** 68 (1901)
(24) KEALY and PAUSON *Nature* **168** 1039 (1931)
    (*b*) MILLER, TEBBOTH and TREMAINE *J. Chem. Soc.* 632 (1952)
(25) (*a*) WILKINSON, ROSENBLUM, WHITING and WOODWARD *J. Amer. Chem. Soc.* **74** 2125 (1952)
    (*b*) FISHER and PFAB *Z. Naturforsch* **7b** 377 (1952)
(26) ISALIEB and BRACK *Z. Naturforsch* **11b** 420 (1956)
(27) WILKINSON *Organic Synthesis* **36** 31 (1956)
(28) WILKINSON, ROSENBLUM, WHITING and WOODWARD *J. Amer. Chem. Soc.* **74** 2125 (1952)
(29) FISCHER and HAFNER *Z. Naturforsch* **10b** 665 (1955)
(30) FISCHER and KOGLER *Z. Naturforsch* **13b** 197 (1958)
(31) MERLING *Ber.* **24** 3108 (1891)
(32) DEWAR *Nature* **155** 50, 141 (1945)
(33) VELPIN, KURSANOV, SHEMYAKIN, MAIMIND and HEYMAN *Chem. and Ind.* (1958)
(34) DEERING and KRAUCH *Angew. Chem.* **68** 661 (1956)
(35) DAUBEN, CADUKI, HARMON and PEARSON *J. Amer. Chem. Soc.* **79** 455 (1957)
(36) GANELLIN and PETTIT *J. Amer. Chem. Soc.* **79** 1767 (1957)
(37) (*a*) RYLANDER, MAYERSON and GRUBB *J. Amer. Chem. Soc.* **79** 842 (1957)
    (*b*) MEYERSON, RYLANDER, ELIELAND and MCCOLLUM *J. Amer. Chem. Soc.* **81** 2606 (1959)
(38) NORZOE, MUKAI, TAKASE and NAGARA *Proc. Imp. Acad. Japan.* **28** 477 (1952)
(39) ANDERSON, COWLES, TAZUMA and NELSON *J. Amer. Chem. Soc.* **77** 6321 (1955)
(40) ANDERSON, SCOTONI, COWLES and FRITZ *J. Org. Chem.* **22** 1193 (1957)
(41) ZEIGENBEIN *Angew. Chem.* **70** 106 (1958)
(42) HAFNER *Angew. Chem.* **71** 378 (1959)
(43) MATHIESON, ROBERTSON, and SINCLAIR *Acta Cryst.* **3** 245 (1950)
(44) CRUICKSHANK *Acta cryst.* **9** 915 (1956)
(45) NATTA *J. Polymer Sci.* **16** 143 (1956)
(46) NATTA *J. Inorg. Nuclear Chem.* **8** 589 (1958)
(47) MARK *Research* **4** 167 (1951)
(48) (*a*) STAVELEY *et al. Ind. Eng. Chem.* **48** 778 (1956)
    (*b*) HORNE *et al. Ind. Eng. Chem.* **48** 784 (1956)
(49) CASE *J. Polymer Sci.* **45** 435 (1960)
(50) CAROTHERS and HILL *J. Amer. Chem. Soc.* **54** 1579 (1932)
(51) (*a*) FLORY *Principles of Polymer Chemistry* p. 653 (Cornell Univ. Press N.Y., 1953)
    (*b*) MANDELKERN *Chem. Rev.* **56** 903 (1956)
(52) SMETS and CLAESON *J. Polymer Sci.* **8** 289 (1952)

(53) SEBBAN–DANON *J. Polymer Sci.* **29** 367 (1958)
(54) PLESCH *Chem. and Ind.* 954 (1958)
(55) COLEMAN *J. Polymer Sci.* **14** 15 (1954)
(56) SMETS and WOODWARD *J. Polymer Sci.* **14** 126 (1954)
(57) KARGIN, KOVARSKAYA, GOLUBENKOVA, AKATIN and SLONIMISKII *Doklady Akad. Nauk S.S.S.R.* **112** 485 (1957)
(58) SEWARE, LEVY and MILKOVICH *J. Amer. Chem. Soc.* **76** 2656 (1956)
(59) COREY and PAULING *Proc. Roy. Soc.* **B141** 10 (1953)
(60) MAGDOFF and CRICK *Acta Cryst.* **8** 468 (1955)
(61) PERUTZ *Trans. Faraday Soc.* **B42** 187 (1946)
(62) GREEN, INGRAM and PERUTZ *Proc. Roy. Soc.* **A225** 287 (1954)
(63) INGRAM *Biochem. J.* **59** 653 (1955)
(64) PERUTZ, ROSSMAN, CULLIS, MUIRHEAD, WILL and NORTH *Nature* **185** 416 (1960)
(65) RHINESMITH, SCHROEDER and MARTIN *J. Amer. Chem. Soc.* **80** 3358 (1958)
(66) INGRAM, GIBSON and PERUTY *Nature* **178** 906 (1956)
(67) HODGKIN, KAMPER, MACKAY, PICKWORTH, TRUEBLOOD and WHITE *Nature* **178** 64 (1956)

# Index

225